Modeling and Electrothermal Simulation of SiC Power Devices

Using Silvaco© ATLAS

Modeling and Electrothermal Simulation of SiC Power Devices
Using Silvaco© ATLAS

Bejoy N. Pushpakaran
Stephen B. Bayne
Texas Tech University, USA

 **World Scientific**

NEW JERSEY · LONDON · SINGAPORE · BEIJING · SHANGHAI · HONG KONG · TAIPEI · CHENNAI · TOKYO

Published by

World Scientific Publishing Co. Pte. Ltd.

5 Toh Tuck Link, Singapore 596224

USA office: 27 Warren Street, Suite 401-402, Hackensack, NJ 07601

UK office: 57 Shelton Street, Covent Garden, London WC2H 9HE

Library of Congress Cataloging-in-Publication Data

Names: Pushpakaran, Bejoy (Bejoy N.), author. | Bayne, Stephen (Stephen B.), author.

Title: Modeling and electrothermal simulation of SiC power devices : using Silvaco© ATLAS /
    Bejoy N. Pushpakaran and Stephen B. Bayne (Texas Tech University).

Description: New Jersey : World Scientific, [2018] | Includes index.

Identifiers: LCCN 2018042653 | ISBN 9789813237827 (hardcover)

Subjects: LCSH: Wide gap semiconductors. | Silicon carbide. | ATLAS TCAD (Computer program)

Classification: LCC QC611.8.W53 P87 2018 | DDC 621.3815/2--dc23

LC record available at https://lccn.loc.gov/2018042653

British Library Cataloguing-in-Publication Data

A catalogue record for this book is available from the British Library.

For any available supplementary material, please visit
https://www.worldscientific.com/worldscibooks/10.1142/10929#t=suppl

Desk Editor: Tay Yu Shan

Typeset by Stallion Press
Email: enquiries@stallionpress.com

Dedication

To God Almighty, without whose blessings this book would never have been a reality.

To Mom and Dad, I could never have done this without your unconditional love, faith, support, and constant encouragement. Thank you for teaching me to believe in myself, in God, and in my dreams. Thank you also for asking a million times the most annoying question ever, "Is your book done yet?"

I would like to dedicate this book to my advisor, teacher, mentor, and friend Prof. Stephen Bayne who has been such an integral part of my career. The knowledge you have imparted to me has been a great asset throughout my career. I appreciate and treasure everything you have taught me.

Bejoy Pushpakaran

Preface

Silicon Carbide (SiC) material has matured to the point that reliable power semiconductor devices are becoming commercially available. Silicon (Si) was the material of choice for power semiconductor devices; however, for applications which require high voltage or high temperature operation, the material limitations of Si make the power devices inefficient and un-manufacturable. Silicon-based power devices consist of Bipolar Junction Transistor (BJTs), Metal Oxide Semiconductor Field Effect Transistor (MOSFETs), and Insulated Gate Bipolar Transistor (IGBTs). Si power MOSFET is the device of choice for low-voltage (<100 V) and high-current applications. There are even commercially available Si MOSFETs which can block up to 1200 V; however, the ON-state resistance and device capacitance limit their usage to low current and slow switching frequency application. Power BJTs are not used in many high-power applications because of its low current gain. The IGBT is the current device of choice for power electronics applications; however, IGBTs are limited in switching frequency because of the injected minority carriers within the drift region. The limitations of Si power semiconductor devices led to the investigation of other materials, and one of the materials that showed promise for high-voltage application was SiC.

SiC is a wide bandgap material with a bandgap of 3.26 eV (4H polytype) as compared to 1.12 eV for Si which makes SiC power devices ideal for pulsed-power applications because of its ability to block high voltage and operate at high junction temperature. In order to understand the performance and limitation of semiconductor devices, physics-based simulation tools such as Silvaco© ATLAS is used to model the structure of the device. Silvaco© ATLAS is a commercial Technology Computer-Aided Design (TCAD) software that is used for modeling semiconductor devices. There are very limited textbooks available for helping students understand how the program works for modeling silicon-based power devices. At the time of this book publication, no text books were available on modeling SiC power devices in Silvaco© Atlas. This book is intended for design engineers and graduate students who are taking a power semiconductor course or conducting research in the area of Si/SiC power semiconductors. This book will significantly reduce the learning curve for the software and will allow the reader to focus more on the design of the semiconductor. The authors have several years of experience in the area of power devices and have modeled many SiC power devices using Silvaco© ATLAS.

This monograph introduces the reader to physics-based modeling and electrothermal simulation of SiC power semiconductor devices using Silvaco© ATLAS TCAD software. The book focuses on steady-state and transient simulation of SiC power devices, while also covering device performance under high current density pulsed applications. In the first chapter, a high-level introduction to various application of power semiconductor devices along with a brief discussion on semiconductor material and device types is provided. Chapter 2 is a brief refresher on basic semiconductor properties and the working of a p–n junction. Chapters 3–5 provide an in-depth discussion on Silvaco© ATLAS TCAD software capabilities and its application in the modeling and simulation of SiC power devices. These chapters include simulation settings, critical modeling techniques, physics-based models and parameters, steady-state and transient simulation methodology, and computational hardware requirements specific to silicon carbide power device modeling and simulation. The last four chapters are devoted to the modeling and simulation of high-voltage SiC p-i-n diode, Schottky diode, Junction Barrier Schottky (JBS) diode, and MOSFET. Chapters 6 and 7 discuss the simulation-based analysis of SiC p-i-n and Schottky diode under steady-state and transient condition, respectively. The modeling of p-i-n and Schottky diode includes the analysis of parallel plane structure followed by more complex device structures. Chapter 8 focuses on the modeling and simulation of JBS diode structure. Chapter 9 is devoted to the modeling and simulation of SiC power MOSFET using the vertical D-MOSFET structure. The MOSFET transient simulations were performed using gate charging, resistive switching, clamped inductive switching, and high current density pulsed switching circuits. The electrothermal parameters obtained during device simulation are shown using graphs and software-generated contour plots to give a better understanding of the device performance. Each device simulation chapter contains numerous tested and fully functional program source code for steady-state and transient simulations. To expedite the learning process for the readers, each simulation program has its own code walkthrough segment which explains each line of code. The authors have also given several key pointers throughout the book that will save the reader significant time while simulating power devices.

About the Authors

Dr. Bejoy N. Pushpakaran received his Bachelor's degree in Electronics and Communication Engineering from Cochin University of Science and Technology, India and M.S. and Ph.D. degrees in Electrical Engineering from Texas Tech University, Lubbock, Texas, USA. During his graduate studies, he was with the Center for Pulsed Power and Power Electronics at Texas Tech University, where his graduate research focused on Technology Computer-Aided Design (TCAD) modeling and simulation of Silicon Carbide (SiC) power devices and pulsed power evaluation of research-grade and commercial SiC power semiconductor devices. After completing his doctoral studies, Dr. Pushpakaran joined X-FAB Texas, where he is currently a SiC Process Development Engineer responsible for semiconductor fabrication projects aimed toward the commercialization of SiC technology by enabling processing and fabrication of SiC power devices on state-of-the-art 6-inch wafers with the support of PowerAmerica institute. His research interests include TCAD modeling, failure analysis, reliability testing, and pulsed power evaluation of SiC power devices, wide bandgap power electronics, and renewable energy.

 **Dr. Stephen B. Bayne** received his Ph.D., M.S., and B.S. degrees in Electrical Engineering from Texas Tech University. After completing his doctoral studies, he joined the Naval Research Lab (NRL) where he was an electronics engineer designing advanced power electronics systems for space power applications. After two and a half years at the NRL, Dr. Bayne transferred to the Army Research Lab (ARL) where he was instrumental in developing the high-temperature Silicon Carbide power electronics program. Dr. Bayne was promoted to Team Lead at ARL where he led the power components team which consisted of five engineers. As the Team Leader, Dr. Bayne was responsible for advanced research in high-temperature and advance power semiconductor devices for Army applications. After one and a half years as Team Lead, Dr. Bayne was promoted to Branch Chief of the Directed Energy Branch where he managed 16 Engineers, technicians, and support staff. Dr. Bayne managed a multi-million dollar budget and was responsible for the recruitment, development, and performance evaluation of members in the branch. After 8 years at the ARL, Dr. Bayne transitioned over to academia where he is currently a Professor at Texas Tech University. His research interests at Texas Tech are power electronics, power semiconductor devices, pulsed power, and renewable energy. Dr. Bayne is a faculty member of ARL South for the Power and Energy research at Texas Tech University. Dr. Bayne has over 150 journal and conference publications. Dr. Bayne is also a veteran of the military, where he served four years in the Air Force.

Contents

Chapter 1

Introduction

Increased awareness of global warming has accelerated research into harnessing renewable energy and the development of energy-efficient power conversion systems. The proliferation of renewable energy-based systems and hybrid electric and all-electric vehicles has increased the magnitude of energy processed by power electronics. The heart of any power electronic circuit is the power semiconductor device. Using the semiconductor device as a switch in a power electronic circuit allows components to operate at higher efficiency and power rating. Before power electronic circuits were developed, DC voltage was regulated by using a linear regulator. Figure 1 shows the basic schematic of a linear regulator circuit.

The output voltage is regulated by adjusting the voltage drop across the control element which is usually a semiconductor transistor. A linear regulator has two major drawbacks: the first limitation of a linear regulator is that the voltage drop across the series pass element caused significant losses in the circuit. The second limitation of a linear regulator is that the circuit could only step down the DC voltage. Switching regulators are well known for their high efficiency (typically >90%) and compact form factor. Depending on the topology, switching regulators can be used to either step down the DC voltage using a Buck converter (Fig. 2) or step up the DC voltage using a Boost converter (Fig. 3). The selection of optimum switching frequency for the power semiconductor device (SW) is based on the application and type of semiconductor device.[1,2]

The following is a list of applications, with primary focus on renewable energy, which are heavily dependent on modern-day power semiconductor devices to ensure efficient and optimum performance.

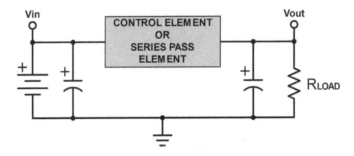

Fig. 1.   Simplified schematic of linear regulator.

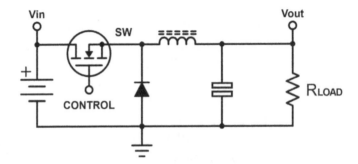

Fig. 2.   Simplified schematic of Buck converter.

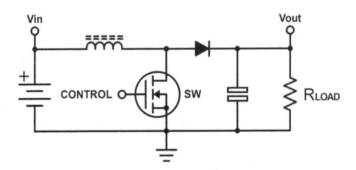

Fig. 3.   Simplified schematic of Boost converter.

• Wind Energy System

Wind energy systems consist of rectifier and inverter circuits which operate in unison to regulate the power flow. Commercial grid-connected wind turbines are implemented based on the two most commonly used topologies, namely Doubly Fed Induction Generator (DFIG)-based design and Direct-Drive design. Figure 4 shows the schematic block diagram of a DFIG-based wind turbine configuration. The DFIG-based wind turbine is a popular system in which the power electronic interface controls the rotor current to achieve the variable speed necessary for maximum energy generation at variable wind speed. Since the power electronics only has to process the rotor power, typically less than 30% of the overall output power, DFIG offers the advantages of speed control with reduced cost and power losses.[3-5]

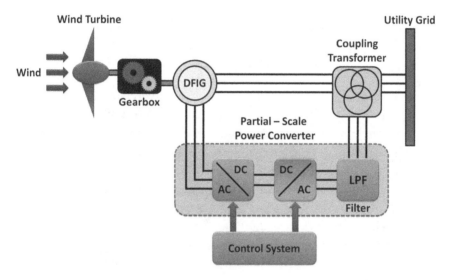

Fig. 4. Simplified schematic of DFIG-based wind turbine.

Figure 5 shows the schematic block diagram of a Direct-Drive wind turbine system. The AC voltage output from the wind turbine is converted to DC by a rectifier circuit. The DC voltage is then converted back to AC voltage by an inverter circuit. The output voltage from the inverter is stepped up to the grid-compatible voltage by a transformer and fed to the utility grid. One of the major differences between a DFIG-based and Direct-Drive wind turbine is the absence of a gearbox in the Direct-Drive system. In this configuration, power electronics must be capable of handling the total power output of the wind turbine, which can be of the order of several megawatts (MW). This could introduce severe electrothermal stress on the power semiconductor devices used in the system. Hence, power semiconductors devices utilized in wind energy systems must be capable of handling high voltage and high current.[6-8]

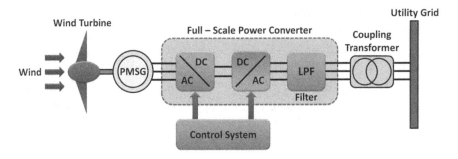

Fig. 5. Simplified schematic of Direct-Drive wind turbine.

• Photovoltaic Energy System

Power electronic circuits are also used extensively in Photovoltaic (PV) energy harvesting systems. PV energy systems can be classified into types based on their configuration: stand-alone or off-grid systems and grid-connected or utility-interactive systems. Stand-alone systems are designed and configured to operate independent of the electric grid and are usually installed to meet the power demands of a small residential community or individual home. Grid-connected PV systems are configured to operate in unison with the electric grid and can be designed for power rating up to several MW. The general block diagram of a PV energy system is shown in Fig. 6. The output from a solar panel is a DC voltage and current. The charge controller incorporates Maximum Power Point Tracking (MPPT) algorithm to extract maximum power from the PV modules. The DC voltage from the charge controller is conditioned using a DC–DC converter to the appropriate voltage level and is converted to AC by a power electronic inverter circuit.[9] The power semiconductors in the circuit must be capable of handling the peak output power from the PV system. Due to the intermittent nature of solar energy, it is imperative to have a Battery Energy Storage System (BESS) to provide power backup.[10]

Figure 6 shows a typical battery system when connected to the grid as a part of the PV energy system. A similar BESS can also be implemented in a wind energy system due to the intermittent nature of the energy source. The power electronics in a battery system must be bidirectional. When the battery is discharging, an inverter circuit is used to convert the DC power from the battery to AC for connection to the grid. When the battery is being charged from the grid, the AC power is converted to DC by a rectifier circuit. In the PV energy system shown in Fig. 6, the battery charging is handled by the charge controller unit. Again, power semiconductor devices are used to manage the flow of energy.[9]

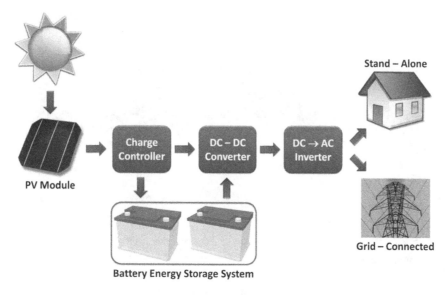

Fig. 6.   Simplified block diagram of PV energy system.

• Hybrid Electric Vehicle

Hybrid Electric Vehicles (HEV) can be classified based on their drive train architecture: Series, Parallel, and Series–Parallel. Detailed discussion of HEV architectures are beyond the scope of this textbook. The block diagram of series hybrid electric drive train is shown in Fig. 7. The power electronics system work the same way as the grid-connected battery system. During vehicle operation, the power electronics circuitry converts DC power from the battery to AC power for the traction motors. The battery bank gets charged either through a generator driven by a small gasoline engine or by an external charging system. HEVs are also designed to charge the battery bank using energy captured from the motor during regenerative braking of the vehicle. Bidirectional energy transfer and management of the battery system are done by the power semiconductor devices.[11,12]

In an all-electric vehicle, the role of power electronics is even more important since the absence of an internal combustion engine is compensated by a high-energy density BESS. The power electronic circuit must be able to operate under the high-temperature condition encountered in an automobile while processing the full rated power of the vehicle. The power semiconductor devices utilized in automotive applications must have high performance and reliability throughout the lifespan of the vehicle.[13]

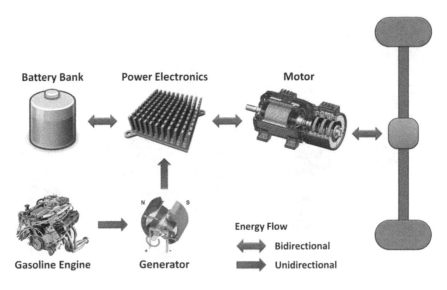

Fig. 7.   Simplified block diagram of series hybrid electric drive train.

• Other Applications

Another fast emerging area for the high-current power device is data centers. Data centers require reliable energy systems to maintain the availability of the data. Data centers are currently powered by low-voltage and high-current systems. Power electronics are used to process the high-current power to the load. Data centers also require battery backup for high-reliability operation.[14,15] Another application is in the area of pulsed power system. Unlike continuous power systems, pulsed power systems charge up over a long period of time and discharge the energy over a short period of time. Power semiconductor switches are used in the following two areas of pulsed power systems: output closing switch to deliver energy to the load, or in the charging circuit for rapid capacitor chargers. Both applications require semiconductor devices with high-voltage, high-current, and high-frequency switching capability.[16,17]

1.1.   Brief Introduction to Power Devices

As stated above, there are many applications that require power semiconductors to process power required by the load. This section will give an introduction to power semiconductor devices and the material used. Silicon (Si) is the dominant material currently used for power semiconductor devices; however, Si is reaching its limits for some high-power and high-temperature

Table 1. Material comparison between Silicon, Gallium Nitride and Silicon Carbide.[18]

Property @ 300 K	Silicon (Si)	Gallium Nitride (GaN)	Silicon Carbide (4H-SiC)
Bandgap (eV)	1.12	3.4	3.26
Relative dielectric constant	11.9	9.7	9.7
Critical electric field (MV/cm)	0.6	3.3	2.5–3
Thermal conductivity (W/cm-K)	1.3	1.3	3–5

applications. Researchers are investigating wide bandgap materials such as Silicon Carbide (SiC) and Gallium Nitride (GaN) for high-voltage and high-temperature applications. Table 1 shows the material properties for Si, SiC, and GaN.

For most applications, power electronic circuits require an active switch and a diode to process power. Typical active switches in a power electronic circuit are Bipolar Junction Transistor (BJT), Metal Oxide Semiconductor Field Effect transistor (MOSFET), and Insulated Gate Bipolar Transistor (IGBT). BJTs and IGBTs are minority carrier devices, whereas a MOSFET is a majority carrier device. The different types of diodes used in power electronics circuits are p-i-n, Schottky, and Junction Barrier Schottky (JBS) diodes. The p-i-n diode is a minority carrier device, whereas Schottky and JBS diodes are majority carrier devices. Minority carrier devices have the advantage of high current capability with low ON-state voltage due to minority carrier injection; however, the injection of minority carriers limits the switching frequency. Majority carrier devices have inherently fast switching capability due to the absence of minority carriers; however, the ON-state losses increase at high forward current.[19] The selection of a power semiconductor device for a given application is based on the aforementioned pros and cons for each device type. In this textbook, modeling and electrothermal simulation of SiC p-i-n diode, Schottky diode, JBS diode, and power MOSFET have been discussed in detail.

References

1. H. Zhang, Basic Concepts of Linear Regulator and Switching Mode Power Supplies, Application Note 140, Analog Devices Inc., 2013.
2. J. Williams, Switching Regulators for Poets, Application Note 25, Linear Technology Corp., 2013.
3. R. D. Richardson and G. M. McNerney, Wind energy systems, *Proceedings of the IEEE*, vol. 81, no. 3, pp. 378–389, Mar 1993.
4. N. S. Patil and Y. N. Bhosle, A review on wind turbine generator topologies, *2013 International Conference on Power, Energy and Control (ICPEC)*, 2013, pp. 625–629.

5. H. Polinder, Overview of and trends in wind turbine generator systems, *2011 IEEE Power and Energy Society General Meeting*, San Diego, CA, 2011, pp. 1–8.

6. R. Jones, Power electronic converters for variable speed wind turbines, *IEEE Colloquium on Power Electronics for Renewable Energy (Digest No: 1997/170)*, London, 1997, pp. 1/1–1/8.

7. J. A. Baroudi, V. Dinavahi and A. M. Knight, A review of power converter topologies for wind generators, *IEEE International Conference on Electric Machines and Drives*, San Antonio, TX, 2005, pp. 458–465.

8. H. Polinder, F. F. A. van der Pijl, G. J. de Vilder and P. J. Tavner, Comparison of direct-drive and geared generator concepts for wind turbines, *IEEE Transactions on Energy Conversion*, vol. 21, no. 3, September 2006, pp. 725–733.

9. Anitha S. Subburaj, Bejoy N. Pushpakaran and Stephen B. Bayne, Overview of grid connected renewable energy based battery projects in USA, *Renewable and Sustainable Energy Reviews*, vol. 45, May 2015, pp. 219–234.

10. B. N. Pushpakaran, A. S. Subburaj, S. B. Bayne and J. Mookken, Impact of silicon carbide semiconductor technology in Photovoltaic Energy System, *Renewable and Sustainable Energy Reviews*, vol. 55, 2016, pp. 971–989.

11. M. Kebriaei, A. H. Niasar and B. Asaei, Hybrid electric vehicles: An overview, *2015 International Conference on Connected Vehicles and Expo (ICCVE)*, Shenzhen, 2015, pp. 299–305.

12. Yimin Gao, M. Ehsani and J. M. Miller, Hybrid Electric Vehicle: Overview and State of the Art, *Proceedings of the IEEE International Symposium on Industrial Electronics, ISIE 2005.*, Dubrovnik, Croatia, 2005, pp. 307–316.

13. A. Z. Khan, A. K. Janjua, S. T. Jan and Z. N. Ahmed, A comprehensive overview on the impact of widespread deployment of electric vehicles on power grid, *2017 IEEE International Conference on Smart Grid and Smart Cities (ICSGSC)*, Singapore, 2017, pp. 195–199.

14. Y. Cui *et al.*, High efficiency data center power supply using wide band gap power devices, *2014 IEEE Applied Power Electronics Conference and Exposition — APEC 2014*, Fort Worth, TX, 2014, pp. 3437–3442.

15. P. T. Krein, Data center challenges and their power electronics, *CPSS Transactions on Power Electronics and Applications*, vol. 2, no. 1, 2017, pp. 39–46.

16. B. J. Le Galloudec *et al.*, Pulsed power projects within the national ignition facility, *2017 IEEE 21st International Conference on Pulsed Power (PPC)*, Brighton, 2017, pp. 1–4.

17. T. Flack *et al.*, Evaluation of high frequency solid state switches for pulsed power applications using a 12 kW variable voltage testbed, *2017 IEEE 21st International Conference on Pulsed Power (PPC)*, Brighton, 2017, pp. 1–4.

18. S. B. Bayne and B. N. Pushpakaran (2012) Silicon carbide technology overview. *Journal of Electrical Engineering and Electronic Technology*, vol. 1, no. 1.

19. B. J. Baliga, *Fundamental of Power Semiconductor Devices*, New York, NY: Springer, 2008.

Chapter 2

Introduction to Semiconductor Properties

In order to correctly model and simulate power semiconductor devices, an understanding of the semiconductor material properties is imperative. This chapter will introduce the reader to the basic concepts required to understand the working of semiconductors. For a greater in-depth understanding of semiconductor physics, reader can refer the chapter references.

2.1. Band Structure

The energy band structure of a material comprises of valence band and conduction band. The valence band is separated from the conduction band by the energy bandgap. Valence band can be defined as the lowest energy level available in the semiconductor, whereas conduction band can be defined as the partially filled upper energy band in the semiconductor. At 0 K, the valence band is nearly completely filled with electrons and the conduction band is devoid of electrons. As the temperature increases, electrons can gain energy and move from the valence band to the conduction band. The bandgap separation depends on the type of semiconductor material. The bandgap for silicon is 1.12 eV, while the bandgap for 4H-SiC (4H polytype of SiC) and GaN are 3.26 eV and 3.4 eV, respectively.[1]

SiC and GaN have a wider bandgap than Si and are called wide bandgap materials. The distance between the conduction and valence band determines if the material is a metal, a semiconductor, or an insulator. For a metal, conduction and the valence bands overlap. The electrons can move easily in the metal even at 0 K. As stated before, in a semiconductor the bands are separated by an energy gap. The energy gap in semiconductors is large enough to allow minimum transitioning of electrons from the valence band to the conduction band under normal conditions. However, when a

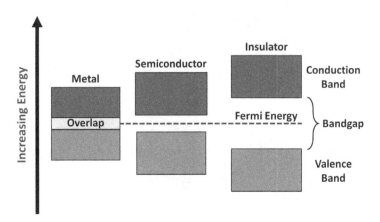

Fig. 1.   Block diagram of energy bandgap for metal, semiconductor and insulator.

reasonable amount of thermal or optical energy is applied, several electrons will transition from the valence band to the conduction band. In an insulator, the bandgap is so large that even when a reasonable amount of thermal or optical energy is applied, minimal electrons are transitioned to the conduction band from the valence band. Figure 1 shows the band diagram for metal, semiconductor, and insulator materials.

The energy gap is not the only parameter that effects the transition of electrons from the valence to the conduction band. Semiconductor band structures can be either direct or indirect. In a band diagram, the x-axis is a function of the momentum vector (k). If the semiconductor has a minimum in the conduction band and a maximum in the valence band at the same k value, then the semiconductor material is direct band. If the minimum of the conduction band and the maximum of the valence band is not at the same k-value, then the material is indirect band. For example, GaAs is a direct band material whereas Si is an indirect band material. Direct and indirect band structure are shown in Figs. 2(a) and 2(b), respectively.[2]

Within the band structure, if the temperature rises above 0 K, some electrons will transition from the valence band to the conduction band. The electrons that transition to the conduction band leave behind a vacant state. This vacant state is referred to as a hole. The electron that is transitioned to the conduction band and the vacant position that is left in the valence band are referred to as an Electron–Hole Pair (EHP). Figure 3 shows the formation of an EHP in a semiconductor.[2]

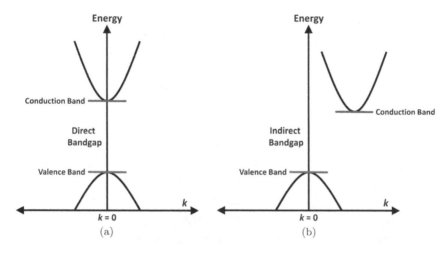

Fig. 2.   (a) Direct band structure. (b) Indirect band structure.

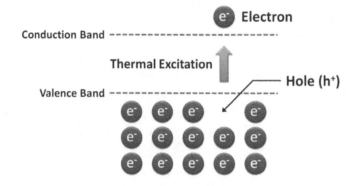

Fig. 3.   EHP generation in a semiconductor.

2.2.   Intrinsic and Extrinsic Semiconductor

Semiconductor material can be classified as intrinsic and extrinsic. In an intrinsic semiconductor material, no foreign atoms or impurities are located in the lattices. At 0 K, the conduction band of an intrinsic semiconductor is completely devoid of electrons and the valence band is filled with electrons. When the temperature goes above 0 K, there is enough thermal energy for electrons to overcome the energy gap and transition to the conduction band. Thermally generated EHPs are the only charge carriers in an intrinsic material. Within an intrinsic material, the concentration of electrons (n) in the conduction band is equal to the concentration of holes (p) in the valence band, which is equal to the intrinsic carrier concentration (n_i). This relationship is shown in Eq. (1).

$$n = p = n_i \tag{1}$$

where n is the electron-concentration per cm^3, p is the hole-concentration per cm^3, and n_i is the intrinsic carrier concentration per cm^3. The conductivity of an intrinsic semiconductor material is very low.[1]

In order to increase the conductivity of a semiconductor material, it is doped with foreign atoms (impurities), thereby making it extrinsic. The nature of the semiconductor can be changed to either n-type or p-type through the process of doping. When the doping concentration of the material increases above the equilibrium carrier concentration of the intrinsic material, the semiconductor is considered to be extrinsic. The two types of dopant atoms are donors and acceptors. When the material is doped with donor atoms, the material becomes n-type and has excess electrons. Considering a group IV semiconductor material, e.g. Silicon, donors are produced from elements in group V of the periodic table. The typical donor atoms include Phosphorus (P), Arsenic (As), and Antimony (Sb). When the material is doped with acceptor atoms, the material becomes p-type and has excess holes. Acceptors are produced from elements in group III of the periodic table. The typical acceptor atoms include Aluminum (Al), Boron (B), and Gallium (Ga). Figure 4 shows the band diagrams of an intrinsic, n-type and p-type semiconductor with their associated Fermi (E_F), donor (E_d), and acceptor (E_a) levels.[1]

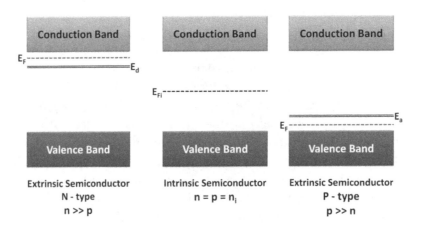

Fig. 4.   Band diagrams of n-type, intrinsic and p-type semiconductor materials.

2.3. Fermi–Dirac Distribution

When the thermal energy (kT) is increased, the number of electrons at a given energy level is also increased. The distribution of electrons in a solid is governed by Fermi–Dirac statistics and it describes the probability that an available energy state is occupied by electrons at absolute temperature. The probability function is defined by Eq. (2) where E_F is the Fermi level energy, E is the energy level of the available state, k is Boltzmann's constant, and T is the absolute temperature.[2]

$$f(E) = \frac{1}{1 + e^{\frac{(E-E_F)}{kT}}} \tag{2}$$

As per Fermi–Dirac function, if energy level E is equal to the Fermi level energy E_F, the probability of the energy level being occupied by an electron is $f(E) = 1/2$. When the absolute temperature is 0 K and $E < E_F$, the exponent term becomes 0 resulting in $f(E) = 1$, and when the absolute temperature is 0 K and $E > E_F$, the exponent term becomes ∞ resulting in $f(E) = 0$. This implies that at absolute temperature of 0 K, $f(E)$ has a rectangular profile such that every energy level up to Fermi level is filled and every energy level above Fermi level is empty. At higher temperature ($T > 0$ K), there is a non-zero probability of having energy states above Fermi level to be filled. Since the Fermi–Dirac distribution is the probability of finding electrons at the energy level, Fermi level (E_{Fi}) is in the middle of the band for intrinsic semiconductor. For n-type material, the Fermi level (E_F) is close to the conduction band and for p-type material, the Fermi level (E_F) is close to the valence band as shown in Fig. 4. If the density of state in the conduction band and the valence band are known, then the Fermi distribution function can be employed to calculate the concentration of electrons and hole in the material. For example, concentration of electrons (n_0) in the conduction band (E_C) under equilibrium can be calculated using the following equation where $f(E)$ is the Fermi–Dirac function and $N(E) \cdot dE$ is the density of states (cm^{-3}) in the energy range dE.[2]

$$n_0 = \int_{E_C}^{\infty} f(E)N(E)dE \tag{3}$$

The product of $f(E)$ and $N(E)$ is integrated over the entire conduction band to obtain the following expression for n_0 where N_C is the effective density of states at the conduction band edge E_C and $f(E_C)$ is the probability of electron occupancy at E_C.

$$n_0 = N_C \cdot f(E_C) \tag{4}$$

At the edge of conduction band, the Fermi function is given by the following equation:

$$f(E_C) = \frac{1}{1 + e^{\frac{E_C - E_F}{kT}}} \approx e^{-\frac{(E_C - E_F)}{kT}} \tag{5}$$

Multiplying the effective density of states with Fermi function given in Eq. (5) gives the concentration of electrons in the conduction band shown in Eq. (6) as follows:

$$n_0 = N_C \, e^{\frac{-(E_C - E_f)}{kT}} \tag{6}$$

The concentration of holes (p_0) at the top of valence band can be calculated in the same way (detailed derivation of equations is out of scope of this textbook). The intrinsic carrier concentration (n_i) in a semiconductor is expressed as the product of n_0 and p_0.

$$n_0 \cdot p_0 = n_i^2 \tag{7}$$

2.4.   Charge Transport

The two main mechanisms for current flow in a semiconductor are drift and diffusion. If a semiconductor has excess carriers that are not evenly distributed at an initial time t_0, over time the excess carriers will diffuse until the carrier concentration is evenly distributed throughout the semiconductor. The diffusion of the carriers to reduce the concentration gradient is called diffusion current. The diffusion current density for electrons (J_n) and holes (J_p) is given by the following equations where D_n is the electron diffusion coefficient, D_p is the hole diffusion coefficient, and $dn(x)/dx$ and $dp(x)/dx$ are electron and hole concentration gradients, respectively.[2]

$$J_n(\text{diff.}) = qD_n \frac{dn(x)}{dx} \tag{8}$$

$$J_p(\text{diff.}) = -qD_p \frac{dp(x)}{dx} \tag{9}$$

The other mode of charge transport within the semiconductor is by the drift of electrons in the presence of an electric field. Carriers in a semiconductor have random motion with an overall net velocity of zero. This random motion of carriers in a semiconductor is a function of temperature. If an electric field is applied to the semiconductor, carriers will move with a velocity v. The electric field exerts a force (F) on the carriers given by:

$$F = qE \tag{10}$$

where q is the charge and E is the electric field. The average drift velocity (v) is a function of the applied electric field E and the mobility μ and is given by the equation below.

$$v = \mu E \tag{11}$$

Electrons will travel in the opposite direction of the applied electric field because of the negative charge on the electron and holes will travel in the same direction of the applied field because of the positive charge on the holes. Equation (12) is used to express current density (J) in terms of drift velocity and number of electrons crossing per unit area (n).

$$J = q\,n\,v \tag{12}$$

Substituting the expression for drift velocity in Eq. (12) and incorporating the hole-current component, the total current density in the semiconductor is given by the below equation where μ_n and μ_p are electron and hole mobilities, respectively.

$$J(\text{drift}) = q(n\,\mu_n + p\,\mu_p)E \tag{13}$$

The conductivity (σ) and resistivity (ρ) of the semiconductor can be extracted from the expression for total drift current density (Eq. (13)) using the following equations:

$$\sigma = q(n\,\mu_n + p\,\mu_p) \tag{14}$$

$$\rho = \frac{1}{q(n\,\mu_n + p\,\mu_p)} \tag{15}$$

It can be seen from the above equations that the electrical parameters are dependent on the mobility of the carriers in the semiconductor. The mobility in a semiconductor can be affected by several parameters such as temperature, doping, surface roughness, and the applied electric field. The total current in the semiconductor consists of the drift and diffusion current components and is defined by the following equations[2]:

$$J_n(x) = q\,\mu_n\,n(x)\,E(x) + qD_n\frac{dn(x)}{dx} \tag{16}$$

$$J_p(x) = q\,\mu_p\,p(x)\,E(x) - qD_p\frac{dp(x)}{dx} \qquad (17)$$

$$J(x) = J_n(x) + J_p(x) \qquad (18)$$

2.5.   Semiconductor P–N Junction

A p-n junction can be defined as the interface between two types of semiconductor material (p-type and n-type) which forms the basic building block for any semiconductor device. When the two different types of material are connected together, a band structure is formed. If p-type and n-type semiconductor materials are connected together without a bias, as shown in Fig. 5, electrons will diffuse to the p-type material and holes will diffuse to the n-type material.

As the carriers diffuse into the n-type and p-type material, an electric field will develop at the p-n junction that will prevent any more carriers from diffusing. The diffused carriers will leave behind fixed charge in the depletion region. In the n-type material, positive donor ions (N_d^+) will remain in the depletion region and in the p-type material negative acceptor ions (N_a^-) will remain in the depletion region. The electric field will establish a potential across the depleted region. This potential across the depletion region is called the built-in potential and is given by the following equation where N_a is acceptor concentration in the p-type material, N_d is the donor concentration in the n-type material, and n_i is the intrinsic carrier concentration:

$$V_{bi} = \frac{kT}{q}\ln\frac{N_d N_a}{n_i^2} \qquad (19)$$

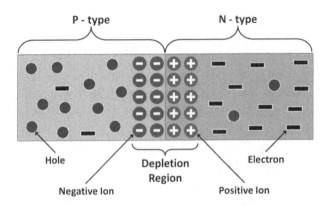

Fig. 5.   P–N junction under zero-bias condition.

In forward-bias mode, the p-type material is given a positive voltage with respect to the n-type material. The applied voltage will decrease the depletion region width, thereby reducing the barrier height. This reduction in the barrier height will allow carriers to flow. In reverse-bias mode, the n-type material is given a positive voltage with respect to the p-type material. The applied voltage will increase the barrier height or the depletion region width, thereby restricting carriers from flowing across the interface. Figures 6 and 7 show the P–N junction in forward- and reverse-bias conditions, respectively.[3,4]

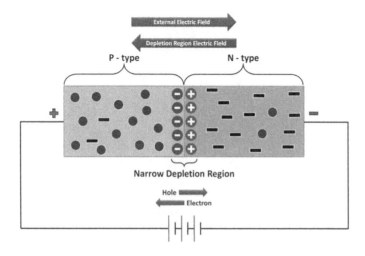

Fig. 6.   P–N junction under forward-bias condition.

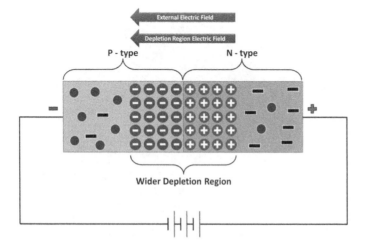

Fig. 7.   P–N junction under reverse-bias condition.

References

1. B. J. Baliga, *Fundamental of Power Semiconductor Devices*, New York, NY: Springer, 2008.
2. B. S. Streetman, *Solid State Electronic Devices*, 3rd edn. New Jersey, NJ: Prentice Hall, 1990.
3. S. Dimitrijev, *Understanding Semiconductor Devices*, Oxford University, New York, 2000.
4. S. M. Sze, *Physics of Semiconductor Devices*, 2nd edn. New York, NY: Wiley, 1981.

Chapter 3

Introduction to Silvaco©
ATLAS TCAD Software

Before any semiconductor device structure is finalized for commercial production, it is important to understand device characteristics and performance. Technology Computer-Aided Design (TCAD) software provides an effective solution for simulating semiconductor device structure under steady-state and transient condition. Analysis of electrothermal parameters like electric field, leakage current, localized heating, and lattice temperature can aid in isolating structural vulnerability and understanding possible causes of device failure. This chapter will provide a detailed description of Silvaco© ATLAS commercial TCAD software and its application in wide bandgap SiC power device simulation.

3.1. Tradeoff Study

Modeling and simulation, in general, help in obtaining information regarding the behavior and functioning of an object under consideration, without actual testing. Irrespective of the object being modeled, any modeling technique must be evaluated for the tradeoffs shown in Fig. 1. The tradeoffs must be carefully studied in order to develop a model which provides the user with specific information that is relevant to the analysis performed. This tradeoff study focuses on the three major factors which determine the efficiency and performance of a model: Speed, Stability, and Accuracy.

Speed of a model is very important from a simulation perspective as it determines the time it would take for the simulation to produce the desired results. Since the simulation speed is dependent on the complexity of the model and the computational hardware, a model should exhibit minimum simulation time on a hardware platform with moderate configuration. One of the primary attributes of a model is the *Accuracy* of its simulation results which must be comparable to the test results of the actual object. Accuracy

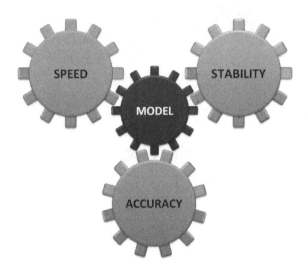

Fig. 1.   Tradeoffs involved in model development.

of a model can be enhanced by including detailed mathematical equations describing the behavior of the object. *Stability* of a model is equally critical as the aforementioned factors. The simulation software must be able to execute the model code without encountering any program execution error like convergence error or mathematical errors like floating point or divide-by-zero error, etc. Based on the above description, it is highly unlikely that a model can be developed which encompasses all the required attributes thereby creating a model which exhibits an extremely high degree of accuracy and stability while maintaining high simulation speed. This is because a high degree of accuracy requires the model to have several complex mathematical equations to replicate the object behavior. However, an increase in the number/complexity of the equations would result in stability issues along with increased simulation time. Similarly, a model comprising of fewer, less complex equations would result in higher stability and reduced simulation time, but at the expense of accuracy of the results. Hence, it is important to understand the objective of the modeling and the information that is expected out of the simulation and acquire an optimum balance between the tradeoff factors.

3.2.   Modeling Techniques

Semiconductor modeling can be defined as the technique of replicating the behavior of a semiconductor device using mathematical equations derived from either fundamental device physics or electrical characteristics. Even though there are different techniques for semiconductor modeling, the two main types of modeling techniques which are crucial to device and application engineers are detailed in the sections that follow.

3.2.1. SPICE-based modeling

Simulation Program with Integrated Circuit Emphasis (SPICE) is a general purpose computer simulation and modeling program which is a popular choice among students and engineers for simulating electronic circuits and predicting its behavior. Due to its open source nature, several SPICE simulators are available as freeware. Programs like LTspice developed by *Linear Technology*, Cadence OrCAD PSPICE developed by *Cadence Design Systems*, and NI Multisim developed by *National Instruments* (NI) are among the major SPICE-based simulators available in the industry. SPICE simulators operate by converting the circuit into nodes and using the *Kirchhoff Current Law* (KCL) to generate nodal equations. These nodal equations are then solved via matrix technique to evaluate the node voltages. Using the node voltage and loop current data, parameters like power dissipation and energy can be calculated.[1,2] Most of the SPICE simulators have a built-in library of active and passive device models and are capable of accepting user-defined or third-party SPICE models. Models include mathematical equations to define the relation between voltage and current at the terminals of a device. Some of the advanced models may also include equations to incorporate the effect of temperature as well as evaluate the variation in junction temperature based on power dissipation. In general, SPICE models are developed based on the semiconductor device behavior rather than charge carrier dynamics, thereby omitting any complex physics-based equation. The absence of complex mathematical equations aids in faster simulation of SPICE-based circuit as compared to physics-based simulation. The ability to simulate complex circuits and analyze major electrical performance parameters is the primary reason behind its widespread use in educational as well as professional establishments.[3,4]

3.2.2. Physics-based modeling

Physics-based modeling involves the design and simulation of semiconductor device structure using fundamental mathematical equations which form the basis for electrostatics and electrodynamics. Even though SPICE-based modeling provides a faster and relatively accurate solution to device response in a circuit, it fails to provide an in-depth analysis of a semiconductor device structure. This particular modeling approach is used to perform a comprehensive analysis of semiconductor device structure before actual fabrication. Analysis includes current distribution, verification of electronic properties, electric field distribution, thermal profiling of device lattice, and study of possible failure mechanisms. Physics-based modeling of a semiconductor device is carried out using a TCAD software.[5,6] TCAD software uses computer simulations to develop and optimize semiconductor fabrication process (Process TCAD) and device technology (Device TCAD). The application suites provided by *Silvaco Inc.* and *Synopsys Inc.* are among the major TCAD software providers in the industry. The development of a TCAD model begins with the creation of the approximate semiconductor device structure on a 2D/3D grid which is divided into a number of grid/mesh points or nodes. The electrical characteristics of the device are then predicted by simulating the transport of carriers through the grid points by applying differential equations derived from Maxwell's laws. Due to the complex mathematical equations used to describe the carrier transport mechanism, TCAD simulations are inherently slow and require powerful computational hardware.[7,8]

Both the aforementioned modeling techniques are important from an engineer's perspective; however, selection of the appropriate modeling scheme is based on whether the analysis is performed at a system level or device level. Table 1 compares the different aspects of SPICE-based and TCAD-based modeling techniques.

Table 1.   Comparison between SPICE and TCAD modeling schemes.

Parameters	SPICE Modeling	TCAD Modeling
Analysis	Circuit and system level.	Device level. Seldom used for large circuit-level analysis due to simulation time.
Device scaling	SPICE-based models can be developed to match the actual device with ratings comparable/equal to the manufacturer ratings.	TCAD modeling limits the size of the device structure due to the complexity involved in the simulation.
Semiconductor mechanism	Each mechanism involved in the particular semiconductor device has to be modeled separately, e.g. BJT latch-up and dV/dt turn ON in power MOSFET.	Since a TCAD model operates on the basis of carrier dynamics, various semiconductor device mechanisms are included by default.

(Continued)

Table 1. (*Continued*)

Parameters	SPICE Modeling	TCAD Modeling
Convergence	Typically not an issue; however, may occur during power electronic circuit simulation.	Serious issue especially for wide bandgap (WBG) devices.
Debugging	Relatively easier as compared to TCAD modeling.	Requires detailed software knowledge.
Hardware	Does not require expensive computational resources. Works on most of the laptops and personal computers.	High-performance computational resources required.
Software license	Full version freeware available, e.g. LTspice.	Mostly licensed.
Simulation time	Minimum	Can be extremely long (hours to days).
Learning curve	SPICE software is relatively easier to learn as compared to TCAD software.	Steep learning curve for TCAD software. Requires extensive knowledge of the semiconductor material.
Literature	Plethora of information including tutorials and sample codes available online and in textbooks.	Lack of tutorials and sample code. Primary source of information is the software manual. Journal and conference publications can also be used for reference.

3.3.   Introduction to Silvaco© TCAD

Silvaco© ATLAS software is designed to simulate the electrical, optical, and thermal behavior of semiconductor devices. It provides a physics-based, modular, and extensible platform to analyze DC, AC, and time domain responses for all semiconductor-based technologies in 2D and 3D. Silvaco© ATLAS is a physics-based simulation software which predicts the electrical and electronic characteristics of a semiconductor device with a specified physical structure, material properties, and bias condition. The Silvaco© TCAD software suite comprises of Process TCAD to simulate the various processing steps like epitaxial growth, etching and deposition, diffusion, implantation, and annealing and Device TCAD for the electrical characterization of 2D/3D devices. In this textbook, modeling and simulation-based characterization of SiC power devices is based on Silvaco© ATLAS 2D Device TCAD software. The analysis of various processing steps involved in SiC device fabrication via Silvaco© Process TCAD tool is beyond the scope of this textbook.[9,10]

3.4.   Silvaco© ATLAS Capabilities

The ATLAS software suite comprises of several modules which provide the capability to model and simulate a variety of semiconductor devices based on the area of application. The wide range of applications that can benefit from ATLAS device TCAD has been summarized in Fig. 2. A detailed explanation of each of the applications can be found on the software website.

In order to cater to the wide range of applications, ATLAS TCAD has several built-in modules to support various semiconductor types. A summary of the module name along with a brief description is shown in Table 2. In this textbook, discussion will be entirely based on the BLAZE, GIGA, and MixedMode modules of the ATLAS simulator.

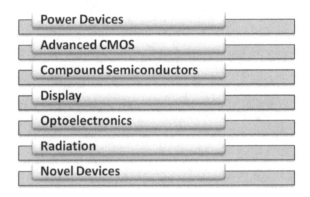

Fig. 2.   Silvaco© ATLAS semiconductor device applications.

Table 2.   Modules incorporated into Silvaco© ATLAS Device TCAD.

Module	Description
1. S-Pisces	Advanced 2D device simulator for silicon-based technologies that incorporates both drift-diffusion and energy balance transport equations.
2. BLAZE	BLAZE is a 2D simulator for semiconductor devices fabricated using advanced materials. Includes a library of physical models and material parameters for binary, ternary, and quaternary semiconductors, e.g. SiC and GaN.
3. GIGA	GIGA 2D non-isothermal device simulator simulates self heating effects when combined with S-Pisces or BLAZE. Models include heat generation, heat flow, lattice heating, heat sinks, and effects of local temperature on physical constants.

(Continued)

Table 2. (*Continued*)

Module	Description
4. MixedMode	MixedMode is a circuit simulator that includes physically based devices in addition to compact analytical models.
5. Luminous	Luminous is an advanced device simulator specially designed to model light absorption and photo-generation in non-planar semiconductor devices.
6. Organic Solar	Organic Solar module enables ATLAS to simulate the electrical and optical properties of organic solar cell devices, photo-detectors, and image sensors.
7. LED	LED is a module used for simulation and analysis of light-emitting diodes.
8. TFT	TFT is an advanced device technology simulator equipped with the physical models and specialized numerical techniques required to simulate amorphous or polysilicon devices including thin film transistors.
9. VCSEL	VCSEL is used in conjunction with the ATLAS framework to produce physically based simulations of vertical cavity surface-emitting lasers (VCSELs).
10. Organic Display	Organic Display module enables ATLAS to simulate the electrical and optical properties of organic display devices such as OTFTs and OLEDs.
11. LASER	World's first commercially available simulator for semiconductor laser diodes.
12. Quantum	Quantum provides a set of models for simulation of various effects of quantum confinement and quantum transport of carriers in semiconductor devices.
13. Ferro	Ferro has been developed to combine the charge-sheet model of FET with Maxwell's first equation, which describes the properties of ferroelectric film.
14. Magnetic	Magnetic is an advanced device simulator specially designed to model light absorption and photo-generation in non-planar semiconductor devices.
15. Noise	Noise combined with S-Pisces or Blaze allows analysis of the small-signal noise generated within semiconductor devices.
16. REM	The Radiation Effect Module (REM) allows Atlas 2D/3D and Victory 3D simulators to model total dose, dose rate, and SEU effects in semiconductors through the generation of defect states, fixed charge, and charge transport within insulating materials.
17. MC Device	Monte Carlo Device simulates the behavior of relaxed and strained silicon devices including non-equilibrium and ballistic effects in 2D.

Source: Silvaco© ATLAS manual.

3.5. Simulation Precision

WBG semiconductor materials like silicon carbide are characterized by their extremely low intrinsic carrier concentration which creates an inherent problem in the simulation of SiC power devices, especially during blocking/breakdown voltage simulation. The breakdown voltage capability of a power device structure is determined in ATLAS via steady-state simulation where the blocking voltage across the device is increased; for example, in a p-i-n diode structure, the cathode (K) to anode (A) voltage (V_{KA}) or $-|V_{AK}|$ is increased. The increase in blocking voltage is accompanied by a proportional increase in electric field within the device to the point where the device undergoes avalanche breakdown due to impact ionization of carriers. The phenomenon of avalanche breakdown in a power device is governed by the concentration/density of high-energy carriers. This can be explained based on the Maxwell–Boltzmann distribution function described by Eq. (1) where $f(E)$ is the probability that a particle will have energy E and A is a normalization constant:

$$f(E) = \frac{1}{A\,e^{\left(\frac{E}{kT}\right)}} \tag{1}$$

It can be inferred from Eq. (1) that the probability for any particle to attain energy E decreases progressively with increasing magnitude of E. This inference can be better understood by the graphical representation of the Maxwell–Boltzmann distribution curve shown in Fig. 3. Hence, it is evident from the Maxwell–Boltzmann energy distribution that the density

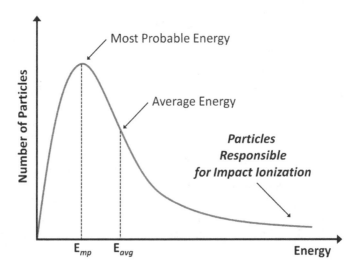

Fig. 3.   Maxwell–Boltzmann energy distribution.

of high-energy particles responsible for impact ionization is very low.[11] When combined with the extremely low intrinsic carrier concentration of SiC, avalanche breakdown simulation of the SiC power device TCAD model becomes extremely difficult. This issue with SiC device simulation can be circumvented by artificially increasing the intrinsic carrier concentration using the following techniques:

- **ATLAS material statement**: The intrinsic carrier concentration of the SiC device can be increased by using the parameter **NI.MIN** in the **MATERIAL** statement. For example, **NI.MIN**= 1.5×10^5 would specify 1.5×10^5 cm^{-3} as the minimum allowable value of the intrinsic carrier density to be used during the simulation.[9]

- **Photo-carrier generation via high-energy optical beam**: Another technique used to artificially increase the carrier concentration is to use a high-energy optical beam like laser to generate electron–hole pairs in the intrinsic/drift region of the power device structure to aid in the avalanche breakdown simulation.

Even though the aforementioned techniques to increase the carrier density are feasible, it is a workaround and not a solution to the issue pertaining to WBG devices since any device structure should be simulated the way it is instead of artificially modifying its properties. The ultra-low intrinsic carrier concentration of WBG material as compared to a small bandgap material like silicon results in extremely low values of carrier current densities being calculated during numerical simulation. If the simulator is not configured for higher precision, results of every iteration will be truncated to the default precision value, resulting in incorrect values being piled up. These incorrect values will prevent avalanche multiplication process as there is no trigger point for the breakdown process. This issue can be better understood by the following analogy — *In reality, no matter how much snow is accumulated on a mountain top, there must be some sort of trigger to initiate the avalanche formation*. Based on the Maxwell–Boltzmann distribution, it can be concluded that, in order to capture events pertaining to the few high-energy particles, device simulator precision must be increased.

Since TCAD simulations are based on numerical calculations, the bit precision of the simulator plays an important role in maintaining the integrity of the simulation results. To ensure convergence of simulation and accuracy of the results, it is imperative to ensure numerical resolution of the quantities $(n - p)$ and $(n + p)$, where n and p are electron and hole concentration, respectively. The term denoting the difference in carrier concentrations is used in the following equation to calculate the electrostatic potential ψ based on the space charge density ρ and local permittivity ε:

$$\text{div}(\varepsilon \nabla \psi) = -\rho \tag{2}$$

The term denoting the sum of carrier concentrations is used implicitly in the calculation of current conservation. In order to accurately resolve the quantities $(n - p)$ and $(n + p)$ during numerical simulation, it is critical to maintain P significant bits of arithmetic precision, where P is approximately given by the following relation:[9]

$$P \sim \frac{|\ln(n) - \ln(p)|}{\ln(2)} \tag{3}$$

Based on the theory of carrier statistics, it can be estimated that, for a convergent and accurate simulation, the significant bit precision should satisfy the following condition where E_G is the semiconductor material bandgap, k is the Boltzmann constant, and T is the lattice temperature:[9]

$$P \geq \frac{1}{\ln(2)} \left(\frac{E_G}{kT} \right) \tag{4}$$

It can be seen from Eq. (4) that the simulation bit precision is directly proportional to the energy bandgap and inversely proportional to the lattice temperature. Table 3 shows the recommended bit precision required for silicon and silicon carbide (4H-SiC) simulation at 300 K lattice temperature. The values shown in Table 3 are solely based on the result obtained by evaluating Eq. (4).

Silvaco© ATLAS runs on a default precision of 64 bits which is typically sufficient for silicon-based devices unless a complex device is being simulated. In order to simulate WBG semiconductor devices, extended precision capability is incorporated into Silvaco© ATLAS. The complete precision capability of ATLAS has been summarized in Table 4. Even though SiC device simulation would ideally require 256-bit precision as per Eq. (4), convergence and accuracy can be obtained at 128-bit and 160-bit precision

Table 3.   Simulation bit precision required for convergence and accuracy.

Material	Energy Bandgap (eV)	Simulation bit Precision (Calculated)
Silicon	1.12	63
Silicon Carbide (4H-SiC)	3.26	183

Table 4.   Silvaco© extended precision scheme.

	Default	Extended	Extended	Extended	Extended
Precision (bits)	64	80	128	160	256
Significant bits	53	64	104	128	209
Type size (bytes)	8	16	16	32	32

Source: Silvaco© ATLAS manual.

since every device presents a different scenario based on the structure, mesh profile, simulation models, and parameter selection.[9] Under the same conditions leading to a well-converged solution, the simulation time increases significantly with the precision especially at 128-bit and above.

 The extended precision mode will only work in the *LINUX* version of Silvaco© ATLAS TCAD software. The *Windows* version will only support the default 64-bit precision.

Extended precision for Silvaco© ATLAS can be enabled via *deckbuild* code; for example, 160-bit precision is enabled using the following statement:

go atlas simflags = "-160"

However, using the above statement alone is not sufficient to implement extended precision. Even though the simulator executes the code with 160-bit precision, the tolerance values for the various convergence criteria specified in the *deckbuild* code must be modified accordingly. Failure to do so will result in abnormal simulation results since the current density value calculated during each numerical iteration will not attain the tolerance required for convergence. Tables 5 and 6 show the various tolerance parameters associated with convergence criteria.

The tolerance parameters shown in Table 5 are used with the **METHOD** statement. If the parameters are not specified, default values will be used by the simulator. During extended-precision SiC device simulation, the tolerance parameters must be set to custom values depending on the bit precision used. Based on the numerous simulations performed on SiC devices, an upper limit for the tolerance parameters was determined and is shown in Table 6. There is no hard and fast rule to use the tolerance values in Table 6 since every device presents a different scenario. Moreover, the values may need to be modified based on steady-state or transient simulation. There is a tradeoff associated with the selection of values for the tolerance parameters. A higher tolerance would ensure the accuracy of results at the expense of

Table 5.   Major simulation convergence parameters.

Parameter	Definition	Default Value
IR.TOL	Absolute current convergence criteria	5.0×10^{-15}
IX.TOL	Relative current convergence criteria	2.0×10^{-5}
CR.TOL	Absolute tolerance for the continuity equation	5.0×10^{-18}
CX.TOL	Relative tolerance for the continuity equation	10^{-5}
PR.TOL	Absolute tolerance for the Poisson equation	5.0×10^{-26}
PX.TOL	Relative tolerance for the potential equation	10^{-5}
TLR.TOL*	Absolute tolerance for convergence of the lattice temperature equation	100
TLX.TOL*	Relative tolerance for convergence of the lattice temperature equation	10^{-3}

Note: *Default values are typically used.
Source: Silvaco© ATLAS manual.

Table 6.   Maximum tolerance value for convergence parameters based on bit precision.

Parameter	Maximum Tolerance Value		
	80-bit Precision	128-bit Precision	160-bit Precision
IR.TOL	10^{-17}	10^{-32}	10^{-39}
IX.TOL	10^{-14}	10^{-28}	10^{-35}
CR.TOL	10^{-17}	10^{-32}	10^{-39}
CX.TOL	10^{-14}	10^{-28}	10^{-35}
PR.TOL	10^{-27}	10^{-44}	10^{-50}
PX.TOL	10^{-17}	10^{-31}	10^{-36}

Note: Values were obtained from simulation and may vary based on the device, models, and nature of the simulation.

extended simulation time since the simulator will keep on iterating and not proceed to the next bias/time step until the tolerance value has been met for the previous step. Similarly, a lower tolerance would result in faster simulation, but may compromise the accuracy of results.[9]

 The tolerance values for simulation parameters may need to be increased or decreased during transient simulation to obtain convergence.

In order to demonstrate the impact of bit precision on the simulation results, 2D structure of a parallel plane p-i-n diode was simulated under varying bit precision. The doping profile contour plot of a 1200 V 4H-SiC p-i-n diode with an active area of 10 μm^2 is shown in Fig. 4 (dimensions in μm).

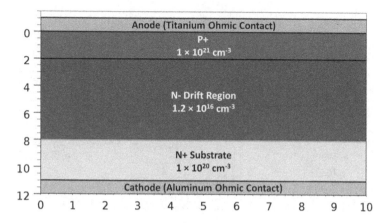

Fig. 4.   1200 V SiC parallel plane p-i-n diode structure.

Doping concentrations of 1×10^{21} cm^{-3}, 1.2×10^{16} cm^{-3}, and 1×10^{20} cm^{-3} were used for the P+, N− drift, and N+ substrate regions, respectively. A heavily doped P+ junction depth of 2 μm and drift region thickness of 6 μm were selected based on design equations. Typically, the substrate thickness of SiC devices is in the order of 150–250 μm; however, a substrate thickness of 3 μm was selected for this example to reduce the number of mesh points and expedite the simulation process.

The p-i-n diode was simulated for its breakdown current density versus voltage (J–V) characteristics under 80-bit, 128-bit and 160-bit simulation precision. The 80-bit and 128-bit simulations were run with default tolerance values, whereas the 160-bit simulations were carried out with both default and user-defined tolerance values. The anode current density data was multiplied throughout by −1 for proper graphical representation. The breakdown J–V characteristics of the p-i-n diode using 80-bit and 128-bit simulation precision are shown in Figs. 5 and 6, respectively. Simulation using 80-bit precision resulted in severe distortion in the breakdown J–V waveform as seen in Fig. 5. Device breakdown was not observed even when the anode voltage was ramped up to −1400 V. Increasing the precision to 128-bit resulted in a much smoother waveform as shown in Fig. 6; however, there is a severe anomaly in the breakdown regime evident from the increase in the anode current density followed by a sudden reversal in the negative direction. This anomaly is followed by the current density re-entering the leakage regime.

In the next phase, the same p-i-n diode structure was simulated using an extended precision of 160-bits with the default values of tolerance parameters specified in Table 5. The resultant J–V waveform during breakdown

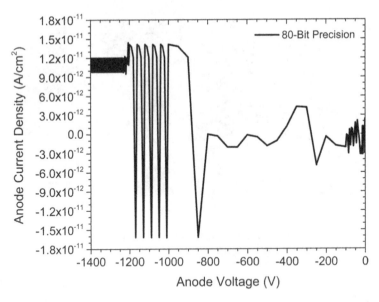

Fig. 5. Breakdown *J–V* characteristics of a 1200 V SiC parallel plane p-i-n diode using 80-bit precision.

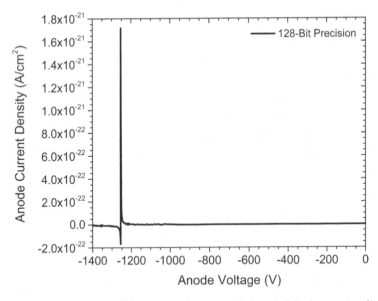

Fig. 6. Breakdown *J–V* characteristics of a 1200 V SiC parallel plane p-i-n diode using 128-bit precision.

simulation is shown in Fig. 7. It is evident from the waveform that despite smooth transition through the leakage regime of the breakdown curve and an abrupt increase in the current density at the expected breakdown voltage, there was a sudden reversal in the anode current density followed by re-entry

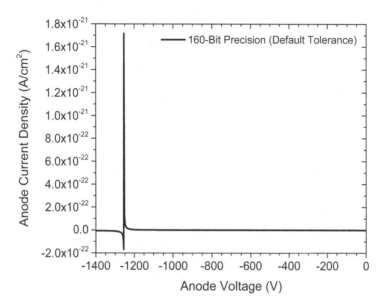

Fig. 7. Breakdown J–V characteristics of a 1200 V SiC parallel plane p-i-n diode using 160-bit precision with default tolerance values.

into the leakage regime. This would represent a scenario similar to that shown in Fig. 6 pertaining to 128-bit simulation, thereby highlighting the importance of tolerance values. In the final phase of simulation, the p-i-n diode was simulated using an extended precision of 160-bits along with higher/tighter tolerance values. The breakdown J–V waveform, shown in Fig. 8, accurately represents p-i-n diode breakdown at the expected reverse-bias anode voltage accompanied by a rapid increase in the anode current density.

Table 7 shows the average time taken for the simulation under varying precision conditions. These simulations were performed individually, and it was made sure that no other simulation was running on the machine. Increase in simulation precision is accompanied by an increase in the simulation time duration with an exception for 160-bit simulation with low tolerance. This exception is due to the mathematical truncation errors that occur when high-precision simulation is not supported by high tolerance values. Even though the time duration values shown in Table 7 appear to be acceptable, the difference can become extremely significant when complex simulations like Mixed-Mode analysis are performed on the particular device model.

The following code was used to simulate the 1200 V parallel plane SiC p-i-n diode structure for its reverse-bias breakdown characteristics

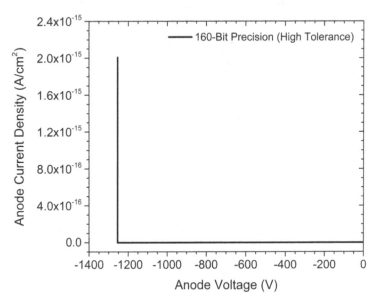

Fig. 8. Breakdown *J–V* characteristics of a 1200 V SiC parallel plane p-i-n diode using 160-bit precision with higher tolerance values.

Table 7. Simulation bit precision and time duration.

Simulation bit Precision	Average simulation time (minutes)
80	1.44
128	2.80
160 (low tolerance)	2.13
160 (high tolerance)	5.80

using 160-bit extended precision and higher tolerance parameters. A brief explanation of the breakdown simulation program is provided in the code walkthrough (Table 8).

```
Sample code: Extended precision simulation of 1200 V parallel plane SiC p-i-n diode structure

1.   GO ATLAS SIMFLAGS="-V 5.18.3.R -P 32 -160"
2.
3.   MESH
4.
5.   x.mesh  loc=0.0    spac=0.5
6.   x.mesh  loc=10.0   spac=0.5
7.
8.   y.mesh  loc=-1.0   spac=1.0
9.   y.mesh  loc=0.00   spac=0.25
```

```
10. y.mesh  loc=1.90  spac=0.01
11. y.mesh  loc=7.50  spac=1.0
12. y.mesh  loc=8.10  spac=0.2
13. y.mesh  loc=11.0  spac=1.0
14. y.mesh  loc=12.0  spac=1.0
15.
16. REGION  num=1  material=4H-SiC   x.min=0  x.max=10  y.min=0  y.max=11
17.
18. ELECTRODE  name=anode    material=titanium   y.min=-1   y.max=0
19. ELECTRODE  name=cathode  material=aluminum   y.min=11   y.max=12
20.
21. DOPING  uniform  n.type  conc=1.2e16  REGION=1
22. DOPING  uniform  p.type  conc=1.e21   y.min=0  y.max=2
23. DOPING  uniform  n.type  conc=1.e20   y.min=8  y.max=11
24.
25. SAVE  outf=PIN_2D_Structure.str
26.
27. MATERIAL  material=4H-SiC  REGION=1  permittivity=9.76   eg300=3.26
    affinity=3.7  egalpha=3.3e-2  egbeta=1.e+5  nc300=1.7e+19  nv300=2.5e+19
    arichn=146  arichp=30  augn=3.e-29  augp=3.e-29  taun0=3.33e-6  taup0=6.7e-7
    nsrhn=3.e+17  nsrhp=3.e+17  edb=0.050  eab=0.20
28.
29. MODELS  REGION=1 MATERIAL=4H-SIC FERMIDIRAC ANALYTIC CONWELL SRH BGN AUGER
    INCOMPLETE  TEMP=300  PRINT
30.
31. MOBILITY  material=4H-SiC REGION=1  vsatn=2.2e7  vsatp=2.2e7  betan=1.2
    betap=2  mu1n.caug=40  mu2n.caug=1136  ncritn.caug=2e17  alphan.caug=-3
    betan.caug=-3  gamman.caug=0.0  deltan.caug=0.76   mu1p.caug=20
    mu2p.caug=125  ncritp.caug=1.e19  alphap.caug=-3  betap.caug=-3
    gammap.caug=0.0  deltap.caug=0.5
32.
33. IMPACT  REGION=1  ANISO  E.SIDE  SELB  SIC4H0001  an1=3.44e6  an2=3.44e6
    bn1=2.58e7  bn2=2.58e7  ap1=3.5e6  ap2=3.5e6  bp1=1.7e7  bp2=1.7e7
    opphe=0.106
34.
35. METHOD  NEWTON autonr  climit=1.e-9  maxtraps=40  itlimit=40   dvmax=1.e8
    ir.tol=1.e-40  cr.tol=1.e-40  ix.tol=1.e-40  px.tol=1.e-30  pr.tol=1.e-45
    cx.tol=1.e-30
36.
37. LOG  outf=PIN2D_Reverse_HP.log
38.
39. SOLVE  init
40. SOLVE  vanode=-0.2  vstep=-0.2     vfinal=-2.0  name=anode
41. SOLVE  vstep=-2     vfinal=-20     name=anode
42. SOLVE  vstep=-5     vfinal=-100    name=anode
43. SOLVE  vstep=-50    vfinal=-1000   name=anode
44. SOLVE  vstep=-10    vfinal=-1200   name=anode
45. SOLVE  vstep=-2     vfinal=-1500   name=anode   compl=1e-22  cname=anode
46.
47. SAVE  outf=PIN2D_Reverse_160_High.str
48.
49. QUIT
```

Table 8. Code walkthrough: Extended precision simulation of 1200 V parallel plane p-i-n diode structure.

Line No:	Functionality
1	Configure ATLAS simulator to use 160-bit extended precision and utilize 32 cores of the CPU if hardware resources are available. The version of ATLAS to be used by the simulator is set to 5.18.3.R using the -V option in the simflags command.
3	Initialize device structure mesh information
5–14	X and Y mesh distribution (Will be discussed later)
16	Declare 4H-SiC as the material for the area of the semiconductor specified by the x and y coordinates.
18–19	Electrode specifications for the p-i-n diode (anode and cathode)
21–23	Specify doping profile, type, and concentration for different areas of the p-i-n diode structure
25	Save the device structure (**.str**) file on the local hard drive. The device structure can be viewed by opening the file via **TonyPlot** to troubleshoot/optimize the structure.
27	Specify material parameters for 4H-SiC. Detailed description of these parameters are available in the Silvaco© ATLAS manual. The values for these parameters can either be obtained via material research or from literature.
29	Specify the various models to be included in the 4H-SiC p-i-n diode simulation
31	Specify mobility parameters for 4H-SiC. Detailed description of these parameters are available in the Silvaco© ATLAS manual. The values for these parameters can either be obtained via material research or from literature.
33	Specify Impact Ionization parameters for 4H-SiC. This statement is mandatory to obtain device breakdown characteristics.
35	Specify the solver type and the tolerance values to be used during the simulation. This is an extremely critical statement which can alter the simulation outcome.
37	Save the simulation log (**.log**) file on the local hard drive. The simulation results can be viewed by opening the file via **TonyPlot**.
39	Solve for the initial bias conditions for the simulation
40–45	Use solve statement to increment the negative anode voltage in discrete steps. The compliance parameter (**compl**) in line 45 forces the simulator to proceed to the next line once the anode current reaches the specified compliance value. This is important, especially in breakdown simulation because once the device enters the breakdown regime, it is not necessary to run the simulation for higher magnitude of current since the breakdown voltage would have already been determined.

(Continued)

Table 8. (*Continued*)

Line No:	Functionality
47	Save the post-simulation device structure (*.str*) file on the local hard drive. Saving the file at this stage of the simulation will enable the user to visualize the variation in various electrothermal parameters within the device structure introduced due to the particular simulation. For example, in this simulation, the user can view the electric field profile in the p-i-n diode during avalanche breakdown.
49	Terminate the simulation

 Simulation error message "Not a Number" could be an indicator of low-precision simulation. Most of the time, this error can be eliminated by using a higher simulation bit-precision.

3.6. Mesh Design

Going back to the basics of physics-based modeling, structure of the semiconductor device has to be designed on a 2D/3D grid which is divided into grid/mesh points or nodes. A well-defined mesh is the key to obtaining accurate simulation results with reasonable computational time and hardware. A complex device structure with sub-micron features will require a large number of mesh points to accurately define the junction boundaries and ensure the accuracy of simulation results. However, increasing the number of mesh points will have an adverse effect on the simulation speed and time. Hence, the device structure design must be optimized to have sufficient mesh points to obtain accurate results while minimizing the simulation time and computational hardware requirements.

3.6.1. Critical regions

As discussed before, tradeoff exists between the mesh density, simulation accuracy, and simulation time. The user has to design a device structure with an efficient mesh profile which provides the optimum balance between accuracy and performance of the model. The following points can be considered to design an efficient mesh profile for the semiconductor device:

(a) Semiconductor junctions

Semiconductor junction is a critical area in the device which requires high mesh point density. Examples of P–N junction in power semiconductor devices include the interface P+/N– Drift region in a power p-i-n diode, emitter-base and collector-base junction in a BJT, P-base/N– drift region in a MOSFET, and P+ gate/N+ source, and P+ gate/N– drain in a vertical JFET. In order to understand the impact of mesh point density on the semiconductor junction, example of a SiC p-i-n diode will be used. The p-i-n diode structure used in the discussion was designed for a breakdown voltage of 1200 V and forward current density of 100 A/cm². The diode regions and their associated mesh profiles are shown in Figs. 9–12, parts (a) and (b), respectively. These diode structures were developed using

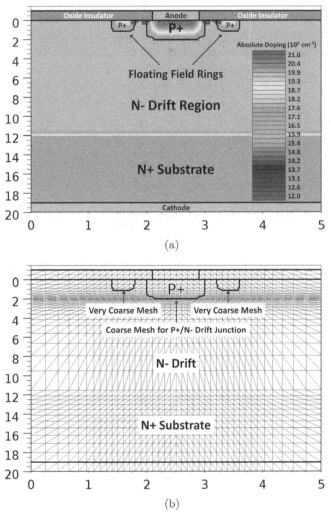

(a)

(b)

Fig. 9.   (a) SiC planar junction p-i-n diode structure with 1517 mesh points. (b) SiC planar junction p-i-n diode structure mesh profile (1517 mesh points).

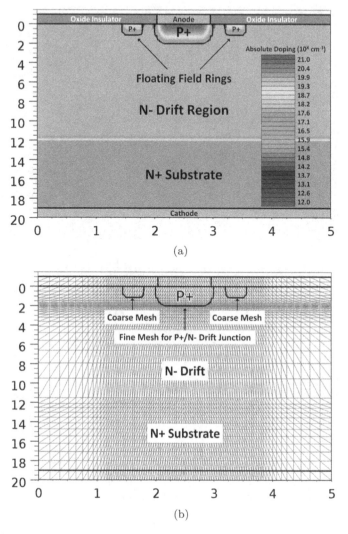

Fig. 10. (a) SiC planar junction p-i-n diode structure with 3330 mesh points. (b) SiC planar junction p-i-n diode structure mesh profile (3330 mesh points).

increasing mesh point density from Figs. 9–12. It can be seen from the diode structures that as the number of mesh points increase, the fine structural details become easier to realize, e.g. floating field rings typically have much smaller dimensions as compared to the active area. This can be explained based on the following: when a coarse mesh approach is used to reduce the simulation time, the software automatically readjusts the dimensions of the device features to the nearest triangle on the 2D grid, thereby resulting in smaller/larger dimension than desired. Similarly, the doping profiles also

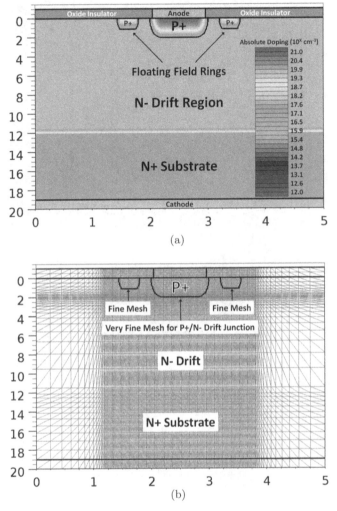

Fig. 11. (a) SiC planar junction p-i-n diode structure with 5809 mesh points. (b) SiC planar junction p-i-n diode mesh profile (5809 mesh points).

become well defined with increased mesh points especially for non-uniform doping profiles like Gaussian.

 Power Device modeling and simulation using TCAD is a time-intensive process. Hence, Mesh profile optimization has to be the highest priority task while developing a semiconductor device model in Silvaco© ATLAS.

The differences induced in the device structure due to the variations in the mesh profile can have a profound impact on the device characteristics.

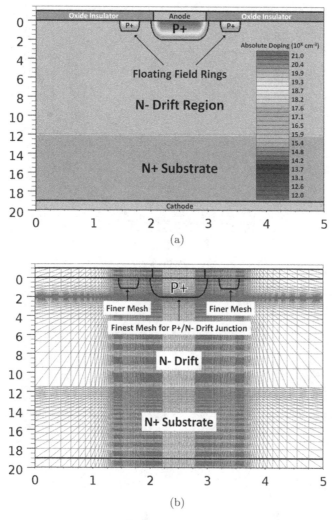

Fig. 12. (a) SiC planar junction p-i-n diode structure with 12,540 mesh points. (b) SiC planar junction p-i-n diode mesh profile (12,540 mesh points).

The easiest way to perform a preliminary test on the device model is to simulate the device structure for its steady-state characteristics and observe the difference based on the variation in the total mesh points. In case of a p-i-n diode, this would pertain to the forward and reverse breakdown J–V characteristics.

The forward and breakdown J–V characteristics of the p-i-n diode using varying mesh point density structures has been plotted in Figs. 13 and 14 on a linear and semi-logarithmic scale, respectively. In the forward J–V characteristics, there is a significant difference in the ON-state characteristics

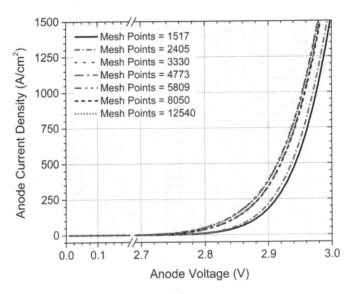

Fig. 13.   Forward *J–V* characteristics of SiC planar junction p-i-n diode at varying mesh point densities on a linear scale.

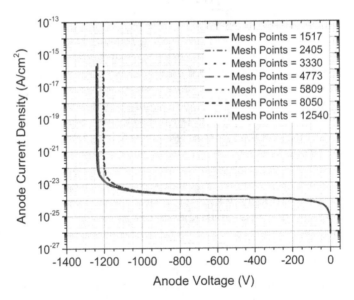

Fig. 14.   Breakdown *J–V* characteristics of SiC planar junction p-i-n diode at varying mesh point densities on a log scale.

especially at 100 A/cm^2 current density. The structures with 1517 and 2405 mesh points had an average ON-state voltage drop of approximately 2.87 V, whereas all the higher mesh point designs had an ON-state voltage drop of approximately 2.83 V at 100 A/cm^2. The diode ON-state loss decreased

Table 9. 4H-SiC p-i-n diode simulation time summary for varying mesh points.

Device	Mesh Points	Total Simulation Time (Minutes)
1	1517	19.7
2	2405	30.5
3	3330	44.5
4	4773	60 (1.0 hours)
5	5809	78 (1.3 hours)
6	8050	120 (2.0 hours)
7	12,540	234 (3.9 hours)

with increasing mesh points; however, it is extremely difficult to determine the exact pattern in which the mesh point density is affecting the device characteristics since a mesh profile can be made fine or coarse by altering either the X-mesh or Y-mesh or both. The breakdown characteristics show a subtle difference between diode structures with lower mesh points and higher mesh points. The p-i-n diode structures with 8050 and 12,540 mesh points had a slightly lower breakdown voltage of 1200 V (average value) as compared to 1232 V (average value) for the lower mesh point designs, a difference of 32 V. This can be explained based on the uniformity of the doping profile and accuracy of dimensions of the field rings, which increases with higher mesh point density.

The aforementioned discussion highlights the effect of variation in mesh points on the device characteristics. But it also raises an important question for students and engineers on the optimum mesh points required for fast and accurate semiconductor device model simulation. In order to assess the model efficacy, the total simulation time taken for the steady-state simulation (forward and reverse breakdown J–V characteristics) has been summarized in Table 9.

The values in Table 9 were obtained using the following code snippet in the complete *deckbuild* code which was kept consistent throughout all the p-i-n diode designs. The anode voltage bias steps were deliberately reduced to 10 mV during forward J–V simulation to obtain a large data set.

```
Code snippet: Forward and reverse J-V simulation of 1200 V parallel plane SiC p-i-n diode

1.  LOG    outf=PIN_Forward_FFR.log
2.  SOLVE  init
3.  SOLVE  vanode=0.01   vstep=0.01     vfinal=3.5     name=anode
4.  SAVE   outf=PIN_Forward_FFR.str     master.out
5.
```

```
6.  LOG     outf=PIN_Reverse_FFR.log
7.  SOLVE   init
8.  SOLVE   vanode=-0.2    vstep=-0.2      vfinal=-2.0   name=anode
9.  SOLVE   vstep=-2.0     vfinal=-20      name=anode
10. SOLVE   vstep=-5.0     vfinal=-100     name=anode
11. SOLVE   vstep=-20.0    vfinal=-1180    name=anode
12. SOLVE   vstep=-2.0     vfinal=-1250    name=anode     compl=1.e-24   cname=anode
13. SAVE    outf=PIN_Reverse_FFR.str       master.out
```

It can be seen from the Table 9 that, under the same simulation condition, increasing the device structure mesh points will result in significant increase in simulation time. If the differences in the steady-state characteristics can be neglected, the user can settle for a device structure with lesser number of mesh points while obtaining reasonably accurate results. Moreover, the number of mesh points become critical especially when the device model becomes a part of another simulation which would affect the total number of mesh points in the circuit, e.g. a diode model is required during the transient simulation of MOSFET in a clamped inductive switching or double-pulse circuit. There are no hard and fast rules to optimize the mesh as demonstrated in this textbook since there are multiple ways to optimize the mesh and it is up to the user to design the best mesh profile which would provide accuracy as well as performance.

(b) Areas of high electric field or impact ionization

SiC Power semiconductor devices are designed for high blocking voltage. This makes it necessary for TCAD models to accurately define the breakdown voltage and the associated electric field. In order to get an accurate picture of the electric field distribution in the breakdown regime, it is important to define a fine mesh in the areas of high electric field, e.g. the P+/N− Drift junction in a p-i-n diode, P-base/N− drift region in a MOSFET, etc. Since, this aspect is similar to the discussion pertaining to the semiconductor junction mesh, it will not be discussed in detail.

(c) Metal–Semiconductor and Insulator–Semiconductor Interface

Due to the larger built-in potential of WBG SiC ($V_{bi} \approx 3$ V) as compared to silicon ($V_{bi} \approx 0.7$ V), majority carrier devices like JBS diode, MOSFET, and JFET are the device of choice for SiC semiconductor. The metal-semiconductor interface in a JBS diode and the oxide-semiconductor interface in a MOSFET are critical since they determine the device behavior. The mesh structure at the interface should be made fine to ensure accurate

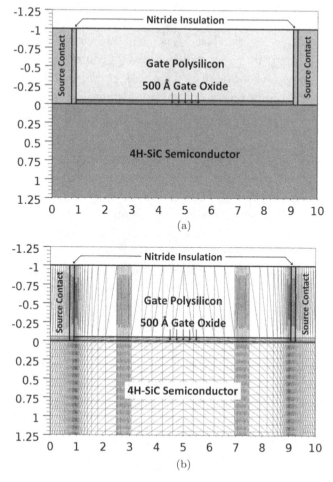

Fig. 15. (a) D-MOSFET gate and source regions. (b) D-MOSFET gate and source region mesh profile.

dimensions and reliable results, e.g. a typical gate oxide thickness of 50 nm (500 Å) used in a SiC MOSFET structure can be divided into 5 mesh points of 0.01 μm width in Y-axis; however, this would result in significant increase in overall mesh points. An enlarged view of the gate and source regions of a D-MOSFET structure is shown in Fig. 15(a). A gate oxide thickness of 50 nm was used for this example and was divided into 2 mesh points of 0.025 μm width in Y-axis. The corresponding mesh profile is shown in Fig. 15(b).

A fine mesh was used in the gate oxide region and at the SiC/SiO$_2$ interface to accurately capture the surface phenomena involved in MOSFET conduction. A similar approach can be used for the Schottky (metal–semiconductor) interface in a JBS diode as well.

(d) Drift region/Epi-layer

Drift region thickness is the largest vertical dimension in a power device (other than the substrate), and its mesh profile can be made coarse in most of the power semiconductor device structures. However, the mesh profile has to be much finer as compared to the substrate mesh.

(e) Substrate

The typical substrate thickness for SiC power devices range from 150 to 250 μm. A fine mesh in such a large vertical thickness would result in an extremely large number of mesh points and, therefore, a painfully long simulation time. Moreover, the substrate doping concentration is of the order of 10^{20} cm^{-3}, thereby contributing relatively lower resistance. Due to the aforementioned reasons, a coarse mesh is typically used in the substrate region unless a thinner substrate region is used in the device model.

3.7.   2D versus 3D Simulation

Silvaco$^\copyright$ ATLAS supports 2D and 3D device modeling and simulation. 3D device modeling can provide a good approximation of the actual device working; however, there are some tradeoffs which must be considered before proceeding with 3D simulations. The major differences between 2D and 3D simulation, highlighted in Table 10, will be discussed in the following sections.

Table 10.   Brief comparison between 2D and 3D TCAD simulation.

Parameter	2D Device Structure	3D Device Structure
Active area (μm^2)	X	$X \times Z$
Simulation time	Precision and mesh dependent	Major issue
Current density	Dependent on device current flow path	Simpler calculations due to 3D structure

3.7.1. Active area

Active area can be defined as the area of the device through which current flow occurs. In general, power semiconductor devices have a vertical structure to support the electric field (pertaining to the blocking voltage) across the drift region. In such a scenario, active area of the device can be calculated as the product of X and Z dimensions (shown in Table 10). In a 3D structure, the active area can be computed as $X \times Z$ μm^2 since it is an approximate representation of a real device. However, in 2D simulation, there is no third dimension and the Z dimension is set to a default value of 1 μm, thereby resulting in an active area of X μm^2.

3.7.2. Simulation time

Simulation time is one of the major bottlenecks of numerical simulation. The simulation time for a particular semiconductor device depends on the simulation precision, complexity of the structure, simulation models, and nature of the circuit simulated. The complexity of the device structure directly affects the mesh point density, which increases as the device structure becomes more and more complex. In 2D simulation, the mesh profile can be greatly optimized to have an optimum balance between accuracy and simulation speed. However, in 3D simulation, the mesh point density cannot be reduced beyond a certain point. For example a 2D diode structure with 2000 mesh points can provide accurate results without adversely affecting the simulation time. However, the addition of just 5 mesh points in the Z direction for a 3D structure results in 10,000 mesh points, which causes a massive increase in simulation time.

3.7.3. Current density

The comparison between 2D and 3D simulation based on current density calculation has been described briefly in Table 10. Irrespective of 2D or 3D simulation, current density is the only way to quantify the simulation result since it is impractical to simulate a complete device. This makes it extremely important to have a clear understanding of current density measurement, which can be further corelated to the lattice temperature rise under high current density pulsed operation. Since 2D simulation was selected for this textbook, following discussion will focus on the current density calculation for 2D device models. Due to the absence of the third dimension in 2D simulation, the current density measurement is dependent on the device current flow path. In order to understand the current flow path in a device,

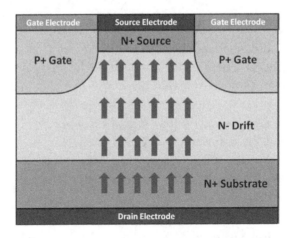

Fig. 16.   Current flow (arrows) direction in a 2D TIV-JFET complete-cell structure.

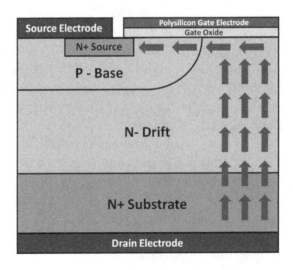

Fig. 17.   Current flow (arrows) direction in a 2D D-MOSFET half-cell structure.

the cross-sectional structures of a Trenched and Implanted Vertical JFET (TIV-JFET) complete-cell and D-MOSFET half-cell are shown in Figs. 16 and 17, respectively. It can be seen in Fig. 16 that the JFET structure exhibits a vertical current flow path from the drain to the source electrode. Under this scenario, the active area can be calculated using the mesa width (width of the source electrode) multiplied by the default Z direction width (1 μm). The value of active area obtained via calculation (using 2D device structure dimensions) was successfully compared with the value obtained through simulation results.

However, the scenario changes when the device structure exhibits multiple current flow paths. The current flow path in a D-MOSFET structure (Fig. 17) is vertical in the drift and JFET regions and horizontal in the accumulation region and channel. Under this circumstance, the active area must include the entire area through which current traverses, as indicated in Fig. 17. In this textbook, the active area for D-MOSFET structure was approximated by using the complete-cell pitch to simplify calculations. However, there was no way to verify the value with simulation results since Silvaco© ATLAS uses the electrode width to calculate current density.

3.8. Simulation Hardware

TCAD software, in general, requires powerful computational hardware to reduce the simulation time. The situation becomes even more critical when WBG devices are being simulated since the simulations are performed with extended bit precision and higher mesh point density. Since Silvaco© ATLAS can utilize up to 64 processor cores, it will be extremely beneficial to have a computer with multi-core processor. The simulation results discussed in this textbook were generated on a Linux Operating System (CentOS)-driven server with the following customized configuration: the Microway 4U AMD Opteron Quadputer Node consists of 4 AMD 'Interlagos' Opteron 6282SE Sixteen Core CPU 2.6 GHz Base Clock Frequency with Turbo CORE supports 3.0 GHz P1, 3.3 GHz P0, and eight Bulldozer modules each with 2MB L2 Cache; 16MB Shared L3 Cache. The system has 256 GB of DDR3 1600 MHz ECC/Registered Memory with 8 TB of RAID-enabled hard drive space and power backup using 2 kVA APC Smart-UPS (*Courtesy: Department of Electrical and Computer Engineering, Texas Tech University*). The multi-core architecture of the computer enables the user to run multiple simulation instances without significant loss in performance.

References

1. R. Pratap, V. Agarwal and R. K. Singh, Review of various available spice simulators. *2014 International Conference on Power, Control and Embedded Systems (ICPCES)*, Allahabad, UP, 2014, pp. 1–6.
2. L. G. Meares, New simulation techniques using spice, *1986 IEEE Applied Power Electronics Conference and Exposition*, New Orleans, LA, 1986, pp. 198–205.
3. A. G. M. Strollo, A new IGBT circuit model for SPICE simulation, *PESC97. Record 28th Annual IEEE Power Electronics Specialists Conference. Formerly Power Conditioning Specialists Conference 1970–71. Power Processing and Electronic Specialists Conference 1972*, St. Louis, MO, 1997, vol. 1, pp. 133–138.
4. B. N. Pushpakaran, S. B. Bayne, G. Wang and J. Mookken, Fast and accurate electro-thermal behavioral model of a commercial SiC 1200V, 80 mΩ power MOSFET, *Pulsed Power Conference (PPC), 2015 IEEE*, May 31 2015–June 4 2015, pp. 1–5.

5. E. Buturla, The use of TCAD in semiconductor technology development, *Proceedings of the IEEE 1991 Custom Integrated Circuits Conference*, San Diego, CA, 1991, pp. 23.1/1–23.1/7.
6. M. Langer and J. Podgorski, Application of TCAD software for numerical simulation of power semiconductor devices, *Experience of Designing and Applications of CAD Systems in Microelectronics. Proceedings of the VI-th International Conference. CADSM 2001 (IEEE Cat. No.01 EX473)*, Lviv-Slavsko, Ukraine, 2001, pp. 305–306.
7. R. Minixhofer, TCAD as an integral part of the semiconductor manufacturing environment, *2006 International Conference on Simulation of Semiconductor Processes and Devices*, Monterey, CA, 2006, pp. 9–16.
8. S. K. Saha, Integrating TCAD in semiconductor foundry companies for an efficient customization of IC manufacturing technology, *Proceedings of the 2000 IEEE Engineering Management Society. EMS — 2000 (Cat. No.00CH37139)*, Albuquerque, NM, 2000, pp. 179–183.
9. *ATLAS User's Manual*, September 11, 2014, [online] Available at: www. silvaco.com.
10. *ATHENA User's Manual*, August 13, 2015, [online] Available at: www. silvaco.com.
11. G. Levin and I. Platzner, Excess kinetic energies of ionization products of electron impact processes, *The Journal of Chemical Physics*, vol. 60, no. 5, 1974, pp. 2007–2011.

Chapter 4

Simulation Models and Parameters

The accuracy of any computer simulation, regardless of the field of engineering, follows the concept of Garbage in, Garbage out (GIGO): the quality of output is determined by the quality of the input, which makes it very important to have accurate parameters for the model to be simulated. The same rule applies to semiconductor TCAD simulation as well. Critical material parameters like electrical and thermal properties must be fairly accurate and reliable to obtain trustworthy simulation results. This chapter will discuss the important simulation models and associated parameters which can be used for SiC power device simulation. The value of parameters discussed in this chapter are based on experimentation and literature study. However, the user may experiment with values beyond the scope of this textbook as long as they are obtained from reliable sources and the simulation results are either in accordance with hardware test data or can be validated in other ways.

Commercial device simulators like Silvaco© TCAD software were by default optimized for Silicon devices, and as and when wide bandgap technology progressed, features were added to support wide bandgap semiconductor device simulation. Since the material properties for silicon are consistent and well-understood due to several decades of existence and technological improvement, the device simulator algorithms are optimized for those conditions. Due to the high level of technology maturity of silicon as compared to newer wide bandgap material, default built-in electrothermal parameters for silicon are accurate and could be used without any modification. However, in case of SiC, extensive research is being conducted to investigate material properties, which results in a wide variety of parameter values reported in scientific literature. The major simulation parameters for SiC power device TCAD simulation have been classified in Fig. 1. Even though the electrical and thermal parameters are shown separately, they are interdependent on

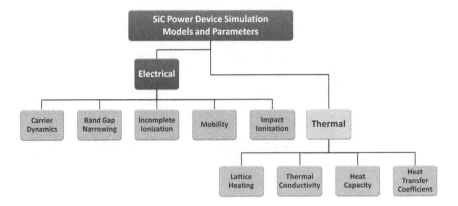

Fig. 1.   SiC power device simulation parameters.

each other, e.g. the effect of temperature on the electrical parameters during steady-state or transient simulation.

Declaring accurate device parameters is critical for SiC power device modeling. Physics-based models must be included to account for carrier generation and recombination, mobility, bandgap narrowing, impact ionization, heat dissipation, and non-isothermal lattice heating. In order to make the model efficient, it is also necessary to incorporate only those models which are required for the particular device. Including models without detailed analysis could result in either longer simulation time without any noticeable difference in the result or simulation errors. Silvaco© ATLAS manual contains model compatibility/precedence data which describes any incompatibility between various combination of models or dominance of one model over the other. The major simulation models and parameters will be discussed in the following sections.

4.1.   Electrical Parameters

The electrical parameters primarily deal with carrier dynamics, bandgap narrowing, incomplete ionization, mobility, and impact ionization.

4.1.1.   Carrier generation and recombination

The two recombination models which were used during SiC power device simulation: *Schottky–Read–Hall* (SRH) and *Auger* recombination. During SRH recombination, either an electron is trapped by an energy state which is introduced through defects in the crystal lattice or a hole moves up to the same energy state before the electron is thermally re-emitted into the conduction band, then it recombines. These defects can either be unintentionally introduced or can be deliberately added to the material to alter its properties. SRH recombination model can be activated using parameter **SRH** in the **MODELS** statement.

The process of Auger Recombination is characterized by the transfer of energy and momentum due to the recombination of an electron and hole to a third mobile particle which may be an electron in case of a heavily doped n-type material or a hole in case of a heavily doped p-type material. This process is only significant at high carrier concentration or high-current densities which is typical for SiC power devices. Auger Recombination can be activated via **AUGER** parameter in the **MODELS** statement.[1,2,3]

4.1.2. Carrier lifetime

Carrier lifetime is defined as the average time it takes for an excess minority carrier to recombine. Electron and hole lifetime values are critical for SiC power device simulation, especially bipolar devices, where processes like conductivity modulation and reverse recovery are critical. Using accurate values for carrier lifetime is important for transient simulation since it affects the switching losses. Electron and hole lifetime can be specified in ATLAS using the parameters **TAUN0** and **TAUP0**, respectively, in the **MATERIAL** statement. The values for the aforementioned parameters could be found either through experimentation or literature review.[2,3]

4.1.3. Bandgap narrowing

The phenomena involving the shrinkage of semiconductor material bandgap when the impurity concentration is very high is known as bandgap narrowing. This effect becomes significant when the doping concentration typically exceeds 10^{18} cm^{-3}. The band structure is basically altered by three effects which can be summarized as the following:

- The interaction between adjacent impurity atoms (due to high concentration) leading to the splitting of the impurity levels into an impurity band.
- The statistical distribution of the dopant atoms in the lattice introduces point-by-point differences in local doping concentration and lattice potential causing the formation of band tails. This effect is significant at doping levels approaching a value of 10^{21} cm^{-3}.
- The interaction between the free carriers and more than one impurity atom leads to a modification of density of states at the band edges.

Bandgap Narrowing model can be activated via **BGN** parameter in the **MODELS** statement. Default values were used for the parameters pertaining to **BGN** model.[2,4]

4.1.4.   Incomplete ionization

Ionization is described as the process in which the dopant atom releases an electron to the conduction band (in case of a donor atom) or hole to the valance band (in case of an acceptor atom). The ionization of impurities is extremely critical in a semiconductor since it determines the free carriers in a semiconductor, and thus the conductivity and other electrical properties. In SiC device processing, Aluminum and Nitrogen are the most commonly used dopants for p-type and n-type doping, respectively. Since n-type nitrogen dopant has a relatively lower ionization energy $(E_{DB} \approx 50$ meV), high degree of ionization (50–100%) can be obtained at room temperature based on the SiC polytype and doping concentration. Due to the high ionization energy of Aluminum ($E_{AB} \approx 200$ meV), at room temperature, the thermal energy within the semiconductor is not sufficient to obtain 100% ionization of the acceptor atoms, i.e. 5–30% of the acceptor concentration gets ionized at room temperature.[5] The ionization energy of dopants decrease with increasing doping concentration due to bandgap narrowing and impurity band formation. Therefore, despite having relatively high ionization energy, almost 100% ionization of aluminum dopant can be achieved if SiC is degenerately doped with an acceptor concentration greater than 5×10^{20} cm^{-3}.

The incomplete ionization model can be activated in Silvaco© ATLAS by using the parameter **INCOMPLETE** in the **MODELS** statement. The critical material parameters pertaining to incomplete ionization include acceptor and donor ionization energies denoted by **EAB** and **EDB**, respectively. Irrespective of the type of simulation being performed, i.e. steady-state or transient, Incomplete Ionization model is critical for device simulation and should always be included in the simulation code.[1]

 The inclusion of incomplete ionization is extremely important for SiC power device simulation which is why it is highly recommended that the user performs simulation with and without the incomplete ionization model to understand the effect of this model on device characteristics.

4.1.5. Mobility

Carrier mobility model is essential to account for the behavior of electron and hole under varying electric field conditions. Physics-based mobility models can be classified into (i) low-field mobility, (ii) high-field mobility, (iii) bulk semiconductor mobility, and (iv) inversion layer mobility. Carriers in low-electric field are affected by phonon and impurity scattering, both of which tend to decrease low-field mobility. Under the influence of high electric field, carriers gain sufficient energy and get accelerated, thereby getting affected by a wider range of scattering phenomena. Due to the scattering processes, mean drift velocity of carriers no longer increases linearly with the applied electric field, instead exhibiting a gradual rise in magnitude. Beyond a certain magnitude of electric field, the drift velocity ceases to rise and saturates at a constant magnitude, which is defined as saturation velocity (V_{sat}). The saturation velocity of carriers in SiC is almost a magnitude higher than that in Silicon. The modeling of carrier mobility in bulk semiconductor material involves specifying the low-field mobility as a function of doping concentration and temperature, dependence of saturation velocity on temperature, and the transition between low-field and high-field regimes. Modeling of inversion layer mobility, encountered in MOS device, e.g. MOSFET, IGBT, etc., is a complicated process since it involves complex mechanisms like surface scattering and carrier-to-carrier scattering.

In this textbook, low-field mobility is modeled using Caughey–Thomas equation which relates the low-field mobility to impurity concentration and temperature as shown in Eqs. (1) and (2) where N is the total impurity concentration and T_L is the lattice temperature.[1,6] Model parameters (***XXXX.CAUG***) can either be defined by the user in the deckfile or the default values may be used. This model can be activated by using **ANALYTIC** parameter in the **MODELS** statement.

$$\mu_{n0} = MU1N.CAUG\left(\tfrac{T_L}{300}\right)^{ALPHAN.CAUG}$$
$$+ \frac{MU2N.CAUG\left(\tfrac{T_L}{300}\right)^{BETAN.CAUG} - MU1N.CAUG\left(\tfrac{T_L}{300}\right)^{ALPHAN.CAUG}}{1+\left(\tfrac{T_L}{300}\right)^{GAMMAN.CAUG} \cdot \left(\tfrac{N}{NCRITN.CAUG}\right)^{DELTAN.CAUG}} \quad (1)$$

$$\mu_{p0} = MU1P.CAUG\left(\tfrac{T_L}{300}\right)^{ALPHAP.CAUG}$$
$$+ \frac{MU2P.CAUG\left(\tfrac{T_L}{300}\right)^{BETAP.CAUG} - MU1P.CAUG\left(\tfrac{T_L}{300}\right)^{ALPHAP.CAUG}}{1+\left(\tfrac{T_L}{300}\right)^{GAMMAP.CAUG} \cdot \left(\tfrac{N}{NCRITP.CAUG}\right)^{DELTAP.CAUG}} \quad (2)$$

In bipolar devices, high-level injection of minority carriers result in carrier–carrier scattering, which plays a significant role in determining the net mobility. The carrier–carrier scattering mechanism has been modeled using Conwell–Weisskopf model where the mobility (μ_{ccs}) is defined as follows:

$$\mu_{ccs} = \frac{D.CONWELL \left(\frac{T_L}{300}\right)^{\frac{3}{2}}}{\sqrt{pn} \left(\ln\left(1 + \frac{F.CONWELL}{(PN)^{\frac{1}{3}}} \left(\frac{T_L}{300}\right)^2\right)\right)} \tag{3}$$

where n and p are electron and hole concentration. When the Conwell model is used in conjunction with another low-field mobility model, e.g. Caughey–Thomas, the net electron and hole mobility is computed using Matthiessens rule, which is given by Eqs. (4) and (5). The Conwell carrier–carrier scattering model can be activated by using **CONWELL** parameter in the **MODELS** statement.[1]

$$\frac{1}{\mu_n} = \frac{1}{\mu_{n0}} + \frac{1}{\mu_{ccs}} \tag{4}$$

$$\frac{1}{\mu_p} = \frac{1}{\mu_{p0}} + \frac{1}{\mu_{ccs}} \tag{5}$$

The field-dependent mobility was implemented using Saturation Velocity model which can be activated by using **FLDMOB** parameter in the **MODELS** statement.[1] The discussion of the various equations and parameters pertaining to the aforementioned models is out of scope of this textbook due to its volume and complexity and can be found in the Silvaco© ATLAS manual. The user is encouraged to experiment with various models available in Silvaco© ATLAS to accurately describe the carrier dynamics. However, as mentioned earlier, the accuracy of a model is solely dependent on the accuracy and reliability of the parameters used in the equations.

4.1.6.   Impact ionization

Impact ionization is described as the process in which carriers in the space–charge region get accelerated by high electric field and gain enough energy to generate more free carriers by collision with the atoms in the crystal lattice. This process leads to avalanche breakdown and consequent destruction of the power device. There are multiple impact ionization models available in Silvaco© ATLAS, but the most commonly used one is the Selberherr model.[7] The ionization rate model proposed by Selberherr is a modified version of

Chynoweth's Law based on the following equations:

$$\alpha_n = AN\ e^{-\left(\frac{BN}{E}\right)^{BETAN}} \tag{6}$$

$$\alpha_p = AP\ e^{-\left(\frac{BP}{E}\right)^{BETAP}} \tag{7}$$

where E is the electric field in the direction of the current flow and parameters **AN**, **AP**, **BN**, **BP**, **BETAN**, and **BETAP** are user definable parameters on the **IMPACT** statement.[1] The Selberherr model can be activated in Silvaco© ATLAS by using the parameter **SELB** in the **IMPACT** statement. Irrespective of the type of simulation being performed, i.e. steady-state or transient, impact ionization model is critical for device simulation and should always be included in the simulation code.

4.2.   Thermal Simulation

In-depth analysis of heat dissipation and temperature rise within the device lattice due to self-heating can be performed by incorporating lattice heating models during device simulation. The various components of GIGA module are summarized below.

4.2.1.   Lattice heat flow

2D thermal profile is generated in ATLAS by solving the 2D heat flow equation shown in Eq. (8) below

$$C\frac{\partial T_L}{\partial t} = \nabla(\kappa \nabla T_L) + H \tag{8}$$

where C is the heat capacitance per unit volume, κ is the thermal conductivity, T_L is the lattice temperature, and H is the heat generated. The heat generated is the sum of three different sources which is computed using Eq. (9):

$$H = \left[\frac{\left|\overrightarrow{J_n}\right|^2}{q \cdot \mu_n \cdot n} + \frac{\left|\overrightarrow{J_p}\right|^2}{q \cdot \mu_p \cdot p} \right] + q(R-G)[\phi_p - \phi_n + T_L(P_p - P_n)]$$

$$- T_L(\overrightarrow{J_n}\nabla P_n - \overrightarrow{J_p}\nabla P_p) \tag{9}$$

where term 1 on the right side denotes the Joule heating component, term 2 denotes the carrier generation and recombination heating and cooling, and term 3 accounts for Peltier and Thomson heating. The various terms used in Eq. (9) are as follows: J is the current density, q is the elementary charge, μ is the mobility, n and q are electron and hole concentration, respectively, G and R are generation and recombination rates, ϕ denotes the quasi-fermi level, and P denotes the thermoelectric power. The subscripts n and p represent electron and hole, respectively. The unit of heat generated (H) is W/cm^3, which is also the volumetric power density. The heat generation model can be configured to either use all the sources of heat generation, or individually select the required components. Using **HEAT.FULL** command activates all the sources of heat generation, whereas the commands **JOULE.HEAT**, **GR.HEAT**, and **PT.HEAT** can be used to individually activate Joule, generation–recombination and Peltier–Thomson heat source, respectively.[1,8]

 Proper analysis of simulation models can avoid the inclusion of unnecessary models and could prevent longer simulation time or simulation errors, e.g. Peltier–Thomson heat generation model can be avoided for SiC Device Simulation.

4.2.2.   Thermal conductivity

Thermal conductivity (W/cm·K) can be modeled in ATLAS using different techniques, but for the discussion presented in this textbook, it was defined as a polynomial function of lattice temperature given by

$$\kappa(T_L) = \frac{1}{TC.A + (TC.B) \cdot T_L + (TC.C) \cdot T_L^2} \tag{10}$$

where **TC.A**, **TC.B**, and **TC.C** are material dependent and calculated based on experimental results. Since thermal conductivity of 4H-SiC decreases with temperature, it provides a fairly accurate model for simulating heat transfer. The electrothermal device simulations discussed in this textbook were carried out using thermal conductivity data shown in Fig. 2. The coefficients **TC.A**, **TC.B**, and **TC.C** were calculated by using polynomial curve fitting for the experimental data in the range of significant temperature. It is evident from the data shown that the thermal conductivity of 4H-SiC decreases with increase in material temperature and the actual value is smaller than the typical values reported at 300 K.

4.2.3.   Heat Capacity

It is defined as volumetric heat capacity or the ability of a given volume of a substance to store internal energy while undergoing a given temperature

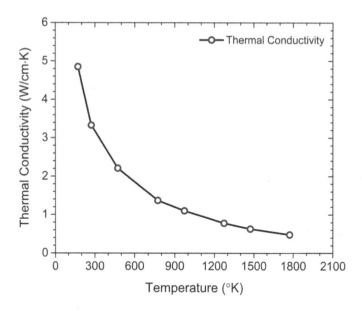

Fig. 2.   Thermal conductivity data for SiC.
Source: Army Research Lab, Adelphi, Maryland, USA.

change, but without undergoing a phase change. Heat capacity $(J/cm^3 \cdot K)$ is implemented in ATLAS GIGA module via Eq. (11)

$$C(T_L) = (HC.A) + (HC.B) \cdot T_L + (HC.C) \cdot T_L^2 + \frac{(HC.D)}{T_L^2} \qquad (11)$$

where coefficients **HC.A**, **HC.B**, **HC.C**, and **HC.D** are material dependent and calculated based on experimental results. It is a function of the lattice temperature and the variation is polynomial in nature. The electrothermal device simulations discussed in this textbook were carried out using volumetric heat capacity data shown in Fig. 3. The experimental data shown in Fig. 3 was calculated using a density of 3.21 g/cm^3 for SiC. The coefficients **HC.A**, **HC.B**, **HC.C**, and **HC.D** were calculated by using polynomial curve fitting for the experimental data in the range of significant temperature.[1]

4.2.4.   Heat transfer coefficient

Heat transfer coefficient can be defined as the rate at which heat leaves a surface. It is a function of the heat flow, the temperature difference between the surface and the ambient and the area of the surface. It has a unit of W/(cm$^2 \cdot$K). Heat transfer coefficient (**ALPHA**) is defined in Silvaco$^\copyright$ ATLAS by Eq. (12) where the quantity on the left-hand side of the equation is the projection of total energy flux on to the unit external normal of the

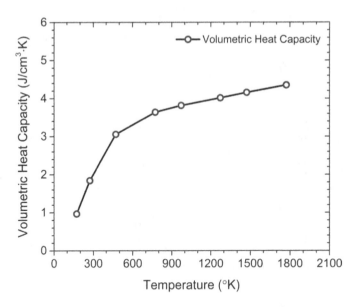

Fig. 3.   Volumetric heat capacity for SiC.

Source: Army Research Lab, Adelphi, Maryland, USA.

boundary. The variable **TEMPER** denotes the ambient temperature of the heat sink boundary.[1]

$$\left(\overrightarrow{J^n_{tot}} \cdot \vec{s}\right) = \frac{1}{R_{th}}(T_L - TEMPER) \tag{12}$$

where the thermal resistance, R_{th}, is given by

$$\frac{1}{R_{th}} = ALPHA \tag{13}$$

This property depends on the interface between the heat source and sink and does not depend on the nature of the material. The value of the heat transfer coefficient has to be carefully selected as it can severely affect the convergence of the program. A low value of the heat transfer coefficient results in excessive heat dissipation, especially during the initial bias voltage calculation in steady-state simulation or device turn-ON in transient simulation. On the other hand, a high value will result in a higher transfer of heat from the source (in this case, semiconductor device lattice) to the sink (boundary condition), thereby resulting in incorrect lattice temperature profile. In a 3D device, the structure is the result of stacking multiple 2D device structures in Z direction, which makes it important to consider heat dissipation to and from adjacent 2D structures. In 2D power device simulation, discussed throughout this textbook, the X–Y plane is used as the thermal boundary condition.

 The value of heat transfer coefficient is perhaps one of the most important parameters in the thermal simulation since it determines the rate at which energy is dissipated to the ambient/heat sink.

References

1. *ATLAS User's Manual*, September 11, 2014, [online] Available at: www.silvaco.com.
2. B. J. Baliga, Material properties and transport physics, *Fundamentals of Power Semiconductor Devices*, Berlin: Springer, 2008, pp. 26–30. Print.
3. S. K. Ghandhi, *Semiconductor Power Devices*, New York, NY: Wiley, 1977.
4. J. Yuan and J. Liou, *Semiconductor Device Physics and Simulation*, New York, NY: Springer, 1998.
5. T. Kimoto and J. A. Cooper, *Fundamentals of Silicon Carbide Technology*, Singapore: Wiley, 2014.
6. D. M. Caughey and R. E. Thomas, Carrier mobilities in silicon empirically related to doping and field, *Proceedings of the IEEE*, vol. 55, no. 12, December 1967, pp. 2192–2193.
7. S. Siegfried, *Analysis and Simulation of Semiconductor Devices*, vol. 2, Wien, Austria: Springer-Verlag, 1984.
8. K. Kells, S. Müller, G. Wachutka, and W. Fichtner, Simulation of self-heating effects in a power pin diode., *Proceedings of the 5th SISDEP Conference*, 1993, pp. 41–44.

Chapter 5

Simulation and Key Factors

The characterization of a power semiconductor device includes the evaluation of steady-state and switching behavior under varying ambient temperature conditions. Silvaco© ATLAS device code is executed using *deckbuild* program either via user interface or command line interface. This chapter will discuss the key points involved in running steady-state and transient simulations using Silvaco© ATLAS.

5.1. Steady-state Simulation

Steady-state simulation is used to generate J–V characteristics for power devices. These would include forward and breakdown J–V characteristics for diodes and MOSFETs. Steady-state simulation performed via voltage biasing involves increasing the voltage steps and recording the change in device current, e.g. forward J–V characteristics of a p-i-n diode can be simulated by increasing the anode voltage while cathode is grounded and reverse breakdown characteristics of a p-i-n diode can be simulated by increasing the cathode voltage with respect to the anode. To optimize the simulation speed, and therefore time, the magnitude of bias voltage step should be varied accordingly. The significance of bias voltage step can be understood by the example of p-i-n diode breakdown simulation. The following code will focus on the gradual ramp-up of forward-bias and reverse-bias voltage for the forward and breakdown simulations of a 3300 V SiC p-i-n diode, respectively.[2,3]

```
Sample code: Parallel plane SiC p-i-n diode forward and breakdown J-V characteristics

1.  GO ATLAS SIMFLAGS="-V 5.18.3.R -P 32 -160"
2.
3.  MESH
4.
5.  X.MESH  loc=0.0    spac=0.5
```

```
6.  X.MESH  loc=10.0    spac=0.5
7.
8.  Y.MESH  loc=-1.0    spac=1.0
9.  Y.MESH  loc=0.0     spac=0.25
10. Y.MESH  loc=2.1     spac=0.01
11. Y.MESH  loc=30.0    spac=10.0
12. Y.MESH  loc=32.1    spac=0.2
13. Y.MESH  loc=33.0    spac=1.0
14. Y.MESH  loc=34.0    spac=20
15. Y.MESH  loc=180.0   spac=20
16. Y.MESH  loc=182.0   spac=1.0
17. Y.MESH  loc=184.0   spac=1.0
18.
19. REGION  num=1          material=4H-SiC x.min=0 x.max=10 y.min=0 y.max=182
20.
21. ELECTRODE  name=anode    material=titanium  x.min=0        x.max=10      y.max=0
22. ELECTRODE  name=cathode  material=aluminum  y.min=182      y.max=184
23.
24. DOPING  UNIFORM  n.type conc=3.8e15 REGION=1
25. DOPING  GAUSS    p.type conc=1.e21 x.min=0  x.max=10  junc=2.0  rat=0.1
26. DOPING  UNIFORM  n.type conc=1.e20 y.min=32 y.max=182
27.
28. SAVE  outf=PIN_Structure.str master.out
29.
30. MATERIAL  material=4H-SiC REGION=1  permittivity=9.76   eg300=3.26
    affinity=3.7   egalpha=3.3e-2   egbeta=1.e+5  nc300=1.7e+19  nv300=2.5e+19
    arichn=146 arichp=30 augn=3.e-29 augp=3.e-29 taun0=3.33e-6 taup0=6.7e-7
    nsrhn=3.e+17 nsrhp=3.e+17 edb=0.050 eab=0.200
31.
32. MODELS  REGION=1 MATERIAL=4H-SiC FERMIDIRAC ANALYTIC CONWELL SRH BGN AUGER
    INCOMPLETE  TEMP=300 PRINT
33.
34. MOBILITY material=4H-SiC REGION=1 vsatn=2.2e7 vsatp=2.2e7 betan=1.2
    betap=2 mu1n.caug=40 mu2n.caug=1136 ncritn.caug=2e17 alphan.caug=-3
    betan.caug=-3 gamman.caug=0.0 deltan.caug=0.76  mu1p.caug=20
    mu2p.caug=125 ncritp.caug=1.e19 alphap.caug=-3 betap.caug=-3
    gammap.caug=0.0 deltap.caug=0.5
35.
36. IMPACT REGION=1 ANISO E.SIDE SELB SIC4H0001 an1=3.44e6 an2=3.44e6
    bn1=2.58e7 bn2=2.58e7 ap1=3.5e6 ap2=3.5e6 bp1=1.7e7 bp2=1.7e7
    opphe=0.106
37.
38. METHOD NEWTON autonr climit=1.e-9 maxtraps=40 itlimit=40 dvmax=1.e8
    ir.tol=1.e-40 cr.tol=1.e-40 ix.tol=1.e-40 px.tol=1.e-30 pr.tol=1.e-45
    cx.tol=1.e-30
39.
40. LOG  outf=PIN_Forward.log
41.
42. SOLVE  init
43. SOLVE  vanode=0.01  vstep=0.01    vfinal=3.5   name=anode
44.
45. SAVE  outf=PIN_Forward.str    master.out
46.
47. LOG  outf=PIN_Reverse.log
48.
49. SOLVE    init
50. SOLVE    vanode=-0.2 vstep=-0.2   vfinal=-2.0 name=anode
51. SOLVE    vstep=-2   vfinal=-20    name=anode
52. SOLVE    vstep=-5   vfinal=-100   name=anode
53. SOLVE    vstep=-50  vfinal=-3000  name=anode
```

```
54. SOLVE    vstep=-10   vfinal=-3250   name=anode
55. SOLVE    vstep=-1.0  vfinal=-3400   name=anode    compl=1e-23  cname=anode
56.
57. SAVE  outf=PIN_Reverse.str    master.out
58.
59. QUIT
```

The deckbuild code used for the initialization of p-i-n diode structure
(**line 3–line 26**) and the associated simulation models and parameters
(**line 30–line 38**) will be discussed in detail in the forthcoming chapters.
The **SOLVE** statement is used to execute the bias voltage on the anode
electrode, and the parameters **VSTEP** and **VFINAL** are used to set the
voltage step and final voltage for the individual statement. Any steady-
state simulation, forward or breakdown J–V, should begin with the **SOLVE**
statement and **INIT** (initial) parameter which sets all voltages to zero.
This is important since it provides an initial guess for the subsequent
solutions. During the forward-bias simulation, **SOLVE** statement is used to
ramp up the anode voltage while the cathode is grounded (**line 43**). During
breakdown simulation, the negative anode voltage is increased until the p-i-
n diode undergoes avalanche breakdown. While solving for breakdown J–V
characteristics, it is necessary to take small bias voltage steps (in the order of
mV) in the beginning of the simulation (**line 50**). This is important because
the change in magnitude of current is high for initial few volts and since the
device simulator uses numerical methods to solve differential equations, any
large bias step will result in convergence error forcing the simulator to reduce
the bias step and if convergence error exists for a given number of iterations,
program will terminate. Once the initial phase is over, the bias voltage steps
are gradually increased (**line 51–line 53**) since the diode is in blocking
phase and the variation in leakage current is minimal.

 If initial parameter is not specified as the first bias point
calculation, the system will automatically insert solve init
statement during code execution; however, it is a good
practice to include it.

Once the anode voltage becomes close to the expected breakdown voltage
of the diode structure, magnitude of leakage current increases significantly
and the bias voltage step is reduced (**line 54**). In the avalanche breakdown
regime, a small change in anode voltage will result in an abrupt increase
in the anode current. Hence, in order to optimize the simulation time, the
voltage bias steps are kept small in the breakdown phase (**line 55**). Normally,

this process is optimized after multiple trial and error runs to get an estimate of the breakdown voltage. The current compliance parameter **COMPL** is used to terminate the solve statement if the anode current exceeds the value specified for the parameter.

Steady-state simulation of a three-terminal device like MOSFET is slightly different from that of a two-terminal device like diode. The simulation of a MOSFET for its forward characteristics (Drain current versus Drain-Source voltage) requires one of the terminal voltages to be set at a constant value, unlike the case of a diode. This can be explained based on the following code snippet where a MOSFET has been simulated for its forward *J–V* characteristics at a fixed gate–source voltage. Detailed description of the code will be discussed in the chapter on MOSFET.

```
Code snippet: Forward J-V characteristics for MOSFET

1.  SOLVE   init
2.  SOLVE   vgate=2
3.  SOLVE   vgate=4
4.  SOLVE   vgate=6
5.  SOLVE   vgate=8
6.  SOLVE   vgate=10
7.  SOLVE   vgate=12
8.  SOLVE   vgate=16
9.  SOLVE   vgate=20     outf=Vgs20
10.
11. LOAD    infile=Vgs20
12. LOG     outf=mosfet_Vgs20.log
13.
14. SOLVE   vdrain=0.05   step=0.05   vfinal=1.00   name=drain
15. SOLVE   vstep=0.5     vfinal=20.0   name=drain
```

As mentioned earlier, the first bias point calculation is performed by setting all terminal voltages to zero via the **INIT** parameter **(line 1)**. However, this would set the gate, drain, and source voltages to zero which would prevent MOSFET turn-ON. In order to successfully run the simulation, the gate voltage is increased from 2 V to 20 V (**vgate = 20**) using multiple solve statements **(line 2–line 8)** and the bias point details are saved to the file **Vgs20** using **OUTF** parameter **(line 9)**. Using multiple **SOLVE** statements helps in attaining faster convergence. Once the gate voltage is set to 20 V, the bias point information which was saved earlier is used as the initial bias condition through the **LOAD** statement with **INFILE** parameter **(line 11)**. The **LOG** statement with **OUTF** parameter is used to generate the data file **(mosfet_Vgs20.log)** which will contain the simulation results **(line 12)**. The drain voltage is ramped up from 0.05 V to 20 V while the gate voltage is set to 20 V in two **SOLVE** steps to avoid any potential convergence issues (**line 14–line 15**). Both the gate and drain voltages are referenced to the source electrode which is set at ground potential. A similar approach can be used for transfer curve simulation where the drain voltage is first set to a constant value followed by ramp up of the gate voltage and recording the drain current.

5.2. Transient Simulation

Simulation of SiC power devices under pulsed/switching conditions can be carried out using Silvaco© ATLAS Mixed-Mode: Mixed Circuit and Device Simulator. Mixed-Mode is a circuit simulator which can be used to simulate compact circuits with the designed device model. The programming syntax for Mixed-Mode is a combination of SPICE-based modeling techniques and ATLAS coding. The circuit topology intended to be simulated is specified as a netlist where each element, active or passive, is described by the node number to which it is connected. The user can combine semiconductor device model(s) with passive components to understand and visualize device performance under actual circuit conditions. However, this complex analysis requires significant computational resources and time, dependent on the type and number of devices involved and the complexity of circuit being simulated.[1]

Data obtained from Mixed-Mode circuit simulation provides us with the following information:

- *I–V* data consisting of voltages in all the circuit nodes and currents in all the circuit branches.
- Internal distribution of solution variables like electron–hole concentration, electric field, potential, and lattice temperature within the numerical device structure.

In this textbook, Mixed-Mode simulator has been used to simulate SiC p-i-n, Schottky, and Junction Barrier Schottky (JBS) diode and MOSFET under high current density pulsed condition. Since each device and circuit presents a new simulation scenario, the user must be prepared to alter the simulation parameters and should not rely on a particular combination of parameters just because it worked for another circuit.

 The ATLAS code can be modified to incorporate a wide variety of solution variables in the output file. However, this would also result in a larger file size, longer file creation time and overall slower program execution.

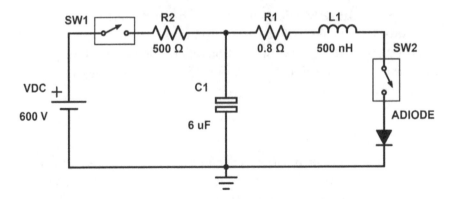

Fig. 1. RLC ring-down circuit schematic.

In order to have a better understanding of implementing transient simulation in ATLAS, an RLC ring-down circuit will be considered, which was designed to generate high peak current density pulse for the evaluation of SiC p-i-n diode. The following example will focus on the important aspects of Mixed-Mode circuit simulator and will skip the details on the diode design, which will be discussed in the next chapter. The circuit schematic of an RLC ring-down circuit is shown in Fig. 1.

The working of an RLC ring-down circuit is as follows. Capacitor (**C1**) gets charged through the voltage source (**VDC**) to 600 V via switch SW1 and charging resistor **R2** while switch SW2 is open. In the discharge phase, SW1 is open and SW2 is closed thereby discharging the capacitor via resistor **R1** and inductor **L1** through the device under test (DUT) denoted by **ADIODE**. The pulse characteristics can be altered by modifying the values of **R1**, **L1**, and **C1**. In order to obtain the required current density without altering the circuit component values, the **WIDTH** parameter in the ATLAS program code was altered. The ATLAS Mixed-Mode implementation of the RLC ring-down circuit is shown in the sample code below.[2,3]

```
Sample code: Parallel plane SiC p-i-n diode mixed-mode transient simulation using RLC ringdown
circuit

1.  GO ATLAS SIMFLAGS="-V 5.18.3.R -P 32 -160"
2.
3.  MESH
4.
5.  X.MESH  loc=0.0    spac=0.5
6.  X.MESH  loc=10.0   spac=0.5
7.
8.  Y.MESH  loc=-1.0   spac=1.0
9.  Y.MESH  loc=0.0    spac=0.25
10. Y.MESH  loc=2.1    spac=0.01
```

```
11. Y.MESH  loc=30.0   spac=10.0
12. Y.MESH  loc=32.1   spac=0.2
13. Y.MESH  loc=33.0   spac=1.0
14. Y.MESH  loc=34.0   spac=20
15. Y.MESH  loc=180.0  spac=20
16. Y.MESH  loc=182.0  spac=1.0
17. Y.MESH  loc=184.0  spac=1.0
18.
19. REGION  num=1 material=4H-SiC  x.min=0  x.max=10 y.min=0 y.max=182
20.
21. ELECTRODE   name=anode    material=titanium  x.min=0   x.max=10  y.max=0
22. ELECTRODE   name=cathode material=aluminum  y.min=182  y.max=184
23.
24. DOPING  UNIFORM n.type conc=3.8e15  REGION=1
25. DOPING  GAUSS   p.type conc=1.e21  x.min=0  x.max=10  junc=2.0  rat=0.1
26. DOPING  UNIFORM n.type conc=1.e20  y.min=32  y.max=182
27.
28. SAVE  outf=PIN_Structure.str  master.out
29.
30. GO ATLAS SIMFLAGS="-V 5.18.3.R -P 32 -160"
31.
32. ##### STEADY STATE SIMULATION #####
33.
34. .BEGIN
35.
36. VDC      1   0   0
37. RSW1     1   2   1.e-12
38. R2       2   3   500
39. C1       3   0   6u
40. R1       3   4   0.80
41. L1       4   5   500n
42. RSW2     5   6   1.e18
43. ADIODE   6=anode  0=cathode   infile=PIN_Structure.str  width=1.2e7
44.
45. .NODESET   v(1)=0  v(2)=0  v(3)=0  v(4)=0  v(5)=0  v(6)=0
46. .NUMERIC   imaxdc=100
47. .LOG       outfile=PIN_DC_log
48. .SAVE      outfile=PIN_RLC_Bias
49. .OPTIONS   m2ln  print  noshift  relpot
50.
51. .DC   VDC   0.   10.   0.25
52. .DC   VDC   10.  100.  10.
53. .DC   VDC   100. 600.  25.
54.
55. .END
56.
57. ##### PHYSICS USED #####
58.
59. CONTACT   DEVICE=ADIODE  NAME=ANODE     EXT.ALPHA=10
60. CONTACT   DEVICE=ADIODE  NAME=CATHODE   EXT.ALPHA=10
61.
62. THERMCONTACT DEVICE=ADIODE  num=3 x.min=0 x.max=10 y.min=-1.0 y.max=184
    alpha=10   ext.temp=300
63.
64. MATERIAL DEVICE=ADIODE  material=4H-SiC REGION=1 permittivity=9.76
    eg300=3.26  affinity=3.7  egalpha=3.3e-2  egbeta=1.e+5  nc300=1.7e+19
    nv300=2.5e+19 arichn=146 arichp=30 augn=3.e-29 augp=3.e-29 taun0=3.33e-6
    taup0=6.7e-7 nsrhn=3.e+17 nsrhp=3.e+17 edb=0.05 eab=0.200 tcon.polyn
    tc.a=0.137534  tc.b=0.00049662  tc.c=0.000000354 hc.a=2.35 hc.b=1.75e-3
    hc.c=1.e-9 hc.d=-6.6e4
```

```
65.
66. ## MODELS USED
67.
68. MODELS  DEVICE=ADIODE  REGION=1  MATERIAL=4H-SIC  FERMIDIRAC  ANALYTIC
    CONWELL  SRH  BGN  AUGER  INCOMPLETE   LAT.TEMP  JOULE.HEAT  GR.HEAT  PT.HEAT
    PRINT
69.
70. ## MOBILITY
71.
72. MOBILITY  DEVICE=ADIODE  material=4H-SiC  REGION=1  vsatn=2.2e7  vsatp=2.2e7
    betan=1.2 betap=2  mu1n.caug=40  mu2n.caug=1136  ncritn.caug=2e17
    alphan.caug=-3  betan.caug=-3  gamman.caug=0.0  deltan.caug=0.76
    mu1p.caug=20  mu2p.caug=125  ncritp.caug=1.e19  alphap.caug=-3  betap.caug=-3
    gammap.caug=0.0  deltap.caug=0.5
73.
74. MOBILITY  DEVICE=ADIODE  material=4H-SiC  REGION=1  n.canali  n.angle=90
    p.angle=90 vsatn=2.2e7  vsatp=2.2e7  betan=1.2 betap=2  mu1n.caug=5
    mu2n.caug=947  ncritn.caug=2e17  alphan.caug=-3  betan.caug=-3
    gamman.caug=0.0  deltan.caug=0.76   mu1p.caug=2.5  mu2p.caug=20
    ncritp.caug=1.e19  alphap.caug=-3  betap.caug=-3  gammap.caug=0.0
    deltap.caug=0.5
75.
76. ## IMPACT IONIZATION
77.
78. IMPACT  DEVICE=ADIODE  REGION=1  ANISO  E.SIDE  SELB  SIC4H0001  an1=3.44e6
    an2=3.44e6  bn1=2.58e7  bn2=2.58e7  ap1=3.5e6  ap2=3.5e6  bp1=1.7e7
    bp2=1.7e7 opphe=0.106
79.
80. METHOD  BLOCK climit=1.e-9  maxtraps=100  itlimit=100   max.temp=1000
    dvmax=1.e8  ir.tol=1.e-35  cr.tol=1.e-35  ix.tol=1.e-35  px.tol=1.e-30
    pr.tol=1.e-45  cx.tol=1.e-30
81.
82. GO ATLAS SIMFLAGS="-V 5.18.3.R -P 32 -160"
83.
84. ##### TRANSIENT SIMULATION #####
85.
86. .BEGIN
87.
88. VDC       1   0   600
89. RSW1      1   2   1.e-12  PULSE  1.e-12  1.e18  5us  50ns  50ns  40us  80us
90. R2        2   3   500
91. C1        3   0   6u
92. R1        3   4   0.80
93. L1        4   5   500n
94. RSW2      5   6   1.e18   PULSE  1.e18  1.e-12  10us  50ns  50ns  40us  80us
95. ADIODE    6=anode   0=cathode    infile=PIN_Structure.str    width=1.2e7
96.
97. .NUMERIC   imaxtr=100  dtmax=1.e-7
98. .OPTIONS   m2ln.tr          print  noshift  relpot  write=25
99. .LOAD      infile=PIN_RLC_Bias
100. .SAVE     master=PIN_Transient
101. .LOG      outfile=PIN_RLC_Ringdown.log
102. .SAVE     outfile=PIN_RLC_Ringdown.str
103.
104. .TRAN        0.01us  45us
105.
106. .END
107.
108. ##### PHYSICS USED #####
109.
```

```
110. CONTACT   DEVICE=ADIODE  NAME=ANODE      EXT.ALPHA=10
111. CONTACT   DEVICE=ADIODE  NAME=CATHODE    EXT.ALPHA=10
112.
113. THERMCONTACT  DEVICE=ADIODE   num=3   x.min=0   x.max=10  y.min=-1.0
     y.max=184   alpha=10   ext.temp=300
114.
115. MATERIAL  DEVICE=ADIODE   material=4H-SiC  REGION=1  permittivity=9.76
     eg300=3.26   affinity=3.7   egalpha=3.3e-2   egbeta=1.e+5  nc300=1.7e+19
     nv300=2.5e+19  arichn=146  arichp=30  augn=3.e-29  augp=3.e-29  taun0=3.33e-6
     taup0=6.7e-7  nsrhn=3.e+17  nsrhp=3.e+17  edb=0.050  eab=0.200  tcon.polyn
     tc.a=0.137534   tc.b=0.00049662   tc.c=0.000000354  hc.a=2.35  hc.b=1.75e-3
     hc.c=1.e-9  hc.d=-6.6e4
116.
117. ## MODELS USED
118.
119. MODELS  DEVICE=ADIODE  REGION=1  MATERIAL=4H-SiC FERMIDIRAC  ANALYTIC
     CONWELL  SRH  BGN  AUGER  INCOMPLETE  LAT.TEMP  JOULE.HEAT  GR.HEAT  PT.HEAT
     PRINT
120.
121. ## MOBILITY
122.
123. MOBILITY  DEVICE=ADIODE  material=4H-SiC  REGION=1  vsatn=2.2e7  vsatp=2.2e7
     betan=1.2 betap=2  mu1n.caug=40  mu2n.caug=1136  ncritn.caug=2e17
     alphan.caug=-3  betan.caug=-3  gamman.caug=0.0  deltan.caug=0.76
     mu1p.caug=20  mu2p.caug=125  ncritp.caug=1.e19  alphap.caug=-3  betap.caug=-3
     gammap.caug=0.0  deltap.caug=0.5
124.
125. MOBILITY  DEVICE=ADIODE  material=4H-SiC  REGION=1  n.canali  n.angle=90
     p.angle=90  vsatn=2.2e7  vsatp=2.2e7  betan=1.2 betap=2  mu1n.caug=5
     mu2n.caug=947  ncritn.caug=2e17  alphan.caug=-3  betan.caug=-3
     gamman.caug=0.0  deltan.caug=0.76   mu1p.caug=2.5  mu2p.caug=20
     ncritp.caug=1.e19  alphap.caug=-3  betap.caug=-3  gammap.caug=0.0
     deltap.caug=0.5
126.
127. ## IMPACT IONIZATION
128.
129. IMPACT  DEVICE=ADIODE  REGION=1  ANISO  E.SIDE  SELB  SIC4H0001  an1=3.44e6
     an2=3.44e6  bn1=2.58e7  bn2=2.58e7  ap1=3.5e6  ap2=3.5e6  bp1=1.7e7
     bp2=1.7e7  opphe=0.106
130.
131. OUTPUT  FLOWLINES  E.MOBILITY  J.DIFFUSION
132.
133. METHOD  BLOCK.TRAN  climit=1.e-9  maxtraps=100  itlimit=100  max.temp=1000
     dvmax=1.e8  ir.tol=1.e-30  cr.tol=1.e-30  ix.tol=1.e-30  px.tol=1.e-25
     pr.tol=1.e-40  cx.tol=1.e-25
134.
135. GO ATLAS SIMFLAGS="-V 5.18.3.R -P 32 -128"
136.
137. QUIT
```

The SiC p-i-n diode structure has been defined in the code from **line 3– line 26** and the resulting device structure with mesh profile, material details, and doping profile was saved to the structure file (**PIN_Structure.str**). Once the structure file is saved, ATLAS is re-initialized using the statement **GO ATLAS** with **SIMFLAGS** parameters (**line 30**). Circuit implementation in ATLAS Mixed-Mode follows the same rules as SPICE, i.e., specifying the circuit elements by the nodes to which they are connected. Each node is assigned a number, and the ground node is always denoted by number 0. The Mixed-Mode circuit information is enclosed within **.BEGIN** and **.END** statements in **line 34** and **line 55**, respectively. The circuit netlist for the DC simulation part is specified in the ATLAS code from **line 36–line 43**. The switches SW1 and SW2 are modeled as resistors **RSW1** and **RSW2** with values $10^{-12}\,\Omega$ and $10^{18}\,\Omega$, respectively. These extreme values of resistance were selected to represent an ideal switch during the close and open positions. Label **ADIODE** is used to represent the DUT, which, in this case, is the SiC p-i-n diode, and parameter **INFILE** was used to load the diode structure into the simulation **(line 43)**.

> It is always a good practice to simulate and verify the functionality of the circuit using any commercial/educational SPICE software like LTspice first before proceeding with Mixed-Mode simulator.

The **WIDTH** parameter is one of the most important factors to be considered during Mixed-Mode simulation. It is specified as a parameter along with the device whose numerical model is being tested. The significance of width parameter is explained as follows: The circuit shown in Fig. 1 was designed to generate a current pulse with a peak magnitude of 600 A; however, forcing 600 A through a diode cell with 10 μm pitch is completely unrealistic and will result in simulation errors. In order to scale down the actual current through the device, width parameter is used. In this example, **WIDTH = 1.2 × 10⁷** would scale down the circuit current of 600 A to p-i-n diode current of 50 μA or a current density of 500 A/cm^2 based on an active area of 10 μm^2.

> Simulation error message "Permittivity not defined for Silicon" may occur if GO command is not used to re-initialize ATLAS (after the creation of device structure file) during transient simulation.

The key to starting off a successful transient simulation is to obtain the initial bias point or steady-state condition for the circuit. Once the netlist is entered in the code, **.NODESET** command is used to initialize the node voltages in the circuit. In this RLC ring-down circuit example, there are 6 nodes as shown in **line 45**. In an RLC ring-down circuit, the initial condition would require the capacitor (C1) to be charged to a voltage equal to 600 V, i.e. nodes $v(1) = 600$ V, $v(2) = 600$ V, $v(3) = 600$ V, $v(4) = 600$ V, $v(5) = 600$ V (can be predicted using SPICE simulation). However, if these values were directly used to describe the initial node voltages (using **.NODESET**), the simulator will not be able to generate solution variables for the device model due to the large voltage bias which would result in simulation error. Parameter **IMAXDC** of **.NUMERIC** statement is used to set the limit for the number of iterations to be performed in DC mode **(line 46)**. A value of 50–100 for **IMAXDC** seems to be working for all the simulations discussed in this textbook. The DC simulation of the circuit is performed in multiple stages using the **.DC** command **(line 51–line 53)**. Every **.DC** statement will generate an individual log file **(line 47)**. Upon completion of the DC simulation, two file types with the same name (**PIN_RLC_Bias**) will be generated which contains the information pertaining to initial condition **(line 48)**. The **.OPTIONS** statement is used to describe the various simulation parameters including solution method **(line 49)**. Modified two-level Newton algorithm (**M2LN**) provides a faster solution when a good initial guess is available. Command **NOSHIFT** is used to disable the shift of voltages for the ATLAS device and **RELPOT** is used to enable relative convergence criteria which is essential for high-voltage devices. The various physics-based models and parameters pertaining to the device being simulated and the numerical solver parameters are included from **line 59–line 80**. After the completion of steady-state Mixed-Mode circuit simulation, ATLAS is re-initialized using the statement **GO ATLAS** with **SIMFLAGS** parameters **(line 82)**.

The circuit netlist for transient simulation is also enclosed between the statements **.BEGIN** and **.END** in **line 86** and **line 106**, respectively. The circuit elements of the netlist are specified in the ATLAS code from **line 88–line 95**; however, there is a difference between the declaration as compared to the DC simulation specified earlier. Since the initial conditions have been established, voltage source **VDC** will have a value of 600 V and the values for **RSW1** and **RSW2** will be as per the switching scheme required for the simulation. In this scenario, **PULSE** type switching of resistance was selected, details of which can be found in either the ATLAS manual or any general SPICE manual. Parameters **IMAXTR** and **DTMAX** of the **.NUMERIC** command are used to specify the maximum number of mixed-circuit iterations and the maximum time step not to be exceeded by the simulator, respectively, **(line 97)**. The value for **DTMAX** should be modified based on the circuit simulated; a large value is favorable for faster simulation; however, a smaller value provides better convergence. The parameters for **.OPTIONS** in **line 98** is similar to that for the DC simulation except for the numerical solution algorithm, i.e. modified two-level Newton for transient simulation (**M2LN.TR**). Parameter **WRITE** is used to save the structure file at user-defined intervals or iterations, in this scenario, a structure file is saved every 25 iterations. The **WRITE** parameter is important since we can obtain simulation information at particular time intervals which is critical in scenarios, e.g. analyze device lattice temperature profile at a certain time step. In the transient section of the code, the **.NODESET** command has not been used but instead **LOAD** command in **line 99** is used to input the file **PIN_RLC_Bias** which contains the circuit and device information including the solution variable and initial condition. **Lines 100–102** are used to save the structure and log files. The initial time step and the total transient simulation time is mentioned using the **.TRAN** command (**line 104**). The various physics-based models and parameters pertaining to the device being simulated and the numerical solver parameters are included from **line 110–line 133**. ATLAS is re-initialized using the statement **GO ATLAS** with **SIMFLAGS** parameters in **line 135**. It may be noted that a different simulation precision can be used during transient simulation depending on the device and circuit being simulated.

 PWLFILE command is used if a file containing piece-wise waveform is required to define the transient parameters and while creating the piece-wise signal, always use units in the .dat file, else the program will not accept the file.

5.3. Mesh Size

For device simulation in ATLAS TCAD, the device must be first modeled on to a 2D or 3D grid which is divided into grid/mesh points. In order to resolve space–charge variations, it is recommended that the mesh size be made smaller than the Debye length of the semiconductor. Debye length of a semiconductor is defined as the distance in semiconductor over which local electric field affects distribution of free charge carriers. The Debye length (L_D) can be calculated using

$$L_D = \sqrt{\frac{\varepsilon k T}{q^2 N}} \tag{1}$$

where ε is the permittivity of the semiconductor material, k is the Boltzmann constant, T is the temperature, q is the magnitude of electronic charge, and

N is the doping concentration. As per Eq. (1), Debye length is directly proportional to the temperature and inversely proportional to the doping concentration, which means a heavily doped region has a smaller magnitude of Debye length. However, it is not always feasible to reduce the mesh size so that it is smaller than the Debye length since there is a tradeoff between the mesh size and the simulation time.[4]

5.4. Dielectric Relaxation Time

During transient simulation, ATLAS simulator automatically increases the time step based on the convergence of the previous time step results to decrease the overall simulation time for the device. Even though ATLAS can regulate the magnitude of time step, user can set the maximum allowable time step during transient simulation which will not be exceeded by the software. Semiconductor dielectric relaxation time can be used as a guide to determine the maximum simulation time step that can be configured into the code during transient simulation. Dielectric Relaxation Time (t_{dr}) can be defined as the characteristic time required by a semiconductor to reach electrical neutrality after carrier injection or extraction. It is estimated using

$$t_{dr} = \frac{\varepsilon}{qN\mu} \tag{2}$$

where ε is the permittivity, q is the magnitude of electronic charge, N is the doping concentration, and μ is the mobility. The simulation time step should be smaller than the dielectric relaxation time in order to avoid convergence errors. However, decreasing the time step also means an extended simulation time which introduces a tradeoff between the time step and overall simulation time.[5]

5.5. Obtuse Triangles

As described in Chapter 3, mesh profile is one of the most critical aspects in TCAD device modeling. An important point to consider while developing the device structure mesh is to make sure that the number of obtuse triangles in the mesh is zero or minimum as it could lead to errors during simulation. As a general rule, the user should try to avoid obtuse triangles or high aspect ratio triangles in the device mesh. The details of the mesh profile are generated when the ATLAS code gets executed. The following output snippet shows an example of the mesh profile details generated during simulation.

```
Output snippet: Mesh details generated during device simulation
─────────────────────────────────────────────────────────────────
Mesh
 Type:                non-cylindrical
 Total  grid points:  6572
 Total  triangles  :  12810
 Obtuse triangles  :  0 (0 %)
```

The highlighted line in the above simulation output snippet shows the number (and percentage) of obtuse triangles present in the mesh. Even though optimizing the mesh for obtuse triangles is an iterative process, it is relatively easier to obtain software feedback on the obtuse triangles since the information is generated immediately once the simulation starts.[1]

References

1. *ATLAS User's Manual*, September 11, 2014, [online] Available at: www.silvaco.com.
2. B. N. Pushpakaran, S. B. Bayne and A. A. Ogunniyi, Electrothermal Simulation-Based Comparison of 4H-SiC p-i-n, Schottky, and JBS Diodes Under High Current Density Pulsed Operation, *IEEE Transactions on Plasma Science*, vol. 45, no. 1, Januray 2017, pp. 68–75.
3. B. N. Pushpakaran, S. B. Bayne and A. A. Ogunniyi, Physics based electro-thermal transient simulation of 4H-SiC JBS diode using Silvaco© ATLAS, in *Pulsed Power Conference (PPC), 2015 IEEE*, May 31 2015–June 4 2015, pp. 1–5.
4. D. Vasileska and S. Goodnick, *Computational Electronics*, 1st edn. San Rafael, CA: Morgan & Claypool Publishers, 2006, pp. 33–37.
5. D. Roy, *Physics of semiconductor devices*, 1st edn. Hyderabad, AP: Universities Press (India) Private Ltd., 2004, pp. 27–33.

Chapter 6

P-i-N Diode

Power p-i-n diodes are known for their high blocking voltage and forward current capability. A simplified cross-sectional structure of a p-i-n diode is shown in Fig. 1. It consists of a heavily doped p-type region which is electrically connected to the device anode, lightly doped n-type region (also known as the drift or intrinsic region), and a heavily doped n-type substrate which is electrically connected to the device cathode. The reverse-blocking voltage in a p-i-n diode is supported at the P+/N− junction by the depletion region that extends into the lightly doped n-type drift region. A larger blocking voltage device would require a thicker drift region with very low doping concentration.

Despite the presence of a thick and lightly doped drift region, p-i-n diode can operate at high forward current density with minimum ON-state voltage drop due to conductivity modulation, a phenomenon where the drift region gets flooded with minority carriers injected from the P+ region such that the injected minority carrier concentration is greater than the background doping. This high-level injection of minority carriers into the lightly doped drift region results in the drastic reduction of ON-state resistance. The ON-state resistance of the p-i-n diode can also be optimized by using a punch-through design approach. In a punch-through approach, the p-i-n diode is designed using a thinner drift region with very low n-type doping concentration. This results in complete depletion of the drift region at much lower reverse-bias voltage followed by a build-up of electric field at the N− Drift/N+ Substrate interface. The difference between reverse-bias electric field profile in non-punch-through (NPT) and punch-through (PT) design is shown in Figs. 2(a) and 2(b), respectively. The electric field profile during reverse-bias operation in a non-punch-through structure is triangular as compared to trapezoidal profile in a punch-though structure.[1,2]

Fig. 1.   Simplified cross-sectional image of power p-i-n diode.

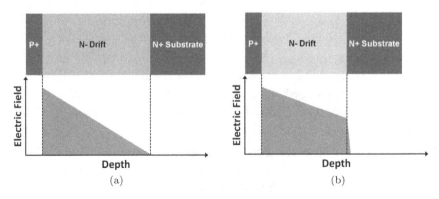

Fig. 2.   (a) Triangular 1D electric field profile in a non-punch-through p-i-n diode during reverse bias. (b) Trapezoidal 1D electric field profile in a punch-through p-i-n diode during reverse bias.

6.1. Forward-bias Characteristics

This section will briefly discuss the forward conduction mechanism in a p-i-n diode. A detailed discussion of the mechanism and derivation of equations is out of scope of this textbook.[2,3] The forward conduction in a p-i-n diode is driven by the following current transport mechanisms:

- ## Space–Charge Recombination current

At low forward bias voltage, current through the p–n junction is very low and is dominated by the recombination of carriers in the space–charge region at the junction.[2] At very low forward current density operation, the ON-state current density (J_{SCR}) of the p-i-n diode is related to the forward voltage drop (V_F) by the following equations:

$$J_{SCR} = \frac{q\, n_i\, W_D}{\tau_{SC}} \cdot e^{\frac{qV_F}{2kT}} \tag{1}$$

$$J_{SCR} \propto e^{\frac{qV_F}{2kT}} \tag{2}$$

where n_i is the intrinsic carrier concentration, W_D is the depletion region width and τ_{SC} is the space–charge region generation lifetime.[2,3]

- ## Low-level Diffusion current

When the forward bias voltage across the p-i-n diode is further increased, current flow through the diode is dominated by diffusion current associated with the injection of minority carriers into the neutral regions on either side of the p–n junction, i.e. injection of electrons into the P+ region and holes into the N− drift region.[2−4] Current density due to diffusion of holes into the N− drift region (J_{LLN}) and electrons into the P+ region (J_{LLP}) is given by the following equations, respectively:

$$J_{LLN} = \frac{q\, D_p\, p_{0N}}{L_p} \cdot \left(e^{\frac{qV_F}{kT}} - 1 \right) \tag{3}$$

$$J_{LLP} = \frac{q\, D_n\, n_{0P}}{L_n} \cdot \left(e^{\frac{qV_F}{kT}} - 1 \right) \tag{4}$$

where D_n and D_p are the diffusion coefficients for electrons and holes, n_{0P} and p_{0N} are electron and hole concentrations in equilibrium in p and n regions, and L_n and L_p are electron and hole diffusion lengths, respectively. It is assumed that the width of the drift region is much larger compared to the carrier diffusion length. Since the P+ region is heavily doped with respect to the N− drift region, minority carrier concentration in the N− drift region is much greater than that in P+ region as per the following equations:

$$n_{0P} = \frac{n_i^2}{N_A} \quad \text{and} \quad p_{0N} = \frac{n_i^2}{N_{\text{Drift}}} \tag{5}$$

$$p_{0N} \gg n_{0P} \tag{6}$$

where N_A and N_{Drift} are the acceptor and donor doping concentrations in the P+ and N− drift regions, respectively. Due to the significant difference between the minority carrier concentration in the P+ and N− regions, current density (J_{LLP}) due to the injection of electrons (minority carrier in p-type region) into the P+ region is negligible compared to the current (J_{LLN}) due to injection of holes (minority carrier in n-type region) into the N− drift region. Hence, forward current density (J_{LL}) in the p-i-n diode under low-level injection, shown in Eq. (7), is dominated by the diffusion current due to the injection of minority carriers into the drift region.[2,3]

$$J_{\text{LL}} = J_{\text{LLN}} = \frac{q\, D_p\, p_{0N}}{L_p} \cdot \left(e^{\frac{qV_F}{kT}} - 1 \right) \tag{7}$$

If the width of the N− drift region is comparable to the diffusion length for holes, Eq. (7) can be re-written as follows, where W_{Drift} is the width of the drift region:

$$J_{\text{LL}} = \frac{q\, D_p\, p_{0N}}{L_p \cdot \tan h \left(\frac{W_{\text{Drift}}}{L_p} \right)} \cdot \left(e^{\frac{qV_F}{kT}} - 1 \right) \tag{8}$$

$$J_{\text{LL}} \propto e^{\frac{qV_F}{kT}} \tag{9}$$

• **High-level injection current**

The n-type drift region in a p-i-n diode is lightly doped to support the large reverse-blocking voltage. As per the Shockley boundary condition shown in Eq. (10), also known as the "law of the junction", the injected minority carrier concentration at the edge of the depletion region on the N− drift side, denoted by $p_N(0)$, increases with the ON-state voltage drop across the diode, which eventually leads to the minority carrier concentration exceeding the background doping concentration (N_{Drift}) in the drift region. The operation of a p-i-n diode in this regime is known as high-level injection.

$$p_N(0) = p_{0N} \cdot e^{\frac{qV_F}{kT}} \tag{10}$$

The elevated concentration of injected minority carriers in the drift region requires an equal concentration of electrons as per charge neutrality.

The extremely high concentration of free carriers in the drift region results in a drastic reduction of the ON-state resistance of the p-i-n diode and is referred to as conductivity modulation of the drift region. This allows the p-i-n diode to operate at very high current density with minimal ON-state losses. The p-i-n diode structure shown in Fig. 3 will be used in the analysis of high-level injection where the drift region is split into two equal regions of width d each.[2]

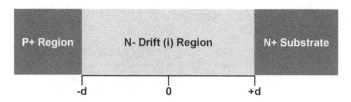

Fig. 3.   Schematic image of p-i-n diode indicating the division of drift region into two equal regions of width d.

The ON-state current density (J_{HL}) of the p-i-n diode as a function of the total ON-state voltage drop (V_{ON}) while operating in the high-level injection regime is given by the following equation:

$$J_{\mathrm{HL}} = \frac{2q\, D_a\, n_i}{d} \cdot F\left(\frac{d}{L_a}\right) \cdot e^{\frac{q V_{\mathrm{ON}}}{2kT}} \tag{11}$$

$$J_{\mathrm{HL}} \propto e^{\frac{q V_{\mathrm{ON}}}{2kT}} \tag{12}$$

where D_a is the ambipolar diffusion coefficient, d is one-half the width of drift region, and $F(d/L_a)$ is the function of the one-half the drift region width to ambipolar diffusion length (L_a). The equation describing $F(d/L_a)$ is given by

$$F\left(\frac{d}{L_a}\right) = \frac{\left(\frac{d}{L_a}\right)\tan h\left(\frac{d}{L_a}\right)}{\sqrt{1 - 0.25\tan h^4\left(\frac{d}{L_a}\right)}} \cdot e^{\frac{-q\,V_{\mathrm{Drift}}}{kT}} \tag{13}$$

where V_{Drift} is the voltage drop across the drift region in the p-i-n diode. The function $F(d/L_a)$ has the maximum value when the ratio (d/L_a) is equal to 1, i.e. the ambipolar diffusion length is equal to one-half the width of drift region.[2] The voltage drop across the drift region (V_{Drift}) is independent of the current density flowing through the region and depends on the device structure and material parameters given by the following equation:

$$V_{\text{Drift}} = \frac{(2d)^2}{(\mu_n + \mu_p) \cdot \tau_{\text{HL}}} \tag{14}$$

where μ_n and μ_p are electron and hole mobilities, respectively, and τ_{HL} is the high-level lifetime. Based on the expression for the total ON-state voltage drop (V_{ON}), derived from Eq. (11), the ON-state voltage drop is minimum for the maximum value of $F(d/L_a)$ given by

$$V_{\text{ON}} = \frac{2kT}{q} \cdot ln \left(\frac{J_{\text{HL}} \cdot d}{2 \, q \, D_a \, n_i \, F\left(\frac{d}{L_a}\right)} \right) \tag{15}$$

It may be noted that during high-level injection, the total current density through the device (J_{HL}) is considered to be equal to the current density through the drift region (J_{Drift}) and the device current flow is based on the injection of minority carriers into the drift region and the recombination of carriers in the drift region.[2,3]

• End Region Recombination Effects

The operation of a p-i-n diode in the high-level injection regime is applicable for current densities in the range 100–200 A/cm^2. Further increase in the ON-state current density (J_{ON}) results in the injection of minority carriers into the P+ and N+ end regions besides drift region, which affects the ON-state characteristics. Under this scenario, current flow in the p-i-n diode needs to take into account not only recombination of carriers in the drift region but also in the heavily doped end regions.[2] This can be expressed via the following equation:

$$J_{\text{ON}} = J_{P+} + J_{\text{Drift}} + J_{N+} \tag{16}$$

Since there is a division of current density in the various regions of the device, current density in the drift region (J_{Drift}) is no longer equal to the total ON-state current density (as discussed during high-level injection), but has a reduced magnitude. For any given magnitude of total ON-state current density, this reduction of injected minority carriers in the drift region increases the ON-state voltage drop across the drift layer of the p-i-n diode. The P+ and N+ end regions are heavily doped which suppresses the injection of minority carriers into the end regions. Hence, the injected minority carrier density in the end regions is well below the background carrier density, a scenario which is comparable to the low-level injection regime.[2] Using the equations derived for low-level injection, current density in the P+ and N+ end regions can be expressed as

$$J_{P+} = \frac{q\, D_{nP+}\, n_{0P+}}{L_{nP+} \cdot \tan h\left(\frac{W_{P+}}{L_{nP+}}\right)} \cdot e^{\frac{qV_{P+}}{kT}} = J_{SP+} \cdot e^{\frac{qV_{P+}}{kT}} \tag{17}$$

$$J_{N+} = \frac{q\, D_{pN+}\, p_{0N+}}{L_{pN+} \cdot \tan h\left(\frac{W_{N+}}{L_{pN+}}\right)} \cdot e^{\frac{qV_{N+}}{kT}} = J_{SN+} \cdot e^{\frac{qV_{N+}}{kT}} \tag{18}$$

where W_{P+} and W_{N+} are the widths of P+ and N+ end regions, L_{nP+} and L_{pN+} are the minority carrier diffusion lengths in the P+ and N+ end regions, D_{nP+} and D_{pN+} are the minority carrier diffusion coefficients in the P+ and N+ end regions, n_{0P+} and p_{0N+} are the minority carrier concentrations in the P+ and N+ end regions, V_{P+} and V_{N+} are the voltages drops across the P+ and N+ end regions, and J_{SP+} and J_{SN+} are the saturation current densities for P+ and N+ end regions, respectively. Considering the effects of bandgap narrowing in the P+ anode and N+ cathode regions, Eqs. (17) and (18) can be expressed in terms of the effective intrinsic carrier concentration in the following equations:

$$J_{P+} = J_{SP+} \cdot \left[\frac{n\left(-d\right)}{n_{ieP+}}\right]^2 \tag{19}$$

$$J_{N+} = J_{SN+} \cdot \left[\frac{n(+d)}{n_{ieN+}}\right]^2 \tag{20}$$

where n_{ieP+} and n_{ieN+} are the effective intrinsic carrier concentrations in the P+ and N+ regions, respectively, under the influence of bandgap narrowing. Terms n($-$d) and n($+$d) denote the drift region carrier concentration at P+/N$-$ drift and N$-$ drift/N+ junctions, respectively. It can be inferred from the above equations that the operation of a p-i-n diode at current densities where end region recombination effects are dominant, carrier density in the drift region increases as the square root of the current density which no longer supports conductivity modulation, and thereby results in an increase in the total ON-state voltage drop.[2]

6.2. Reverse-bias Characteristics

This section will briefly discuss the behavior of the p-i-n diode in reverse-blocking phase. Typically, high-voltage p-i-n diodes are designed using a punch-though (PT) design approach since it facilitates the reduction of drift region thickness which is beneficial for lower ON-state voltage drop. In this discussion, p-i-n diode design based on punch-through approach will be considered. Doping concentration of the drift region in a punch-through design is much lower as compared to a non-punch-through design which causes depletion of the drift region to occur at a relatively lower reverse-bias voltage.[2] The reverse-bias voltage (V_{PT}) at which the drift region completely depletes is given by Eq. (21) where the total drift region width is denoted by $2d$.

$$V_{PT} = \frac{q \, N_{Drift} \, (2d)^2}{2 \, \varepsilon_{SiC}} \qquad (21)$$

The leakage current in a p-i-n diode during reverse bias is a result of space–charge generation current and diffusion current. The brief discussion of these mechanism is as follows:

- **Space–Charge Generation Current**

This component of leakage current is due to the electron–hole pairs that are generated within the depletion region and get swept across by the electric field due to the reverse voltage. The space–charge generation current density (J_{SCG}) is given by Eq. (22) where W_D is the width of the depletion region and τ_{SC} is the space-charge generation lifetime.[2]

$$J_{SCG} = \frac{q \, n_i \, W_D}{\tau_{SC}} \qquad (22)$$

Since the entire drift region gets depleted in punch-through design at a lower voltage, the width of the depletion region W_D in Eq. (22) can be replaced by the thickness of the drift region $(2d)$. Hence, Eq. (22) can re-written in terms of the drift region thickness as follows:[2,3]

$$J_{SCG} = \frac{q \, n_i \, (2d)}{\tau_{SC}} \qquad (23)$$

- **Diffusion Current**

This component of leakage current is due to the generation of minority carriers near the p–n junction. These minority carriers can diffuse to the depletion region boundary and get swept across to the opposite side of the junction by the electric field. Renamed Eqs. (3) and (4) will be used to define the hole diffusion current $(J_{Diff,N})$ into the n-type region and electron diffusion current ($J_{\text{Diff},P}$) into the p-type region, respectively, and the reverse-bias voltage is denoted by V_R.

$$J_{\text{Diff},N} = \frac{q\,D_p\,p_{0N}}{L_p} \cdot \left(e^{\frac{qV_R}{kT}} - 1 \right) \tag{24}$$

$$J_{\text{Diff},P} = \frac{q\,D_n\,n_{0P}}{L_n} \cdot \left(e^{\frac{qV_R}{kT}} - 1 \right) \tag{25}$$

Since $V_R \ll 0$, the magnitude of leakage current component in Eqs. (24) and (25) can be re-written as

$$J_{\text{Diff},N} = \frac{q\,D_p\,p_{0N}}{L_p} = \frac{q\,D_p\,n_i^2}{L_p \cdot N_D} \tag{26}$$

$$J_{\text{Diff},P} = \frac{q\,D_n\,n_{0P}}{L_n} = \frac{q\,D_n\,n_i^2}{L_n \cdot N_A} \tag{27}$$

Since the depletion region extends all the way from the P+/N− Drift junction to the N− drift/N+ substrate boundary, it can be assumed that the diffusion currents are generated in the P+ and N+ end regions. Hence, the total reverse-bias leakage current (J_{Leakage}) for the p-i-n diode can be defined by the following equation as the sum of the individual components described by Eqs. (23), (26), and (27) where $N_{\text{AP+}}$ and $N_{\text{DN+}}$ are the doping concentrations in the P+ and N+ end regions, respectively[2,3]:

$$J_{\text{Leakage}} = \frac{q\,D_n\,n_i^2}{L_n \cdot N_{\text{AP+}}} + \frac{q\,n_i(2d)}{\tau_{\text{SC}}} + \frac{q\,D_p\,n_i^2}{L_p \cdot N_{\text{DN+}}} \tag{28}$$

6.3. Switching Characteristics

Power conversion circuits like rectifiers, DC–DC converters, RLC ring-down pulse generators depend on the switching characteristics of the power semiconductor device for their optimum performance. Unlike steady-state operation, in a switching circuit, the device alternates rapidly between the ON-state (forward conduction) and OFF-state (reverse-blocking) per switching cycle depending on the switching frequency. To minimize power loss during switching phase, it is necessary for the device to make a smooth and rapid transition between the ON-state and OFF-state. In case of a p-i-n diode, the switching performance is determined by two major phenomena known as *forward recovery* and *reverse recovery*, which will be discussed briefly in the following sections.

6.3.1. Forward Recovery

The transition of the p-i-n diode from reverse-blocking mode to forward conduction mode in a switching circuit often results in a transient increase in the forward voltage drop across the diode, especially when the diode current increases at a rapid rate. This phenomenon is known as *forward recovery*. This overshoot in the ON-state voltage drop can be significantly higher than the voltage drop under steady-state operation when the positive rate of change of diode current (typically expressed in $A/\mu s$) is high during device turn-ON. The mechanism of forward recovery can be explained using the concept of conductivity modulation. As discussed earlier, steady-state operation of a p-i-n diode in high-level injection regime is attributed by the injection of minority carriers into the drift region, thereby exceeding the background doping concentration and resulting in low ON-state voltage drop across the diode. However, for conductivity modulation to take place, there is a finite time interval required to inject enough minority carriers into the drift region to surpass the background doping concentration. Under transient operation, if the external circuit forces the diode current to ramp up in a short duration of time (high di/dt), there may not be sufficient time for the drift region of the p-i-n diode to undergo conductivity modulation due to the finite rate for the diffusion of minority carriers. This causes a portion of the drift region to remain un-modulated, thereby increasing the overall resistance of the drift-region, which leads to a higher ON-state voltage drop across the p-i-n diode for a transient duration. Once the drift region gets flooded with minority carriers and the device undergoes conductivity modulation, the voltage drop across the diode decays back to its steady-state value. Detailed analysis of forward recovery in a p-i-n diode is out of scope of this textbook.[2,3]

6.3.2. Reverse Recovery

The previous section discussed the transition of a p-i-n diode from reverse-blocking to forward conduction during switching operation. This section will discuss the transition from forward-conduction to reverse-blocking during switching operation. Conductivity modulation in a p-i-n diode is responsible for maintaining the low ON-state voltage drop across the diode during forward-conduction, even at high current density despite a thick and lightly-doped drift region to support the high reverse-blocking voltage. As discussed earlier, conductivity modulation can be defined as the mechanism responsible for the reduction of ON-state resistance across the lightly-doped drift region due to the high-level injection of minority carriers which exceeds the background doping concentration. However, to block voltage across the diode, it is imperative to remove free carriers from the drift region to enable the formation and extension of depletion region into the drift region to support the high electric field.

Under switching condition, when the voltage across a p-i-n diode is reversed, i.e. anode voltage is negative with respect to the cathode, diode current does not undergo a steady transition to zero. There is a momentary reversal of current which continues to flow from cathode to anode until the stored charge in the p-i-n diode is removed to a magnitude where the p–n junction can support the depletion region pertaining to the applied reverse-bias. The process of switching the p-i-n diode from forward-conduction mode to reverse-blocking mode, which is accompanied by a transient reversal in the diode current is known as *reverse recovery*.[2,3]

Reverse recovery process in a p-i-n diode is characterized by the following parameters:

- **ON-State Current Density**

  Current density through the p-i-n diode during conduction phase under switching application. Since the injected minority carrier concentration is proportional to the ON-state current density, it affects the reverse recovery characteristics as more carriers need to be removed from the drift region before the p-i-n diode can enter blocking phase.

- **Current Density Ramp Rate During Turn-OFF**

  The reverse recovery current is affected by the negative slope of the ON-state current density ($-dJ/dt$) during the diode turn-OFF. A faster decrease in the diode current would result in a larger reverse recovery current.

- **Peak Reverse Recovery Current Density**

  The peak reverse recovery current ($J_{\text{RR,Peak}}$) is proportional to the current density ramp rate during turn-OFF. The magnitude of $J_{\text{RR,Peak}}$ is important since it affects power dissipation within the diode and adds to the primary circuit current thereby increasing switching loss.

- **Reverse Recovery Time**

  The time duration needed to restore the blocking state in a p-i-n diode after the anode current changes from positive to negative is known as reverse recovery time (t_{RR}). It is usually defined as the time difference between the instant the current passes through zero during transition from forward-conduction to reverse-blocking state and the instant where the reverse current has decayed to 10% of its peak value $J_{RR,Peak}$.

- **Junction Temperature**

Peak reverse recovery current ($J_{RR,Peak}$) and reverse recovery time (t_{RR}) increase with junction temperature (T_J) of the bipolar device due to increase in minority carrier concentration.

The simultaneous presence of reverse recovery current and reverse-bias voltage during the diode turn-OFF process results in excessive power dissipation in the device thereby increasing the junction temperature. This could lead to thermal runaway since reverse recovery becomes worse with increase in device temperature. The transient reversal of current in a p-i-n diode can induce large voltage across parasitic inductance which could damage circuit components. Moreover, in a typical application, power semiconductor device (e.g. MOSFET, BJT, or IGBT) controlling the switching event must be rated to handle the reverse recovery current generated in the diode during turn-OFF cycle. A detailed analysis of reverse recovery in a p-i-n diode is out of the scope of this textbook.[2,3]

6.4.   Silvaco© ATLAS Modeling and Simulation

Irrespective of the device being simulated, it is highly recommended that the user starts off the modeling process by developing a TCAD model for the most basic device design. This would not only streamline the overall modeling process by reducing the initial simulation time, enabling faster troubleshooting and better understanding of the device model, but also helps in optimizing the more complex device design approach. In case of a p-i-n diode, the most basic design consists of the parallel plane diode.

The following sections will discuss the modeling and simulation of a 3300 V SiC p-i-n diode using parallel plane, half-cell, and complete-cell structure designs. A detailed discussion of the design equations used for the p-i-n diode is out of scope of this textbook. The simulations will consist of steady-state and transient characterization.

6.4.1.   Simulation models

The physics-based models used for p-i-n diode simulation accounted for Shockley–Read–Hall recombination (**SRH**), auger recombination (**AUGER**), bandgap narrowing (**BGN**), low-field mobility (**ANALYTIC**), mobility due to carrier–carrier scattering (**CONWELL**), incomplete ionization of dopants (**INCOMPLETE**), and impact ionization (**SELB**). The **MODELS** statement was used to implement these models in the deckbuild code. The temperature parameter (**TEMP**) can be used to change the steady-state lattice temperature of the simulation. For non-isothermal Mixed-Mode or transient simulation, in addition to the aforementioned models, lattice temperature model (**LAT.TEMP**) was included to account for the change in device lattice temperature during the course of simulation. The lattice temperature model was used in conjunction with models to account for heat generation due to joule heating (**JOULE.HEAT**), Carrier Generation and Recombination heating (**GR.HEAT**), and Peltier–Thomson heating (**PT.HEAT**). Performing non-isothermal simulations also requires models and parameters to define thermal conductivity and heat capacity and its variation as a function of lattice temperature. The p-i-n diode simulations discussed in this chapter use the polynomial function (**TCON.POLYN**) for thermal conductivity and the standard model for heat capacity.[4]

6.4.2. Parallel plane P-i-N diode

The parallel plane p-i-n diode structure was designed for a rated blocking voltage of 3300 V and an ON-state current density of 100 A/cm^2. Since the rated blocking voltage is typically 80% of the actual breakdown voltage, the diode was designed for a breakdown voltage of approximately 4200 V. The P+ anode region had a junction depth of 2 μm and was heavily doped with a peak acceptor concentration of 1.0×10^{21} cm^{-3} using a Gaussian profile. The N− epitaxial/drift region was 30 μm thick with a doping concentration of 3.8×10^{15} cm^{-3}. The N+ substrate had a thickness of 150 μm and doping concentration of 1.0×10^{20} cm^{-3}. In this model, the p-type and n-type dopants are assumed to be aluminum and nitrogen, respectively. Electron and hole lifetimes of 3.33 μs and 0.67 μs were selected based on research and literature review, respectively.[5-7] Titanium and aluminum were selected for the P+ anode and N+ cathode ohmic contacts, respectively.[8] The 2D device structure had a cell pitch of 10 μm and an active area of 10 μm^2. The active area was calculated using complete-cell pitch (X-axis) in the parallel plane structure and the default value of Z-dimension, i.e. 1 μm. The parallel plane p-i-n diode structure does not involve any field termination and assumes an ideal scenario. A simplified cross-sectional view of a parallel plane p-i-n diode highlighting the critical regions and design parameters is shown in Fig. 4.

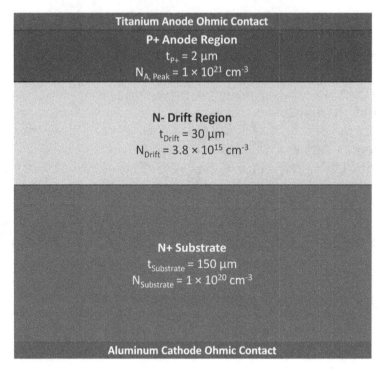

Fig. 4.   Simplified cross-sectional view of parallel plane p-i-n diode structure with design parameters (not drawn to scale).

 Even though implementing a thicker substrate in the device model is a closer approximation to an actual fabricated device, it is highly recommended to start off with a much thinner substrate.

Due to the large substrate thickness as compared to the drift layer, the complete device structure designed using Silvaco© ATLAS has been split into two Figs. 5(a) and 5(b), respectively. The Gaussian doping profile used for the P+ region can be seen in Fig. 5(b). The p-type doping concentration peaks close to the anode contact followed by a gradual decrease closer to the P+/ N− junction. The p-i-n diode parallel plane diode structure can also be designed using uniformly doped P+ region.

6.4.2.1.   *Steady-state simulation*

Steady-state/DC simulation helps in verifying the basic operation of the device model. This section will discuss the forward conduction and reverse

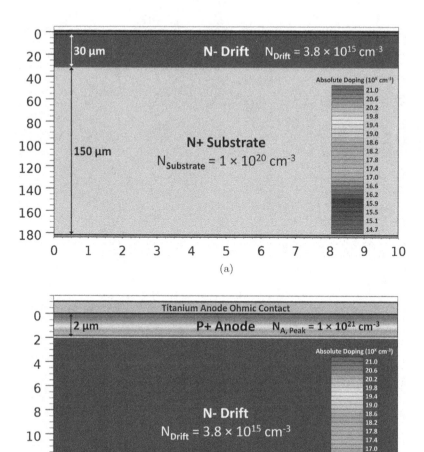

Fig. 5. (a) 3300 V SiC p-i-n diode parallel plane structure designed in Silvaco© ATLAS. (b) 3300 V SiC p-i-n diode parallel plane structure designed in Silvaco© ATLAS (zoomed-in view).

breakdown current density versus anode voltage (J–V) characteristics at 27°C, 75°C, 125°C, and 175°C device temperatures. Steady-state simulations help the user to refine the device model which includes optimization of the mesh profile and doping concentration adjustment to fine-tune the breakdown voltage. The following code was used to simulate the p-i-n diode J–V characteristics, which includes forward conduction and reverse breakdown. A brief explanation of the Steady-State simulation program is provided in the code walkthrough (Table 1).

```
Sample code: Parallel plane SiC p-i-n diode forward and breakdown J-V characteristics @ 27°C

1.   GO ATLAS SIMFLAGS ="-V 5.18.3.R -P 32 -160"
2.
3.   ##### 3300V PARALLEL PLANE PIN DIODE #####
4.
5.   MESH
6.
7.   ## X-MESH
8.
9.   X.MESH  loc=0.0      spac=0.5
10.  X.MESH  loc=10.0     spac=0.5
11.
12.  ## Y-MESH
13.
14.  Y.MESH  loc=-1.0     spac=1.0
15.  Y.MESH  loc=0.0      spac=0.25
16.  Y.MESH  loc=2.1      spac=0.01
17.  Y.MESH  loc=30.0     spac=10.0
18.  Y.MESH  loc=32.1     spac=0.2
19.  Y.MESH  loc=33.0     spac=1.0
20.  Y.MESH  loc=34.0     spac=20
21.  Y.MESH  loc=180.0    spac=20
22.  Y.MESH  loc=182.0    spac=1.0
23.  Y.MESH  loc=184.0    spac=1.0
24.
25.  ## Defining Regions
26.
27.  REGION  num=1 material=4H-SiC   x.min=0  x.max=10  y.min=0  y.max=182
28.
29.  ## Electrode
30.
31.  ELECTRODE  name=anode    material=titanium  x.min=0    x.max=10  y.max=0
32.  ELECTRODE  name=cathode  material=aluminum  y.min=182  y.max=184
33.
34.  ## Doping Distribution
35.
36.  ## Bulk Doping
37.  DOPING  uniform  n.type  conc=3.8e15  REGION=1
38.
39.  ## P+ Doping
40.  DOPING  gauss  p.type  conc=1.e21  x.min=0   x.max=10   junc=2.0   rat=0.1
41.
42.  ## N+ Substrate Region Doping
43.  DOPING  uniform  n.type  conc=1.e20   y.min=32   y.max=182
44.
45.  SAVE  outf=PIN_Parallel_Plane.str  master.out
46.
47.  MATERIAL  material=4H-SiC REGION=1 permittivity=9.76  eg300=3.26
     affinity=3.7   egalpha=3.3e-2   egbeta=1.e+5  nc300=1.7e+19  nv300=2.5e+19
     arichn=146  arichp=30  augn=3.e-29  augp=3.e-29  taun0=3.33e-6  taup0=6.7e-7
     nsrhn=3.e+17  nsrhp=3.e+17  edb=0.05  eab=0.20
48.
49.  ## MODELS USED
50.
51.  MODELS  REGION=1 MATERIAL=4H-SIC FERMIDIRAC ANALYTIC CONWELL  INCOMPLETE SRH
     BGN  AUGER TEMP=300 PRINT
52.
53.  ## MOBILITY
```

```
54.
55. MOBILITY  material=4H-SiC  REGION=1  vsatn=2.2e7  vsatp=2.2e7  betan=1.2
      betap=2  mu1n.caug=40  mu2n.caug=1136  ncritn.caug=2e17  alphan.caug=-3
      betan.caug=-3  gamman.caug=0.0  deltan.caug=0.76   mu1p.caug=20  mu2p.caug=125
      ncritp.caug=1.e19  alphap.caug=-3  betap.caug=-3  gammap.caug=0.0
      deltap.caug=0.5
56.
57. IMPACT  REGION=1  ANISO  E.SIDE  SELB  SIC4H0001  an1=3.44e6  an2=3.44e6
      bn1=2.58e7  bn2=2.58e7  ap1=3.5e6  ap2=3.5e6  bp1=1.7e7  bp2=1.7e7  opphe=0.106
58.
59. METHOD  NEWTON AUTONR  climit=1.e-9  maxtraps=40  itlimit=40   dvmax=1.e8
      ir.tol=1.e-36  cr.tol=1.e-36  ix.tol=1.e-36  px.tol=1.e-30  pr.tol=1.e-45
      cx.tol=1.e-30
60.
61. OUTPUT FLOWLINES
62.
63. LOG  outf=PIN_Forward_27C.log
64.
65. SOLVE  init
66. SOLVE  vanode=0.05  vstep=0.05  vfinal=2.6    name=anode
67. SOLVE  vstep=0.02              vfinal=3.2    name=anode
68. SOLVE  vstep=0.1               vfinal=4.0    name=anode
69.
70. SAVE  outf=PIN_Forward_27C.str
71.
72. LOG    outf=PIN_Reverse_27C.log
73.
74. SOLVE  init
75. SOLVE  vanode=-0.2  vstep=-0.2    vfinal=-2.0    name=anode
76. SOLVE  vstep=-2    vfinal=-20    name=anode
77. SOLVE  vstep=-5    vfinal=-100   name=anode
78. SOLVE  vstep=-10   vfinal=-1000  name=anode
79. SOLVE  vstep=-25   vfinal=-4000  name=anode
80. SOLVE  vstep=-10   vfinal=-4200  name=anode
81. SOLVE  vstep=-5    vfinal=-4500  name=anode    compl=1e-25  cname=anode
82.
83. SAVE outf=PIN_Reverse_27C.str
84.
85. QUIT
```

Table 1. Code walkthrough: parallel plane p-i-n diode forward and breakdown J–V characteristics.

Line No:	Functionality
1	Configure ATLAS simulator to use 160-bit extended precision and utilize 32 cores of the CPU if hardware resources are available. The version of ATLAS to be used by the simulator is set to 5.18.3.R using the $-V$ option in the simflags command.
5	Initialize device structure mesh information.
7–23	X-axis and Y-axis mesh distribution.
27	Declare 4H-SiC as the material for the area of the semiconductor specified by the x and y coordinates.

(Continued)

Table 1. (*Continued*)

Line No:	Functionality
31–32	Electrode specifications for the p-i-n diode (Anode and Cathode)
36–43	Specify doping profile, type, and concentration for different areas of the PIN diode structure.
45	Save the device structure (**.str**) file on the local hard drive. The device structure can be viewed by opening the file via **TonyPlot** to troubleshoot/optimize the structure.
47	Specify material parameters for 4H-SiC. Detailed description of these parameters are available in the Silvaco© ATLAS manual. The values for these parameters can either be obtained via material research or from literature.
51	Specify the various models to be included in the 4H-SiC p-i-n diode simulation.
55	Specify mobility parameters for 4H-SiC. Detailed description of these parameters are available in the Silvaco© ATLAS manual. The values for these parameters can either be obtained via material research or from literature.
57	Specify impact ionization parameters for 4H-SiC. This statement is mandatory to obtain device breakdown characteristics.
59	Specify the solver type and the tolerance values to be used during the simulation. This is an extremely critical statement which can alter the simulation outcome.
61	Include current flowlines in the output structure file.
63	Save the forward-bias simulation log (**.log**) file on the local hard drive. The simulation results can be viewed by opening the file via **TonyPlot**.
65–68	Solve for the initial bias conditions for the simulation followed by positive sweep of anode voltage for steady-state forward characteristics.
70	Save the post-forward-bias simulation device structure (*.str*) file on the local hard drive. Saving the file at this stage of the simulation will enable the user to visualize the variation in various electrothermal parameters within the device structure introduced due to the particular simulation. For example in this simulation, the user can view the carrier concentration profile in the p-i-n diode during forward conduction.
72	Save the reverse-bias simulation log (**.log**) file on the local hard drive. The simulation results can be viewed by opening the file via **TonyPlot**.
74–81	Solve for the initial bias conditions for the simulation followed by negative sweep of anode voltage for steady-state reverse-bias characteristics. The compliance parameter (**compl**) in line 81 forces the simulator to proceed to the next line once the anode current reaches the specified compliance value. This is important, especially in breakdown simulation because once the device enters the breakdown regime, it is not necessary to run the simulation for higher magnitude of current since the breakdown voltage would have already been determined.

(*Continued*)

Table 1. (*Continued*)

Line No:	Functionality
83	Save the post-reverse-bias simulation device structure (`.str`) file on the local hard drive. Saving the file at this stage of the simulation will enable the user to visualize the variation in various electrothermal parameters within the device structure introduced due to the particular simulation. For example in this simulation, the user can view the electric field profile in the p-i-n diode during avalanche breakdown.
85	Terminate the simulation

 The user can have separate programs for forward-conduction and reverse-breakdown simulation. Having multiple steady-state simulations in a single program helps in minimizing the error introduced when changes made (especially mesh structure) in one program do not reflect in the other. Also, the user can comment the various code segments to run a specific code segment.

6.4.2.2. *Steady-state simulation results*

The forward conduction J–V characteristics for the 3300 V SiC p-i-n diode on a linear and semi-log scale are shown in Figs. 6(a) and 6(b), respectively. The anode voltage scale on the linear plot shown in Fig. 6(a) starts from 2 V to provide the reader with a clearer view of the diode turn-ON regime and a better understanding of the effect of temperature on diode turn-ON. There is a steady decrease in the diode turn-ON voltage as the lattice temperature increases from 27°C to 175°C. However, beyond 450 A/cm^2 current density, the dynamic ON-state resistance of the p-i-n diode increases with temperature, thereby resulting in higher ON-state losses. The semi-log plot shown in Fig. 6(b) highlights the various regimes which define the forward conduction mechanism in a p-i-n diode. The slope of current density indicates space–charge recombination, low-level injection, and high-level injection regimes. Once the current density exceeds 100 A/cm^2, there is significant increase in the ON-state voltage drop due to the end region resistance effects. At an ON-state current density of 100 A/cm^2, voltage drop of 3.05 V was observed across the diode at 27°C device temperature.

The reverse-bias breakdown J–V characteristics are shown in Fig. 7. Breakdown voltage of 4350 V was obtained for the p-i-n diode at 27°C device temperature. There is a progressive increase in the leakage current

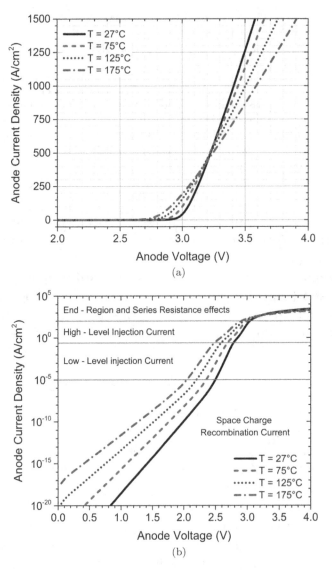

Fig. 6.   (a) Forward J–V characteristics for the SiC parallel plane p-i-n diode on a linear scale. (b) Forward J–V characteristics for the SiC parallel plane p-i-n diode on a semi-log scale.

with device temperature without any change in the breakdown voltage. The breakdown characteristics are dependent on the impact ionization coefficients (**line 57 in the simulation code**), and it is up to the user to specify them based on experimental data or literature review.

The electric field distribution in the p-i-n diode structure during breakdown is shown in the contour plot in Fig. 8. The contour plot has been

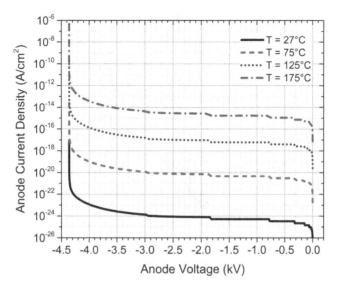

Fig. 7. Reverse breakdown J–V characteristics for the SiC parallel plane p-i-n diode on a semi-log scale.

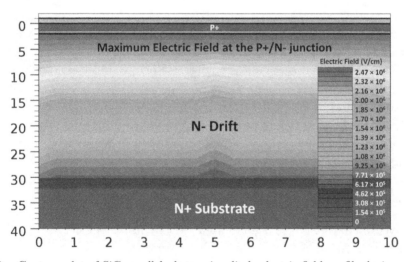

Fig. 8. Contour plot of SiC parallel plane p-i-n diode electric field profile during reverse breakdown.

scaled to focus on the electric field in the critical regions of the device, i.e. P+ and N− drift region. Maximum electric field of 2.47 MV/cm was observed at the P+/N− drift junction and gradually decreases towards the N− drift/N+ substrate junction. Due to the parallel plane design, peak electric field is uniform across the active diode area at the P+/N− drift junction. The magnitude of electric field in the substrate is approximately

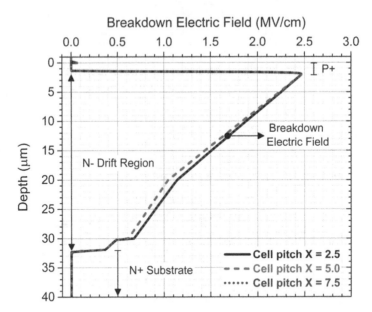

Fig. 9.   1D electric field profile in a parallel plane SiC p-i-n diode as a function of device depth.

zero; hence, only a segment of the substrate width is shown in Fig. 8. Using the **cutline** feature in **TonyPlot**, 1D electric field profile as a function of device depth was generated and is shown in Fig. 9. The electric field profiles were generated for three points along the cell pitch/active area: $x = 2.5\,\mu$m, $x = 5.0\,\mu$m, and $x = 7.5\,\mu$m. Ideally, for a parallel plane structure, the electric field profiles should be overlapping; however, in Fig. 9, there is slight difference in the profile at $x = 5.0\,\mu$m due to the merger of mesh from the left and right halves of the complete structure.

6.4.2.3.   *Mixed-mode transient simulation*

Transient simulation of the p-i-n diode model helps in predicting the behavior of the device in an actual circuit. This section will discuss the transient simulation of a parallel plane SiC p-i-n diode using the Mixed-Mode circuit simulator. An RLC ring-down circuit was used to simulate the p-i-n diode structure under high current density pulsed operation. The working of an RLC ring-down circuit shown in Fig. 10 has already been discussed in Chapter 5. The circuit was designed to generate a current pulse with pulse-width of $5\,\mu$s and the peak current was varied using the **width** parameter in the deckbuild code.[9,10]

The RLC ring-down circuit elements have been renamed according to their usage in the SPICE netlist mentioned in the transient simulation

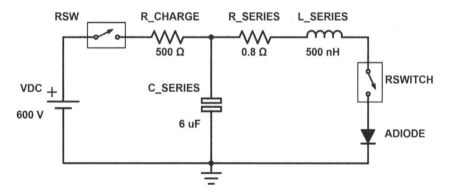

Fig. 10.   RLC ring-down circuit used for high current density pulsed simulation.

program. The following code was used to simulate the p-i-n diode for a peak current density of $5000\,\text{A/cm}^2$ under pulsed condition. A brief explanation of the Mixed-Mode simulation program is provided in the code walkthrough (Table 2).

```
Sample code: Parallel plane SiC p-i-n diode transient simulation

1.  GO ATLAS SIMFLAGS ="-V 5.18.3.R -P 32 -160"
2.
3.  ##### PARALLEL PLANE PIN DIODE RLC RINGDOWN PULSE 5000A/cm2 ######
4.
5.  MESH  WIDTH=1.2e6
6.
7.  ## X-MESH
8.
9.   X.MESH  loc=0.0        spac=0.5
10.  X.MESH  loc=10.0       spac=0.5
11.
12. ## Y-MESH
13.
14. Y.MESH  loc=-1.0        spac=1.0
15. Y.MESH  loc=0.0         spac=0.25
16. Y.MESH  loc=2.1         spac=0.01
17. Y.MESH  loc=30.0        spac=10.0
18. Y.MESH  loc=32.1        spac=0.2
19. Y.MESH  loc=33.0        spac=1.0
20. Y.MESH  loc=34.0        spac=20
21. Y.MESH  loc=180.0       spac=20
22. Y.MESH  loc=182.0       spac=1.0
23. Y.MESH  loc=184.0       spac=1.0
24.
25. ## Defining Regions
26.
27. REGION  num=1  material=4H-SiC   x.min=0   x.max=10   y.min=0  y.max=182
28.
29. ## Electrode
30.
31. ELECTRODE  name=anode    material=titanium   x.min=0    x.max=10   y.max=0
```

```
32. ELECTRODE  name=cathode  material=aluminum   y.min=182   y.max=184
33.
34. ## Doping Distribution
35.
36. ## Bulk Doping
37. DOPING  uniform  n.type  conc=3.8e15  REGION=1
38.
39. ## P+ Doping
40. DOPING  gauss    p.type  conc=1.e21  x.min=0  x.max=10  junc=2.0   rat=0.1
41.
42. ## N+ Substrate Region Doping
43. DOPING  uniform  n.type  conc=1.e20   y.min=32    y.max=182
44.
45. SAVE outf=PIN_Structure.str  master.out
46.
47. ##### STEADY STATE SIMULATION CIRCUIT #####
48.
49. GO ATLAS SIMFLAGS ="-V 5.18.3.R -P 32 -160"
50.
51. .BEGIN
52.
53. VDC         1   0   0
54. RSW         1   2   1.e-12
55. R_CHARGE    2   3   500
56. C_SERIES    3   0   6u
57. R_SERIES    3   4   0.80
58. L_SERIES    4   5   500n
59. RSWITCH     5   6   1.e18
60. ADIODE      6=anode   0=cathode   infile=PIN_Structure.str   WIDTH=1.2e6
61.
62. .NODESET  v(1)=0  v(2)=0  v(3)=0  v(4)=0  v(5)=0  v(6)=0
63. .NUMERIC  imaxdc=100
64.
65. .DC   VDC   0.    10.   0.25
66. .DC   VDC   10.   100.  10.
67. .DC   VDC   100.  600.  25.
68.
69. .LOG  outfile=PIN_DC_log
70. .SAVE   outfile=PIN_RLC_Bias
71. .OPTIONS  m2ln print noshift relpot
72.
73. .END
74.
75. ##### PHYSICS USED #####
76.
77. CONTACT  DEVICE=ADIODE  NAME=ANODE      EXT.ALPHA=10
78. CONTACT  DEVICE=ADIODE  NAME=CATHODE    EXT.ALPHA=10
79.
80. THERMCONTACT DEVICE=ADIODE num=3  x.min=0   x.max=10  y.min=-1.0  y.max=184
    alpha=10   ext.temp=300
81.
82. MATERIAL DEVICE=ADIODE   material=4H-SiC REGION=1  permittivity=9.76
    eg300=3.26  affinity=3.7  egalpha=3.3e-2  egbeta=1.e+5  nc300=1.7e+19
    nv300=2.5e+19  arichn=146  arichp=30  augn=3.e-29  augp=3.e-29  taun0=3.33e-6
    taup0=6.7e-7  nsrhn=3.e+17 nsrhp=3.e+17 edb=0.050  eab=0.20  tcon.polyn
    tc.a=0.137534   tc.b=0.00049662   tc.c=0.000000354  hc.a=2.35  hc.b=1.75e-3
    hc.c=1.e-9  hc.d=-6.6e4
83.
84. ## MODELS USED
85.
```

```
86. MODELS   DEVICE=ADIODE   REGION=1   MATERIAL=4H-SIC FERMIDIRAC ANALYTIC CONWELL
    SRH BGN AUGER INCOMPLETE LAT.TEMP   JOULE.HEAT GR.HEAT   PT.HEAT PRINT
87.
88. ## MOBILITY
89.
90. MOBILITY  DEVICE=ADIODE  material=4H-SiC REGION=1  vsatn=2.2e7  vsatp=2.2e7
    betan=1.2 betap=2  mu1n.caug=40  mu2n.caug=1136  ncritn.caug=2e17
    alphan.caug=-3  betan.caug=-3  gamman.caug=0.0  deltan.caug=0.76   mu1p.caug=20
    mu2p.caug=125  ncritp.caug=1.e19  alphap.caug=-3  betap.caug=-3
    gammap.caug=0.0  deltap.caug=0.5
91.
92. MOBILITY  DEVICE=ADIODE  material=4H-SiC REGION=1   n.canali  n.angle=90
    p.angle=90 vsatn=2.2e7  vsatp=2.2e7  betan=1.2 betap=2  mu1n.caug=5
    mu2n.caug=947  ncritn.caug=2e17  alphan.caug=-3  betan.caug=-3  gamman.caug=0.0
    deltan.caug=0.76   mu1p.caug=2.5  mu2p.caug=20  ncritp.caug=1.e19
    alphap.caug=-3  betap.caug=-3  gammap.caug=0.0  deltap.caug=0.5
93.
94. ## IMPACT IONIZATION
95.
96. IMPACT   DEVICE=ADIODE   REGION=1   ANISO  E.SIDE  SELB  SIC4H0001  an1=3.44e6
    an2=3.44e6  bn1=2.58e7  bn2=2.58e7  ap1=3.5e6  ap2=3.5e6  bp1=1.7e7  bp2=1.7e7
    opphe=0.106
97.
98. METHOD BLOCK  climit=1.e-9  maxtraps=100  itlimit=100   max.temp=1000
    dvmax=1.e8  ir.tol=1.e-35  cr.tol=1.e-35  ix.tol=1.e-35  px.tol=1.e-30
    pr.tol=1.e-45  cx.tol=1.e-30
99.
100. ##### TRANSIENT SIMULATION CIRCUIT #####
101.
102. GO ATLAS SIMFLAGS ="-V 5.18.3.R -P 32 -160"
103.
104. .BEGIN
105.
106. VDC        1    0    600
107. RSW        1    2    1.e-12  PULSE   1.e-12  1.e18  5us  50ns  50ns  40us  80us
108. R_CHARGE  2    3    500
109. C_BANK    3    0    6u
110. R_SERIES  3    4    0.80
111. L_SERIES  4    5    500n
112. RSWITCH   5    6    1.e18   PULSE   1.e18  1.e-12  10us  50ns  50ns  40us   80us
113. ADIODE    6=anode    0=cathode   infile=PIN_Structure.str   WIDTH=1.2e6
114.
115. .NUMERIC  imaxtr=100  dtmax=5.e-8
116. .OPTIONS  m2ln.tr  print  noshift  relpot  write=20
117. .LOAD       infile=PIN_RLC_Bias
118. .SAVE       master=PIN_Transient
119. .LOG        outfile=PIN_RLC_Ringdown.log
120. .SAVE       outfile=PIN_RLC_Ringdown.str
121. .TRAN   0.01us 45us
122.
123. .END
124.
125. ##### PHYSICS USED #####
126.
127. CONTACT  DEVICE=ADIODE  NAME=ANODE      EXT.ALPHA=10
128. CONTACT  DEVICE=ADIODE  NAME=CATHODE    EXT.ALPHA=10
129.
130. THERMCONTACT DEVICE=ADIODE   num=3   x.min=0   x.max=10  y.min=-1.0  y.max=184
     alpha=10   ext.temp=300
131.
```

```
132. MATERIAL  DEVICE=ADIODE   material=4H-SiC  REGION=1  permittivity=9.76
     eg300=3.26   affinity=3.7  egalpha=3.3e-2   egbeta=1.e+5  nc300=1.7e+19
     nv300=2.5e+19  arichn=146  arichp=30  augn=3.e-29  augp=3.e-29  taun0=3.33e-6
     taup0=6.7e-7  nsrhn=3.e+17 nsrhp=3.e+17 edb=0.050  eab=0.200  tcon.polyn
     tc.a=0.137534   tc.b=0.00049662   tc.c=0.000000354  hc.a=2.35  hc.b=1.75e-3
     hc.c=1.e-9  hc.d=-6.6e4
133.
134. ## MODELS USED
135.
136. MODELS  DEVICE=ADIODE   REGION=1 MATERIAL=4H-SIC FERMIDIRAC ANALYTIC CONWELL
     SRH BGN AUGER INCOMPLETE LAT.TEMP  JOULE.HEAT  GR.HEAT  PT.HEAT PRINT
137.
138. ## MOBILITY
139.
140. MOBILITY  DEVICE=ADIODE  material=4H-SiC REGION=1  vsatn=2.2e7  vsatp=2.2e7
     betan=1.2 betap=2  mu1n.caug=40  mu2n.caug=1136  ncritn.caug=2e17
     alphan.caug=-3  betan.caug=-3  gamman.caug=0.0  deltan.caug=0.76   mu1p.caug=20
     mu2p.caug=125  ncritp.caug=1.e19  alphap.caug=-3  betap.caug=-3
     gammap.caug=0.0  deltap.caug=0.5
141.
142. MOBILITY  DEVICE=ADIODE  material=4H-SiC REGION=1  n.canali  n.angle=90
     p.angle=90 vsatn=2.2e7  vsatp=2.2e7  betan=1.2 betap=2  mu1n.caug=5
     mu2n.caug=947  ncritn.caug=2e17  alphan.caug=-3  betan.caug=-3  gamman.caug=0.0
     deltan.caug=0.76   mu1p.caug=2.5  mu2p.caug=20  ncritp.caug=1.e19
     alphap.caug=-3  betap.caug=-3  gammap.caug=0.0  deltap.caug=0.5
143.
144. ## IMPACT IONIZATION
145.
146. IMPACT  DEVICE=ADIODE  REGION=1  ANISO  E.SIDE  SELB  SIC4H0001  an1=3.44e6
     an2=3.44e6  bn1=2.58e7  bn2=2.58e7  ap1=3.5e6  ap2=3.5e6  bp1=1.7e7  bp2=1.7e7
     opphe=0.106
147.
148. OUTPUT  FLOWLINES  E.MOBILITY
149.
150. METHOD  BLOCK.TRAN  climit=1.e-9  maxtraps=100  itlimit=100   max.temp=1000
     dvmax=1.e8  ir.tol=1.e-25  cr.tol=1.e-25  ix.tol=1.e-30  px.tol=1.e-30
     pr.tol=1.e-36  cx.tol=1.e-30
151.
152. GO ATLAS SIMFLAGS ="-V 5.18.3.R -P 32 -128"
153.
154. QUIT
```

Table 2.   Code walkthrough: Parallel plane p-i-n Diode mixed-mode.

Line No:	Functionality
1	Configure ATLAS simulator to use version 5.18.3.R, 160-bit extended precision and utilize 32 cores of the CPU if hardware resources are available.
5	Initialize device structure mesh information with width parameter.
7–23	X-axis and Y-axis mesh distribution.
27	Declare 4H-SiC as the material for the area of the semiconductor specified by the x and y coordinates.
31–32	Electrode specifications for the p-i-n diode (Anode and Cathode).

(Continued)

Table 2. (*Continued*)

Line No:	Functionality
36–43	Specify doping profile, type, and concentration for different areas of the p-i-n diode structure.
45	Save the device structure (**.str**) file on the local hard drive.
49	Initialize ATLAS simulator using GO ATLAS command (same as line 1).
51	Initialize the starting of SPICE-like code in Mixed-Mode steady-state simulation.
53–60	RLC ring-down circuit description in SPICE-like format.
62	Declare the initial node voltage for the RLC ring-down circuit nodes.
63	Set the maximum number of mixed circuit-device iterations to be performed during steady-state analysis (**imaxdc**) to 100.
65–67	Ramp up DC voltage to attain steady-state condition, i.e. VDC = 600 V. This can be split into multiple steps.
69	Save log file after steady-state simulation completion.
70	Save file with bias information which will be used for transient simulation
71	Specify Mixed-Mode steady-state simulation conditions. Modified two-level Newton solution method (**m2ln**), disable the shift of voltage for ATLAS devices (**noshift**), and enable the use of relative convergence criteria for potential especially when large voltage biases are involved (**relpot**).
73	Initialize the ending of SPICE-like code in Mixed-Mode steady-state simulation.
77–78	Specify heat transfer coefficient (**ext.alpha**) for the anode and cathode contacts.
80	Specify the thermal boundary for the p-i-n diode. Parameters include boundary dimensions, heat transfer coefficient (**alpha**), and temperature of the thermal boundary (**ext.temp**) which is typically at 300 K.
82	Specify material parameters for 4H-SiC.
86	Specify the various models to be included in the 4H-SiC p-i-n diode simulation.
90	Specify parameters for mobility in 4H-SiC.
92	Specify parameters for anisotropic mobility in 4H-SiC.
96	Specify Impact Ionization parameters for 4H-SiC.
98	Specify the steady-state Block Newton solver type (**BLOCK**) and the tolerance values to be used during the simulation.
102	Initialize ATLAS simulator using GO ATLAS command (same as line 1) for steady-state bias point simulation.
104	Initialize the starting of SPICE-like code in Mixed-Mode transient simulation.

(*Continued*)

Table 2.   (*Continued*)

Line No:	Functionality
106–113	RLC ring-down circuit description in SPICE-like format. The magnitude of DC voltage source is initialized at 600 V which is the result of the earlier steady-state simulation performed. Transient parameters have been added to the Resistor which is acting like a switch.
115	Set the maximum number of mixed circuit-device iterations to be performed during transient analysis (***imaxtr***) to 100 and the maximum transient simulation time step (***dtmax***) to 50 ns.
116	Specify Mixed-Mode transient simulation conditions. Modified two-level Newton solution method for transient simulation (***m2ln.tr***), disable the shift of voltage for ATLAS devices (***noshift***), enable the use of relative convergence criteria for potential especially when large voltage biases are involved (***relpot***), and write structure file after every 20 time-step iterations.
117	Load the steady-state simulations results saved in line 70.
118	Save the structure file after every 20 time-step iterations specified in line 116.
119	Save log file after the completion of transient simulation.
120	Save the structure file after the completion of transient simulation.
121	Specify the initial time interval of 10 ns and total simulation time of 45 μs.
123	Initialize the ending of SPICE-like code in Mixed-Mode transient simulation.
127–146	Same as line 77 to line 96.
148	Include current flowlines (***FLOWLINES***) and Electron Mobility (***E.MOBILITY***) in the output structure file.
150	Specify the transient Block Newton solver type (***BLOCK.TRAN***) and the tolerance values to be used during the simulation.
152	Initialize ATLAS simulator using GO ATLAS command (same as line 1) for transient simulation. A lower simulation precision of 128-bit has been used due to forward conduction mode of operation.
154	Terminate the simulation

6.4.2.4.   *Mixed-mode transient simulation results*

The transient simulation for the p-i-n diode was carried out for varying magnitudes of peak current density ranging from 500 A/cm^2 to 5000 A/cm^2 in steps of 500. The ***width*** parameter was used to change the peak current density through the diode without altering the waveform. In this section, the results pertaining to the maximum current density scenario of 5000 A/cm^2 will be discussed followed by a summary of all the other cases. The anode voltage and current density waveforms are shown in Fig. 11 and the power

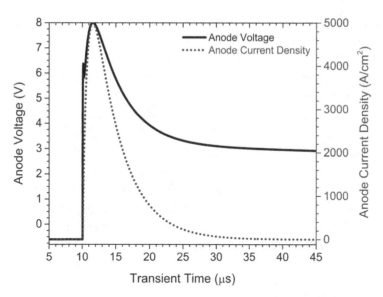

Fig. 11.   Anode voltage (solid) and current density (dotted) waveforms pertaining to 5000 A/cm^2 peak current density simulation.

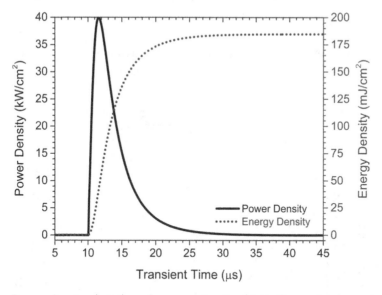

Fig. 12.   Power density (solid) and energy density (dotted) waveforms pertaining to 5000 A/cm^2 peak current density simulation.

and energy density waveforms are shown in Fig. 12. An overshoot in the anode voltage waveform can be observed during the current ramp-up phase in Fig. 11. This sudden rise in anode voltage is due to the finite time required for conductivity modulation to occur, also known as forward recovery. In the latter part of this section, a summary of anode voltage waveforms will be provided to explain the difference in the forward recovery voltage with varying peak pulsed current density.

A $10\,\mu s$ delay was introduced during the Mixed-Mode transient simulation to provide a well-defined starting point for the electrical parameters, purely from a graphical representation standpoint. The delay value can be seen in the transient parameter **PULSE** of the resistor element **RSWITCH** in **line 112**. Hence, the time scale in the waveforms are starting from $5\,\mu s$ instead of zero. A peak voltage drop of $8\,V$ was observed across the p-i-n diode at peak current density of $5000\,A/cm^2$ which corresponds to a peak power dissipation density of $40\,kW/cm^2$. Integration of the power density waveform yielded an energy density of $184\,mJ/cm^2$. A peak lattice temperature of $309.2\,K$ was observed in the p-i-n diode lattice during this pulsed operation. The variation in lattice temperature with power dissipation density and energy density during simulation is shown in Figs. 13 and 14, respectively. The simulation was run for only $45\,\mu s$, and hence does not show the complete decay of temperature waveform back to the ambient value. To identify the area of heat dissipation in the p-i-n diode structure, intermediate structure files were generated during the simulation (in this scenario, a structure file was generated every 20 time-step iterations). These structure files were manually scanned for the transient time instant which corresponds to the maximum lattice temperature.

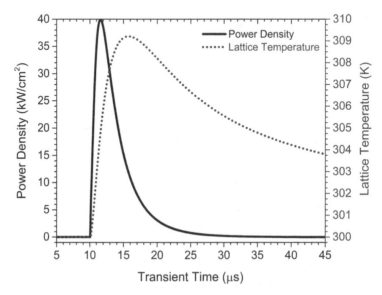

Fig. 13.   Power Density (solid) and lattice temperature (dotted) waveforms pertaining to $5000\,A/cm^2$ RLC ring-down simulation.

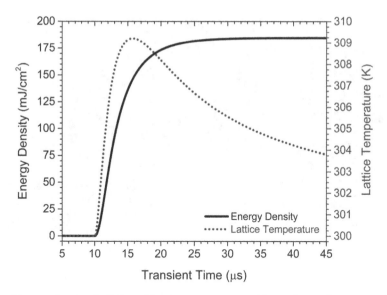

Fig. 14.   Energy density (solid) and lattice temperature (dotted) waveforms pertaining to 5000 A/cm^2 RLC ring-down simulation.

The lattice temperature profile of the p-i-n diode structure recorded at the time instant corresponding to maximum temperature during high current density pulsed simulation are shown in Figs. 15(a) and 15(b). A maximum temperature of 309.2 K was observed in the P+ anode region.

To investigate the heat dissipation source, recombination heat power and joule heat power profiles were extracted from the structure file and are shown in Figs. 16 and 17, respectively (p–n junction at 2 μm depth is marked by a white line). The heat power sources are expressed in W/cm^3 in **TonyPlot**, and the contour plots have been scaled to highlight the areas of interest.

 The heat power sources (Carrier Generation– Recombination, Joule, and Peltier–Thomson) are expressed in W/cm^3 in TonyPlot software for a 2D device structure which can result in very large values for the parameter.

 The Joule heat power values can range from positive to negative and may require adjustment of the upper and lower limits of the contour plot in TonyPlot software. Discussion of the internal calculation of heat power is beyond the scope of this textbook.

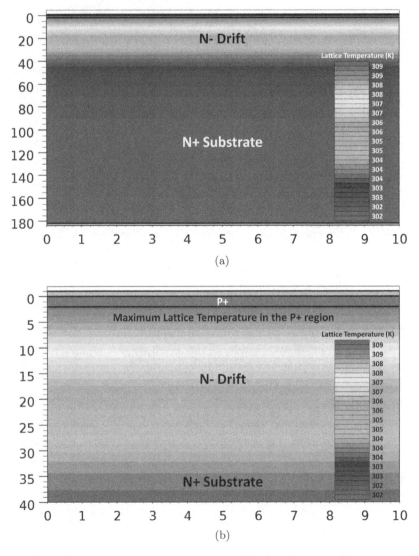

Fig. 15.   (a) Lattice temperature profile of parallel plane p-i-n diode structure during 5000 A/cm² RLC ring-down simulation. (b) Lattice temperature profile of parallel plane p-i-n diode structure during 5000 A/cm² RLC ring-down simulation (zoomed-in view).

It can be seen from the heat power profiles that there is significant power dissipation in the P+ region due to carrier generation and recombination and joule/resistive heating effects. This heat generation is due to the end region recombination effects (discussed earlier) which increases the ON-state resistance especially at higher current density forward operation.[11]

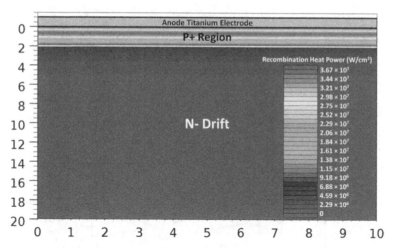

Fig. 16. Recombination heat power profile of parallel plane p-i-n diode structure during $5000\,\mathrm{A/cm^2}$ RLC ring-down simulation (zoomed-in view).

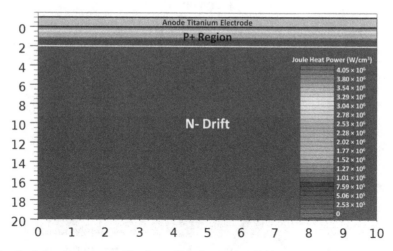

Fig. 17. Joule heat power profile of parallel plane p-i-n diode structure during $5000\,\mathrm{A/cm^2}$ RLC ring-down simulation (zoomed-in view).

The summary of lattice temperature and anode voltage waveforms for the parallel plane p-i-n diode for all the values of peak pulsed current density are shown in Figs. 18 and 19, respectively. The anode voltage waveforms have been scaled to highlight the instant when the RLC ring-down circuit current density ramps up through the diode in Fig. 19. During the initial phase of current density ramp up, voltage drop across the p-i-n diode increases due to incomplete conductivity modulation within the drift region. Soon after the onset of conductivity modulation, voltage drop across diode decreases back

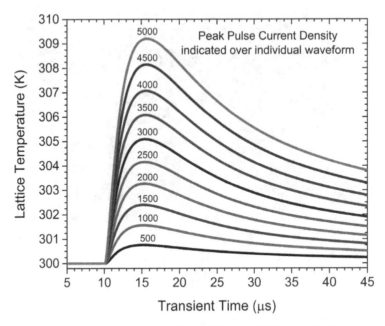

Fig. 18.   Lattice temperature summary of parallel plane SiC p-i-n diode structure during RLC ring-down simulation.

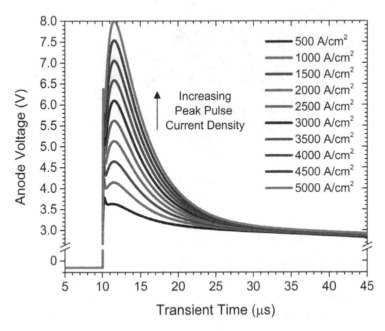

Fig. 19.   Anode voltage summary of parallel plane SiC p-i-n diode structure during RLC ring-down simulation.

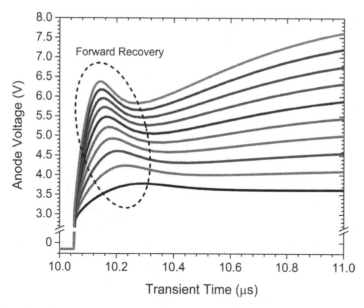

Fig. 20. Anode voltage summary of parallel plane SiC p-i-n diode structure during RLC ring-down simulation with emphasis on the forward recovery process.

to a value which is determined by the forward current density through the device. As the magnitude of peak circuit current density increases, the effect of end region recombination becomes more and more dominant, thereby resulting in an increase in the voltage drop.

It can be seen from Fig. 20 that the anode voltage waveform corresponding to $500\,A/cm^2$ has the lowest variation as compared to the $5000\,A/cm^2$ simulation waveform due to the impact of peak pulsed current density on forward recovery process and end region recombination effects.

6.4.3. PIN diode structure with planar junction and floating field rings (Half-cell)

Parallel plane structure is an ideal design which is good for simulation and basic understanding of device performance. However, it is not a practical design that can be fabricated into a production device. The primary design parameters for the p-i-n diode with planar junction including drift region thickness and doping concentration are kept same as the parallel plane structure. The main difference between a parallel plane and planar junction p-i-n diode structure is the profile of the p-type junction. The p–n junction in a parallel plane design presents an ideal scenario due to the uniform electric field distribution at the P+/N− junction across the device active area as seen in Fig. 8, thereby attaining the maximum possible breakdown voltage, whereas the planar junction has a lower breakdown voltage due to electric field enhancement at the edge of the cylindrical junction. In this p-i-n diode design, the P+ anode region had a junction depth of $2\,\mu$m and was heavily doped with a peak acceptor concentration of $1.0 \times 10^{21}\,\mathrm{cm}^{-3}$ using a Gaussian profile. The floating field rings also had a junction depth of $2\,\mu$m and were heavily doped with a peak acceptor concentration of $1.0 \times 10^{20}\,\mathrm{cm}^{-3}$ (slightly lower than the anode region) using a Gaussian profile. The N− epitaxial/drift region was $30\,\mu$m thick with a doping concentration of $3.8 \times 10^{15}\,\mathrm{cm}^{-3}$. The N+ substrate had a thickness of $150\,\mu$m and doping concentration of $1.0 \times 10^{20}\,\mathrm{cm}^{-3}$. Electron and hole lifetimes of $3.33\,\mu$s and $0.67\,\mu$s were selected based on research and literature review, respectively.[5–7] Titanium and aluminum were selected for the P+ anode and N+ cathode ohmic contacts, respectively.[8] Due to the presence of floating field rings, the 2D device structure had a cell pitch of $16\,\mu$m and an active area of $10\,\mu\mathrm{m}^2$ based on the $10\,\mu$m wide P+ anode region. A $1\,\mu$m thick oxide layer is used as the Inter-Layer Dielectric (ILD) over the floating field rings. The width of the P+ implanted regions forming the field rings and the spacing between them are critical and optimizable parameters and are unique to each diode design. Since each semiconductor designer has their own unique way of defining field rings, it will not be discussed in this textbook.

Due to the large substrate thickness as compared to the drift layer, the complete device structure designed using Silvaco© ATLAS has been split into two sections: complete structures shown in Figs. 21(a) and 21(b) respectively. The Gaussian doping profile has been used for the P+ anode region and floating field rings which can be seen in Fig. 21(b).

6.4.3.1. *Steady-state simulation*

This section will discuss the forward conduction and reverse breakdown current density versus anode voltage (J–V) characteristics at 27°C, 75°C, 125°C, and 175°C device temperature. The steady-state simulation code is similar to the one used for the parallel plane diode except for change in device mesh profile and the inclusion of oxide material. The following code was used to simulate the p-i-n diode J–V characteristics which includes forward conduction and reverse breakdown. A brief explanation of the steady-state simulation program is provided in the code walkthrough (Table 3).

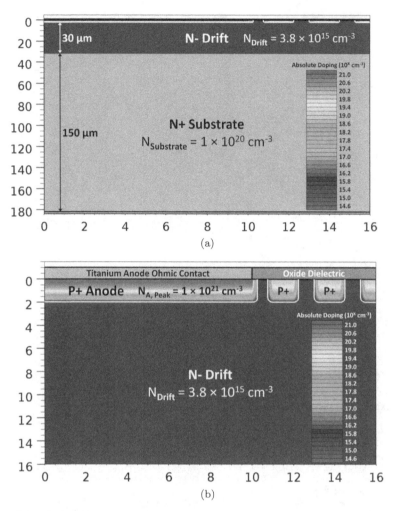

Fig. 21. (a) 3300 V SiC p-i-n diode planar junction half-cell structure designed in Silvaco©
ATLAS. (b) 3300 V SiC p-i-n diode planar junction half-cell structure designed in Silvaco©
ATLAS (zoomed-in view).

```
Sample code: Planar junction SiC p-i-n diode half-cell forward and breakdown J-V
characteristics @ 27°C

1.   GO ATLAS SIMFLAGS ="-V 5.18.3.R -P 32 -160"
2.
3.   ##### 3300V PLANAR JUNCTION PIN DIODE - HALF CELL #####
4.
5.   MESH
6.
7.   ## X-MESH
8.
```

```
9.   X.MESH   loc=0.0     spac=0.5
10.  X.MESH   loc=9.0     spac=0.5
11.  X.MESH   loc=10.0    spac=0.25
12.  X.MESH   loc=16.0    spac=0.25
13.
14.  ## Y-MESH
15.
16.  Y.MESH   loc=-1.0      spac=1.0
17.  Y.MESH   loc=0.0       spac=0.25
18.  Y.MESH   loc=2.1       spac=0.01
19.  Y.MESH   loc=30.0      spac=4.0
20.  Y.MESH   loc=32.1      spac=0.2
21.  Y.MESH   loc=33.0      spac=1.0
22.  Y.MESH   loc=34.0      spac=20
23.  Y.MESH   loc=180.0     spac=20
24.  Y.MESH   loc=182.0     spac=1.0
25.  Y.MESH   loc=184.0     spac=1.0
26.
27.  ## Defining Regions
28.
29.  REGION   num=1   material=Oxide    y.max=0
30.  REGION   num=2   material=4H-SiC   x.min=0    x.max=16    y.min=0  y.max=182
31.
32.  ## Electrode
33.
34.  ELECTRODE  name=anode    material=titanium   x.min=0     x.max=10    y.max=0
35.  ELECTRODE  name=cathode  material=aluminum   y.min=182   y.max=184
36.
37.  ## Bulk Doping
38.  DOPING  uniform  n.type  conc=3.8e15  REGION=2
39.
40.  ## P+ Doping
41.  DOPING  gauss  p.type conc=1.e21  x.min=0    x.max=10    junc=2.0    rat=0.1
42.
43.  ## P+ Floating Field Rings
44.  DOPING  gauss  p.type conc=1.e20  x.min=11.00  x.max=12.00  junc=2.0  rat=0.1
45.  DOPING  gauss  p.type conc=1.e20  x.min=13.25  x.max=14.25  junc=2.0  rat=0.1
46.  DOPING  gauss  p.type conc=1.e20  x.min=15.50  x.max=16     junc=2.0  rat=0.1
47.
48.  ## N+ Substrate Region Doping
49.  DOPING  uniform  n.type  conc=1.e20   y.min=32    y.max=182
50.
51.  SAVE   outf=PIN_Planar_FFR.str.str  master.out
52.
53.  MATERIAL  material=4H-SiC  REGION=2  permittivity=9.76  eg300=3.26
     affinity=3.7  egalpha=3.3e-2  egbeta=1.e+5  nc300=1.7e+19  nv300=2.5e+19
     arichn=146  arichp=30  augn=3.e-29  augp=3.e-29  taun0=3.33e-6  taup0=6.7e-7
     nsrhn=3.e+17  nsrhp=3.e+17  edb=0.05  eab=0.20
54.
55.  ## MODELS USED
56.
57.  MODELS  REGION=2 MATERIAL=4H-SIC FERMIDIRAC ANALYTIC CONWELL INCOMPLETE SRH BGN
     AUGER TEMP=300 PRINT
58.
59.  ## MOBILITY
60.
61.  MOBILITY  material=4H-SiC REGION=2 vsatn=2.2e7  vsatp=2.2e7  betan=1.2 betap=2
     mu1n.caug=40  mu2n.caug=1136  ncritn.caug=2e17  alphan.caug=-3  betan.caug=-3
     gamman.caug=0.0  deltan.caug=0.76   mu1p.caug=20  mu2p.caug=125
     ncritp.caug=1.e19  alphap.caug=-3  betap.caug=-3  gammap.caug=0.0
     deltap.caug=0.5
```

```
62.
63. IMPACT  REGION=2  ANISO  E.SIDE  SELB  SIC4H0001 an1=3.44e6  an2=3.44e6
    bn1=2.58e7  bn2=2.58e7  ap1=3.5e6  ap2=3.5e6  bp1=1.7e7  bp2=1.7e7 opphe=0.106
64.
65. METHOD  NEWTON AUTONR  climit=1.e-9  maxtraps=40  itlimit=40    dvmax=1.e8
    ir.tol=1.e-36  cr.tol=1.e-36  ix.tol=1.e-36  px.tol=1.e-30  pr.tol=1.e-45
    cx.tol=1.e-30
66.
67. OUTPUT  FLOWLINES
68.
69. LOG  outf=PIN_Forward_27C.log
70.
71. SOLVE  init
72. SOLVE  vanode=0.05  vstep=0.05  vfinal=2.6      name=anode
73. SOLVE  vstep=0.02              vfinal=3.2      name=anode
74. SOLVE  vstep=0.1               vfinal=4.0      name=anode
75.
76. SAVE  outf=PIN_Forward_27C.str
77.
78. LOG  outf=PIN_Reverse_27C.log
79.
80. SOLVE  init
81. SOLVE  vanode=-0.2  vstep=-0.2      vfinal=-2.0     name=anode
82. SOLVE  vstep=-2    vfinal=-20              name=anode
83. SOLVE  vstep=-5    vfinal=-100     name=anode
84. SOLVE  vstep=-10   vfinal=-1000    name=anode
85. SOLVE  vstep=-25   vfinal=-4000    name=anode
86. SOLVE  vstep=-10   vfinal=-4200    name=anode
87. SOLVE  vstep=-5    vfinal=-4500    name=anode    compl=1e-25  cname=anode
88.
89. SAVE  outf=PIN_Reverse_27C.str
90.
91. QUIT
```

Table 3. Code walkthrough: Planar junction p-i-n diode forward and breakdown J–V characteristics.

Line No:	Functionality
1	Configure ATLAS simulator to use 160-bit extended precision and utilize 32 cores of the CPU if hardware resources are available. The version of ATLAS to be used by the simulator is set to 5.18.3.R using the $-V$ option in the simflags command.
5	Initialize device structure mesh information.
7–25	X-axis and Y-axis mesh distribution.
29–30	Declare oxide and 4H-SiC as the material for the area of the semiconductor specified by the x and y coordinates.
34–35	Electrode specifications for the p-i-n diode (Anode and Cathode).
38–49	Specify doping profile, type, and concentration for different areas of the p-i-n diode structure.
51	Save the device structure (**.str**) file on the local hard drive. The device structure can be viewed by opening the file via **TonyPlot** to troubleshoot/optimize the structure.

(Continued)

Table 3. (*Continued*)

Line No:	Functionality
53	Specify material parameters for 4H-SiC. Detailed description of these parameters is available in the Silvaco© ATLAS manual. The values for these parameters can either be obtained via material research or from literature.
57	Specify the various models to be included in the 4H-SiC PIN diode simulation.
61	Specify mobility parameters for 4H-SiC. Detailed description of these parameters is available in the Silvaco© ATLAS manual. The values for these parameters can either be obtained via material research or from literature.
63	Specify Impact Ionization parameters for 4H-SiC. This statement is mandatory to obtain device breakdown characteristics.
65	Specify the solver type and the tolerance values to be used during the simulation. This is an extremely critical statement which can alter the simulation outcome.
67	Include current flowlines in the output structure file.
69	Save the forward-bias simulation log (*.log*) file on the local hard drive. The simulation results can be viewed by opening the file via **TonyPlot**.
71–74	Solve for the initial bias conditions for the simulation followed by positive sweep of anode voltage for steady-state forward characteristics.
76	Save the post-forward-bias simulation device structure (*.str*) file on the local hard drive. Saving the file at this stage of the simulation will enable the user to visualize the variation in various electrothermal parameters within the device structure introduced due to the particular simulation. For example in this simulation, the user can view the carrier concentration profile in the p-i-n diode during forward conduction.
78	Save the reverse-bias simulation log (*.log*) file on the local hard drive. The simulation results can be viewed by opening the file via **TonyPlot**.
80–87	Solve for the initial bias conditions for the simulation followed by negative sweep of anode voltage for steady-state reverse-bias characteristics. The compliance parameter (**compl**) in line 87 forces the simulator to proceed to the next line once the anode current reaches the specified compliance value. This is important, especially in breakdown simulation because once the device enters the breakdown regime, it is not necessary to run the simulation for higher magnitude of current since the breakdown voltage would have already been determined.
89	Save the post-reverse-bias simulation device structure (*.str*) file on the local hard drive. Saving the file at this stage of the simulation will enable the user to visualize the variation in various electrothermal parameters within the device structure introduced due to the particular simulation. For example in this simulation, the user can view the electric field profile in the p-i-n diode during avalanche breakdown.
91	Terminate the simulation.

6.4.3.2.   *Steady-state simulation results*

The forward conduction J–V characteristics for the 3300 V planar junction
SiC p-i-n diode on a linear and semi-log scale are shown in Figs. 22(a)
and 22(b), respectively. The simulations were carried out at varying lattice
temperature values like the parallel plane diode simulation. At an ON-state

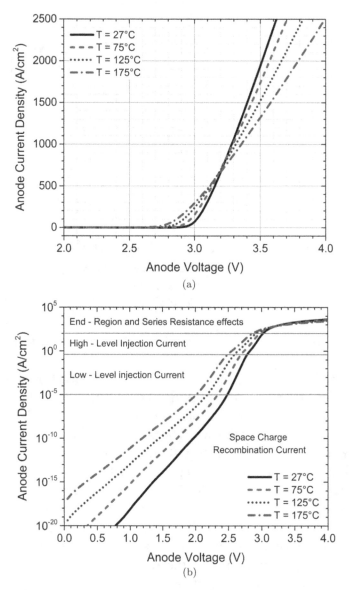

Fig. 22.   (a) Forward J–V characteristics for the SiC planar junction p-i-n diode half-cell
on a linear scale. (b) Forward J–V characteristics for the SiC planar junction p-i-n diode
half-cell on a semi-log scale.

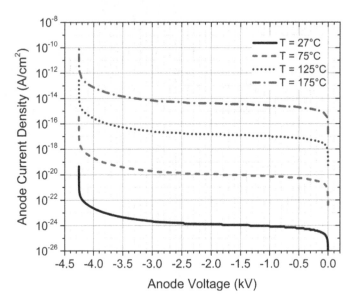

Fig. 23.   Reverse breakdown *J–V* characteristics for the SiC planar junction p-i-n diode half-cell structure on a semi-log scale.

current density of $100\,\mathrm{A/cm^2}$, a voltage drop of $3.02\,\mathrm{V}$ was observed across the diode at $27°\mathrm{C}$ device temperature. The various regions of p-i-n diode forward operation can be seen in the semi-log plot in Fig. 22(b).

The reverse-bias breakdown *J–V* characteristics for varying lattice temperature conditions are shown in Fig. 23. Breakdown voltage of $4254\,\mathrm{V}$ was obtained for the planar junction p-i-n diode structure with floating field rings at $27°\mathrm{C}$ device temperature.

The electric field distribution in the p-i-n diode structure during breakdown is shown in the contour plot in Fig. 24 (Image has been scaled to highlight the area of interest). A maximum electric field of $2.62\,\mathrm{MV/cm}$ was observed at the point of breakdown. The presence of floating field rings aid in the distribution of the electric field and prevent premature breakdown at the edge of P+ anode region due to electric field enhancement. The conduction current density contour plot during breakdown is shown in Fig. 25 (Image has been scaled to highlight the area of interest). It can be seen in Fig. 25 that avalanche breakdown occurs at the edge of the anode P+ region which should be the case since floating field rings should not undergo breakdown. However, there is an exception in the case of Schottky diode simulation, which will be discussed in the next chapter.

1D electric field profile as a function of device depth is shown in Fig. 26(a). The plot has been scaled to highlight the region of interest. The electric field

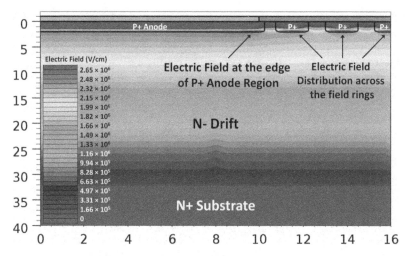

Fig. 24.   Electric field contour plot during reverse-bias breakdown in planar junction p-i-n diode half-cell structure.

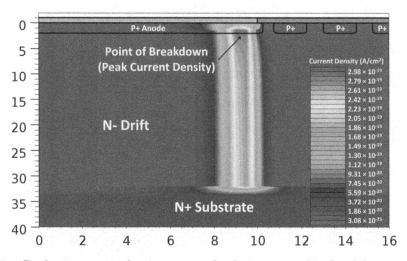

Fig. 25.   Conduction current density contour plot during reverse-bias breakdown in planar junction p-i-n diode half-cell structure.

data was extracted for the following points: middle of the active area P+ anode region ($x = 5\,\mu$m), edge of the active area P+ anode region which is also the point of breakdown ($x = 10\,\mu$m), and floating field ring P+ regions ($x = 11.5\,\mu$m, $x = 14\,\mu$m, and $x = 16\,\mu$m) using the **cutline** feature in **TonyPlot**. To have a closer look at the electric field distribution in the aforementioned points, individual electric field profiles are shown in

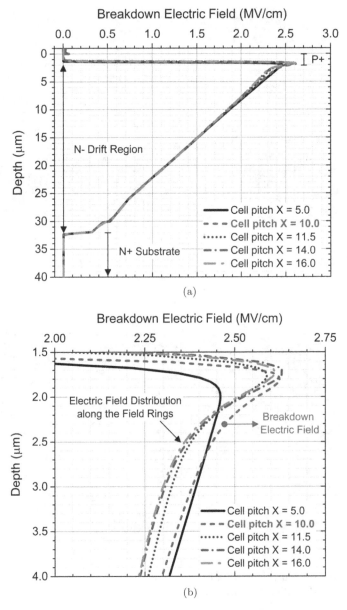

Fig. 26.   (a) 1D electric field profile as a function of device depth at varying points across the diode active area/cell pitch. (b) 1D electric field profile as a function of device depth at varying points across the diode active area/cell pitch (zoomed-in view).

Fig. 26(b), which is a zoomed-in version of Fig. 26(a). It can be seen from Fig. 26(b) that the minimum value of electric field exists in the middle of the P+ anode region. There is also a uniform distribution of electric field across the floating field rings.

6.4.3.3. *Mixed-mode transient simulation — forward pulsing*

The forward pulsing Mixed-Mode transient simulation was performed using the RLC ring-down circuit shown in Fig. 10.[9,10] The simulation code was similar to that used in the parallel plane diode structure with changes pertaining to the planar junction structure. These changes include device mesh profile, inclusion of floating field rings, and dimensions of the thermal boundary using **Thermcontact** statement. The following code was used to simulate the p-i-n diode for a peak forward current density of $5000\,\mathrm{A/cm^2}$ under pulsed condition. A brief explanation of the Mixed-Mode simulation program is provided in the code walkthrough (Table 4).

```
Sample code: Planar junction SiC p-i-n diode half-cell transient simulation

1.   GO ATLAS SIMFLAGS ="-V 5.18.3.R -P 32 -160"
2.
3.   ## 3300V PLANAR JUNCTION PIN DIODE - HALF CELL RLC RINGDOWN PULSE 5000A/cm2 ##
4.
5.   MESH  WIDTH=1.2e6
6.
7.   ## X-MESH
8.
9.   X.MESH  loc=0.0    spac=0.5
10. X.MESH  loc=9.0    spac=0.5
11. X.MESH  loc=10.0   spac=0.25
12. X.MESH  loc=16.0   spac=0.25
13.
14. ## Y-MESH
15.
16. Y.MESH  loc=-1.0    spac=1.0
17. Y.MESH  loc=0.0     spac=0.25
18. Y.MESH  loc=2.1     spac=0.01
19. Y.MESH  loc=30.0    spac=4.0
20. Y.MESH  loc=32.1    spac=0.2
21. Y.MESH  loc=33.0    spac=1.0
22. Y.MESH  loc=34.0    spac=20
23. Y.MESH  loc=180.0   spac=20
24. Y.MESH  loc=182.0   spac=1.0
25. Y.MESH  loc=184.0   spac=1.0
26.
27. ## Defining Regions
28.
29. REGION  num=1  material=Oxide    y.max=0
30. REGION  num=2  material=4H-SiC   x.min=0   x.max=10   y.min=0  y.max=182
31.
32. ## Electrode
33.
34. ELECTRODE  name=anode    material=titanium   x.min=0     x.max=10    y.max=0
35. ELECTRODE  name=cathode  material=aluminum   y.min=182   y.max=184
36.
37. ## Doping Distribution
38.
39. ## Bulk Doping
40. DOPING  uniform n.type  conc=3.8e15  REGION=2
```

```
41.
42. ## P+ Doping
43. DOPING  gauss  p.type  conc=1.e21  x.min=0     x.max=10     junc=2.0   rat=0.1
44.
45. ## P+ Field Rings
46. DOPING  gauss  p.type  conc=1.e20  x.min=11.00  x.max=12.00  junc=2.0   rat=0.1
47. DOPING  gauss  p.type  conc=1.e20  x.min=13.25  x.max=14.25  junc=2.0   rat=0.1
48. DOPING  gauss  p.type  conc=1.e20  x.min=15.50  x.max=16     junc=2.0   rat=0.1
49.
50. ## N+ Substrate Region Doping
51. DOPING  uniform  n.type  conc=1.e20  y.min=32    y.max=182
52.
53. SAVE  outf=PIN_Structure.str  master.out
54.
55. ##### STEADY STATE SIMULATION CIRCUIT #####
56.
57. GO ATLAS SIMFLAGS ="-V 5.18.3.R -P 32 -160"
58.
59. .BEGIN
60.
61. VDC          1    0    0
62. RSW          1    2    1.e-12
63. R_CHARGE     2    3    500
64. C_BANK       3    0    6u
65. R_SERIES     3    4    0.80
66. L_SERIES     4    5    500n
67. RSWITCH      5    6    1.e18
68. ADIODE       6=anode   0=cathode    infile=PIN_Structure.str    WIDTH=1.2e6
69.
70. .NODESET  v(1)=0  v(2)=0  v(3)=0  v(4)=0  v(5)=0  v(6)=0
71. .NUMERIC  imaxdc=100
72.
73. .DC   VDC   0.    10.    0.25
74. .DC   VDC   10.   100.   10.
75. .DC   VDC   100.  600.   25.
76.
77. .LOG      outfile=PIN_DC_log
78. .SAVE     outfile=PIN_RLC_Bias
79. .OPTIONS  m2ln print noshift relpot
80.
81. .END
82.
83. ##### PHYSICS USED #####
84.
85. CONTACT  DEVICE=ADIODE  NAME=ANODE      EXT.ALPHA=10
86. CONTACT  DEVICE=ADIODE  NAME=CATHODE    EXT.ALPHA=10
87.
88. THERMCONTACT  DEVICE=ADIODE  num=3  x.min=0  x.max=16  y.min=-1.0  y.max=184
    alpha=10  ext.temp=300
89.
90. MATERIAL  DEVICE=ADIODE   material=4H-SiC  REGION=2  permittivity=9.76
    eg300=3.26  affinity=3.7  egalpha=3.3e-2  egbeta=1.e+5  nc300=1.7e+19
    nv300=2.5e+19  arichn=146  arichp=30  augn=3.e-29  augp=3.e-29  taun0=3.33e-6
    taup0=6.7e-7  nsrhn=3.e+17  nsrhp=3.e+17  edb=0.050  eab=0.20  tcon.polyn
    tc.a=0.137534  tc.b=0.00049662  tc.c=0.000000354  hc.a=2.35  hc.b=1.75e-3
    hc.c=1.e-9  hc.d=-6.6e4
91.
92. ## MODELS USED
93.
```

```
94. MODELS   DEVICE=ADIODE   REGION=2 MATERIAL=4H-SIC FERMIDIRAC ANALYTIC CONWELL SRH
    BGN AUGER INCOMPLETE LAT.TEMP   JOULE.HEAT GR.HEAT   PT.HEAT PRINT
95.
96. ## MOBILITY
97.
98. MOBILITY   DEVICE=ADIODE   material=4H-SiC REGION=2   vsatn=2.2e7  vsatp=2.2e7
    betan=1.2 betap=2  mu1n.caug=40  mu2n.caug=1136  ncritn.caug=2e17
    alphan.caug=-3  betan.caug=-3  gamman.caug=0.0  deltan.caug=0.76   mu1p.caug=20
    mu2p.caug=125  ncritp.caug=1.e19  alphap.caug=-3  betap.caug=-3
    gammap.caug=0.0  deltap.caug=0.5
99.
100. MOBILITY   DEVICE=ADIODE   material=4H-SiC REGION=2   n.canali  n.angle=90
     p.angle=90  vsatn=2.2e7  vsatp=2.2e7 betan=1.2 betap=2  mu1n.caug=5
     mu2n.caug=947  ncritn.caug=2e17  alphan.caug=-3  betan.caug=-3  gamman.caug=0.0
     deltan.caug=0.76   mu1p.caug=2.5  mu2p.caug=20  ncritp.caug=1.e19
     alphap.caug=-3  betap.caug=-3  gammap.caug=0.0  deltap.caug=0.5
101.
102. ## IMPACT IONIZATION
103.
104. IMPACT   DEVICE=ADIODE   REGION=2  ANISO  E.SIDE  SELB  SIC4H0001  an1=3.44e6  an2=3.44e6
     bn1=2.58e7  bn2=2.58e7  ap1=3.5e6  ap2=3.5e6  bp1=1.7e7  bp2=1.7e7
     opphe=0.106
105.
106. METHOD  BLOCK climit=1.e-9  maxtraps=100  itlimit=100   max.temp=1000
     dvmax=1.e8  ir.tol=1.e-35  cr.tol=1.e-35  ix.tol=1.e-35  px.tol=1.e-30
     pr.tol=1.e-45  cx.tol=1.e-30
107.
108. ##### TRANSIENT SIMULATION CIRCUIT #####
109.
110. GO ATLAS SIMFLAGS ="-V 5.18.3.R -P 32 -160"
111.
112. .BEGIN
113.
114. VDC          1   0    600
115. RSW          1   2    1.e-12   PULSE  1.e-12  1.e18  5us  50ns  50ns  40us    80us
116. R_CHARGE     2   3    500
117. C_BANK       3   0    6u
118. R_SERIES     3   4    0.80
119. L_SERIES     4   5    500n
120. RSWITCH      5   6    1.e18    PULSE  1.e18  1.e-12  10us  50ns  50ns  40us  80us
121. ADIODE       6=anode    0=cathode     infile=PIN_Structure.str    WIDTH=1.2e6
122.
123. .NUMERIC  imaxtr=100  dtmax=5.e-8
124. .OPTIONS  m2ln.tr  print  noshift  relpot  write=10
125. .LOAD     infile=PIN_RLC_Bias
126. .SAVE     master=PIN_Transient
127. .LOG      outfile=PIN_RLC_Ringdown.log
128. .SAVE     outfile=PIN_RLC_Ringdown.str
129. .TRAN   0.01us 45us
130.
131. .END
132.
133. ##### PHYSICS USED #####
134.
135. CONTACT  DEVICE=ADIODE  NAME=ANODE      EXT.ALPHA=10
136. CONTACT  DEVICE=ADIODE  NAME=CATHODE    EXT.ALPHA=10
137.
138. THERMCONTACT  DEVICE=ADIODE  num=3  x.min=0  x.max=16  y.min=-1.0  y.max=184
     alpha=10   ext.temp=300
139.
```

```
140. MATERIAL  DEVICE=ADIODE   material=4H-SiC  REGION=2  permittivity=9.76
     eg300=3.26   affinity=3.7  egalpha=3.3e-2   egbeta=1.e+5  nc300=1.7e+19
     nv300=2.5e+19  arichn=146  arichp=30  augn=3.e-29  augp=3.e-29  taun0=3.33e-6
     taup0=6.7e-7  nsrhn=3.e+17 nsrhp=3.e+17 edb=0.050   eab=0.200  tcon.polyn
     tc.a=0.137534   tc.b=0.00049662   tc.c=0.000000354  hc.a=2.35  hc.b=1.75e-3
     hc.c=1.e-9  hc.d=-6.6e4
141.
142. ## MODELS USED
143.
144. MODELS DEVICE=ADIODE   REGION=2 MATERIAL=4H-SIC FERMIDIRAC ANALYTIC CONWELL
     SRH BGN AUGER INCOMPLETE LAT.TEMP  JOULE.HEAT  GR.HEAT  PT.HEAT PRINT
145.
146. ## MOBILITY
147.
148. MOBILITY  DEVICE=ADIODE  material=4H-SiC  REGION=2  vsatn=2.2e7  vsatp=2.2e7
     betan=1.2 betap=2  mu1n.caug=40  mu2n.caug=1136  ncritn.caug=2e17
     alphan.caug=-3  betan.caug=-3  gamman.caug=0.0  deltan.caug=0.76   mu1p.caug=20
     mu2p.caug=125  ncritp.caug=1.e19  alphap.caug=-3  betap.caug=-3
     gammap.caug=0.0  deltap.caug=0.5
149.
150. MOBILITY  DEVICE=ADIODE  material=4H-SiC  REGION=2  n.canali  n.angle=90
     p.angle=90 vsatn=2.2e7  vsatp=2.2e7  betan=1.2 betap=2  mu1n.caug=5
     mu2n.caug=947  ncritn.caug=2e17  alphan.caug=-3  betan.caug=-3  gamman.caug=0.0
     deltan.caug=0.76   mu1p.caug=2.5  mu2p.caug=20  ncritp.caug=1.e19
     alphap.caug=-3  betap.caug=-3  gammap.caug=0.0  deltap.caug=0.5
151.
152. ## IMPACT IONIZATION
153.
154. IMPACT  DEVICE=ADIODE  REGION=2  ANISO  E.SIDE  SELB  SIC4H0001  an1=3.44e6
     an2=3.44e6  bn1=2.58e7  bn2=2.58e7  ap1=3.5e6  ap2=3.5e6  bp1=1.7e7  bp2=1.7e7
     opphe=0.106
155.
156. OUTPUT  FLOWLINES  E.MOBILITY
157.
158. METHOD  BLOCK.TRAN  climit=1.e-9  maxtraps=100  itlimit=100   max.temp=1000
     dvmax=1.e8  ir.tol=1.e-25  cr.tol=1.e-25  ix.tol=1.e-30  px.tol=1.e-30
     pr.tol=1.e-36  cx.tol=1.e-30
159.
160. GO ATLAS SIMFLAGS ="-V 5.18.3.R -P 32 -128"
161.
162. QUIT
```

Table 4. Code walkthrough: Planar junction p-i-n diode half-cell mixed-mode forward pulsing simulation.

Line No:	Functionality
1	Configure ATLAS simulator to use version 5.18.3.R, 160-bit extended precision and utilize 32 cores of the CPU if hardware resources are available.
5	Initialize device structure mesh information with width parameter.
7–25	X-axis and Y-axis mesh distribution.
29–30	Declare oxide and 4H-SiC as the material for the area of the semiconductor specified by the x and y coordinates.

(Continued)

Table 4. (*Continued*)

Line No:	Functionality
34–35	Electrode specifications for the p-i-n diode (Titanium Anode and Aluminum Cathode).
37–51	Specify doping profile, type, and concentration for different areas of the p-i-n diode structure.
53	Save the device structure (*.str*) file on the local hard drive.
57	Initialize ATLAS simulator using GO ATLAS command (same as line 1).
59	Initialize the starting of SPICE-like code in Mixed-Mode steady-state simulation.
61–68	RLC ring-down circuit description in SPICE-like format.
70	Declare the initial node voltage for the RLC ring-down circuit nodes.
71	Set the maximum number of mixed circuit-device iterations to be performed during steady-state analysis (*imaxdc*) to 100.
73–75	Ramp up DC voltage to attain steady-state condition, i.e. VDC = 600 V. This can be split into multiple steps.
77	Save log file after steady-state simulation completion.
78	Save file with bias information which will be used for transient simulation.
79	Specify Mixed-Mode steady-state simulation conditions. Modified two-level Newton solution method (*m2ln*), disable the shift of voltage for ATLAS devices (*noshift*), and enable the use of relative convergence criteria for potential especially when large voltage biases are involved (*relpot*).
81	Initialize the ending of SPICE-like code in Mixed-Mode steady-state simulation.
85–86	Specify heat transfer coefficient (*ext.alpha*) for the anode and cathode contacts.
88	Specify the thermal boundary for the p-i-n diode. Parameters includes boundary dimensions, heat transfer coefficient (*alpha*), and temperature of the thermal boundary (*ext.temp*) which is typically at 300 K.
90	Specify material parameters for 4H-SiC.
94	Specify the various models to be included in the 4H-SiC p-i-n diode simulation.
98	Specify parameters for mobility in 4H-SiC.
100	Specify parameters for anisotropic mobility in 4H-SiC.
104	Specify impact ionization parameters for 4H-SiC.
106	Specify the steady-state Block Newton solver type (*BLOCK*) and the tolerance values to be used during the simulation.
110	Initialize ATLAS simulator using GO ATLAS command (same as line 1) for steady-state bias point simulation.

(*Continued*)

Table 4.   (*Continued*)

Line No:	Functionality
112	Initialize the starting of SPICE-like code in Mixed-Mode transient simulation.
114–121	RLC ring-down circuit description in SPICE-like format. The magnitude of DC voltage source is initialized at 600 V which is the result of the earlier steady-state simulation performed. Transient parameters have been added to the Resistor which is acting like a switch.
123	Set the maximum number of mixed circuit-device iterations to be performed during transient analysis (***imaxtr***) to 100 and the maximum transient simulation time step (***dtmax***) to 50 ns.
124	Specify Mixed-Mode transient simulation conditions. Modified two-level Newton solution method for transient simulation (***m2ln.tr***), disable the shift of voltage for ATLAS devices (***noshift***), enable the use of relative convergence criteria for potential especially when large voltage biases are involved (***relpot***), and write structure file after every 10 time-step iterations.
125	Load the steady-state simulations results saved in line 78.
126	Save the structure file after every 10 time-step iterations specified in line 124.
127	Save log file after the completion of transient simulation.
128	Save the structure file after the completion of transient simulation.
129	Specify the initial time interval of 10 ns and total simulation time of 45 μs.
131	Initialize the ending of SPICE-like code in Mixed-Mode transient simulation.
133–154	Same as line 83 to line 104.
156	Include current flowlines (***FLOWLINES***) and Electron Mobility (***E.MOBILITY***) in the output structure file.
158	Specify the transient Block Newton solver type (***BLOCK.TRAN***) and the tolerance values to be used during the simulation.
160	Initialize ATLAS simulator using GO ATLAS command (same as line 1) for transient simulation. A lower simulation precision of 128-bit has been used due to forward conduction mode of operation.
162	Terminate the simulation

6.4.3.4. *Mixed-mode transient simulation — forward pulsing results*

The forward pulsing transient simulation for the planar junction p-i-n diode was carried out for varying magnitudes of peak current density ranging from 500 A/cm^2 to 5000 A/cm^2 in steps of 500. The width parameter was used to change the peak current density through the diode without altering the waveform. In this section, the results pertaining to the maximum current density

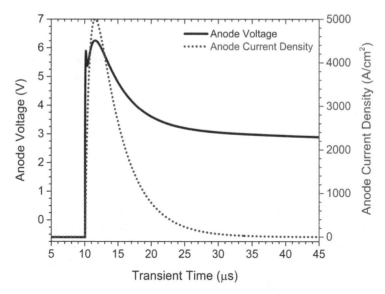

Fig. 27. Anode voltage (solid) and current density (dotted) waveforms pertaining to 5000 A/cm² peak current density simulation.

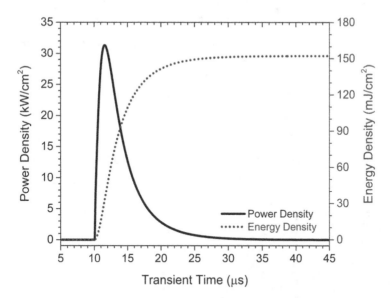

Fig. 28. Power density (solid) and energy density (dotted) waveforms pertaining to 5000 A/cm² peak current density simulation.

scenario of 5000 A/cm² will be discussed followed by a summary of all the other cases. The anode voltage and current density waveforms are shown in Fig. 27, and the power dissipation and energy density waveforms are shown in Fig. 28. An overshoot in the anode voltage waveform can be observed during the current ramp-up phase in Fig. 27. This sudden rise in anode voltage is due to the finite time required for conductivity modulation to occur, also known as forward recovery. In the latter part of this section, a summary of anode voltage waveforms will be provided to explain the difference in the forward recovery voltage with varying peak pulsed current density.

A peak voltage drop of 6.25 V was observed across the p-i-n diode at peak current density of 5000 A/cm^2 which corresponds to a peak power dissipation density of 31.3 kW/cm^2. Integration of the power density waveform yielded an energy density of 152 mJ/cm^2. A peak lattice temperature of 304.3 K was observed in the p-i-n diode lattice during this pulsed operation. The variation of lattice temperature with power dissipation density and energy density during simulation is shown in Figs. 29 and 30, respectively. The simulation was run for only 45 μs, and hence does not show the complete decay of temperature waveform back to the ambient value. To identify the area of heat dissipation in the p-i-n diode structure, intermediate structure files were generated during the simulation. These structure files were manually scanned for the transient time instant which corresponds to the maximum lattice temperature.

The lattice temperature profile of the planar junction p-i-n diode structure recorded at the time instant corresponding to maximum temperature

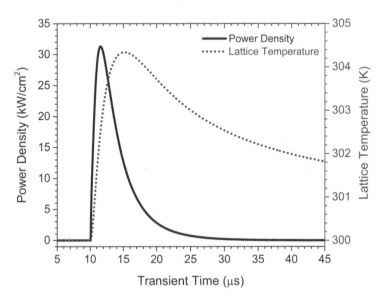

Fig. 29. Power density (solid) and lattice temperature (dotted) waveforms pertaining to 5000 A/cm^2 RLC ring-down simulation.

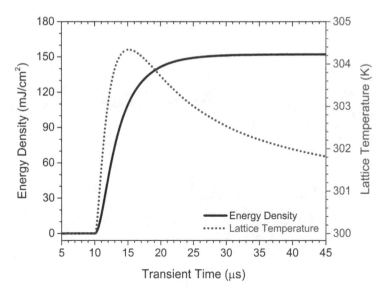

Fig. 30. Energy density (solid) and lattice temperature (dotted) waveforms pertaining to 5000 A/cm² RLC ring-down simulation.

during high current density pulsed simulation is shown in Figs. 31(a) and 31(b). A maximum temperature of 304.3 K was observed in the P+ anode region.

To investigate the heat dissipation source, recombination heat power and joule heat power profiles were extracted from the structure file and are shown in Figs. 32 and 33, respectively (p–n junctions are marked by in white). The heat power sources are expressed in W/cm³ in **TonyPlot**, and the contour plots have been scaled to highlight the areas of interest. It can be seen from the heat power profiles that there is significant power dissipation in the P+ region due to carrier generation and recombination effects. The joule/resistive heat power dissipation is dominant only at the edges of P+ anode due to current crowding. This heat generation is due to the end region recombination effects which increases the ON-state resistance especially at higher current density forward operation.[11]

The summary of lattice temperature and anode voltage waveforms for the planar junction p-i-n diode for all the values of peak pulsed current density are shown in Figs. 34 and 35, respectively. To highlight the impact of forward recovery on the anode voltage, the anode voltage waveforms have been scaled to highlight the instant when the RLC ring-down circuit current density ramps up through the diode in Fig. 36.

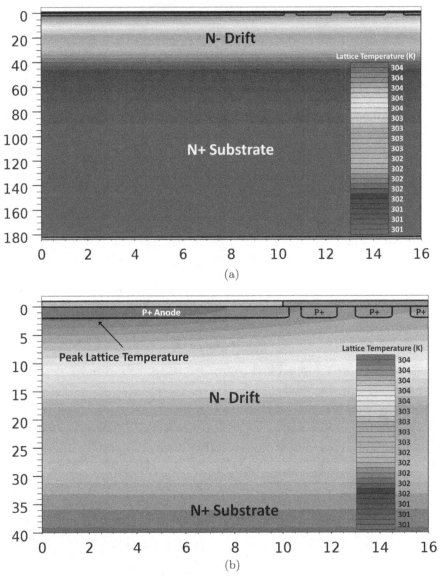

Fig. 31.   (a) Lattice temperature profile of planar junction p-i-n diode half-cell structure during 5000 A/cm² RLC ring-down simulation. (b) Lattice temperature profile of planar junction p-i-n diode half-cell structure during 5000 A/cm² RLC ring-down simulation (zoomed-in view).

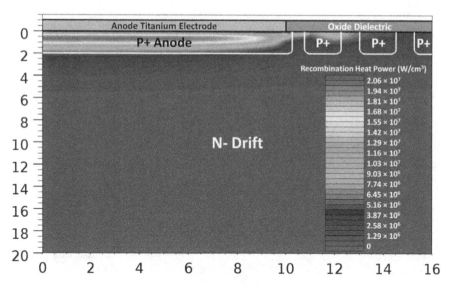

Fig. 32. Recombination heat power profile of planar junction p-i-n diode half-cell structure during $5000\,\text{A}/\text{cm}^2$ RLC ring-down simulation (zoomed-in view).

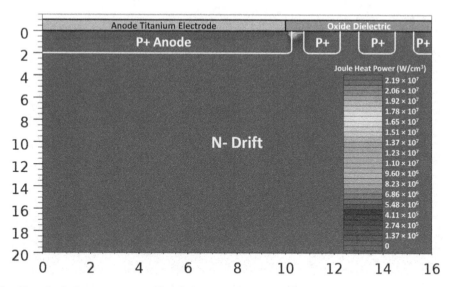

Fig. 33. Joule heat power profile of planar junction p-i-n diode half-cell structure during $5000\,\text{A}/\text{cm}^2$ RLC ring-down simulation (zoomed-in view).

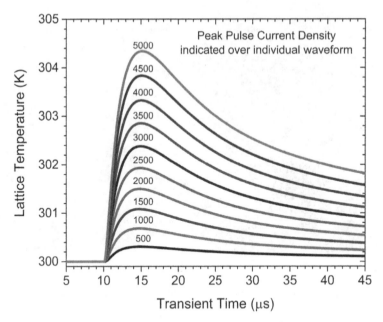

Fig. 34. Lattice temperature summary of planar junction SiC p-i-n diode half-cell structure during RLC ring-down simulation.

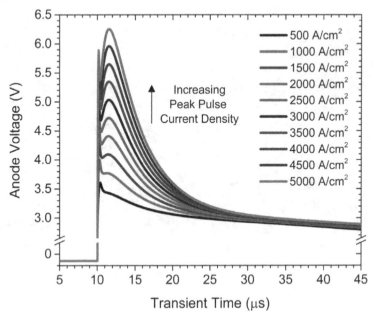

Fig. 35. Anode voltage summary of planar junction SiC p-i-n diode half-cell structure during RLC ring-down simulation.

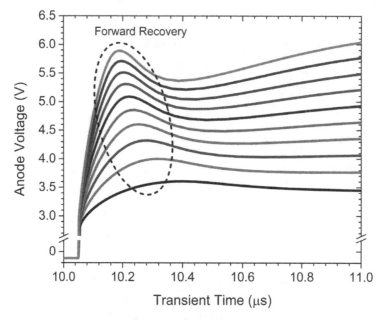

Fig. 36. Anode voltage summary of planar junction SiC p-i-n diode half-cell structure during RLC ring-down simulation with emphasis on the forward recovery process.

6.4.3.5. *Mixed-mode transient simulation-reverse recovery*

Reverse recovery is not a favorable phenomenon since it not only limits the switching frequency in power converter design but also puts additional stress on the switching device (MOSFET/IGBT) by forcing the reverse recovery current through the switch along with the primary circuit current. Reverse recovery simulation is typically done using a Clamped Inductive Switching (CIS) circuit, also known as clamped inductive double-pulse circuit.[12] A CIS circuit requires a controlled switching element like MOSFET or IGBT in addition to the diode under test. Implementing a CIS circuit in a SPICE-based software is a trivial scenario and the simulation is generally very fast; however, simulating a CIS circuit with two devices in a TCAD environment is complex and could take several weeks to months depending on the number of mesh points defined for each device structure (*based on author's personal experience!*). In order to circumvent this issue, a simpler circuit (shown in Fig. 37) was used to simulate the p-i-n diode structure for its reverse recovery characteristics.[9]

   In this circuit, the pulsed voltage source (VPULSE) was configured to deliver a single square wave cycle which alternates between +30 V DC and −3300 V DC. The series resistance (R_SERIES) was designed for a fixed

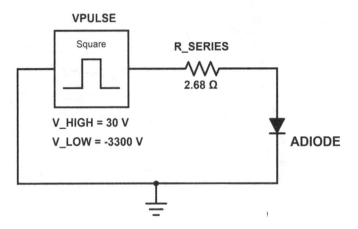

Fig. 37. Reverse recovery simulation circuit.

current density of $100\,\mathrm{A/cm^2}$ through the diode (ADIODE) during ON-state. During the positive voltage ($+30\,\mathrm{V}$) phase of the square wave, the diode will conduct with an ON-state current density of $100\,\mathrm{A/cm^2}$. When the voltage source reverses its polarity, the p-i-n diode transitions from ON-state to reverse-blocking state, which is accompanied by a reversal in the diode current which is proportional to the negative rate of change of current density ($-dJ/dt$). The value of $-dJ/dt$ can be varied by changing the ramp down rate of source voltage from positive to negative. The following code was used to simulate the p-i-n diode for its reverse recovery characteristics, and a brief explanation of the Mixed-Mode simulation program is provided in the code walkthrough (Table 5).

```
Sample code: Planar junction SiC p-i-n diode half-cell structure reverse recovery transient
simulation

1.   GO ATLAS SIMFLAGS ="-V 5.18.3.R -P 32 -160"
2.
3.   ##### 3300V PLANAR JUNCTION PIN DIODE - HALF CELL REVERSE RECOVERY #####
4.
5.   MESH  WIDTH=1.2e6
6.
7.   ## X-MESH
8.
9.   X.MESH  loc=0.0      spac=0.5
10.  X.MESH  loc=9.0      spac=0.5
11.  X.MESH  loc=10.0     spac=0.25
12.  X.MESH  loc=16.0     spac=0.25
13.
14.  ## Y-MESH
15.
16.  Y.MESH  loc=-1.0     spac=1.0
17.  Y.MESH  loc=0.0      spac=0.25
```

```
18. Y.MESH   loc=2.1        spac=0.01
19. Y.MESH   loc=30.0       spac=4.0
20. Y.MESH   loc=32.1       spac=0.2
21. Y.MESH   loc=33.0       spac=1.0
22. Y.MESH   loc=34.0       spac=20
23. Y.MESH   loc=180.0      spac=20
24. Y.MESH   loc=182.0      spac=1.0
25. Y.MESH   loc=184.0      spac=1.0
26.
27. ## Defining Regions
28.
29. REGION  num=1  material=Oxide   y.max=0
30. REGION  num=2  material=4H-SiC  x.min=0   x.max=10   y.min=0  y.max=182
31.
32. ## Electrode
33.
34. ELECTRODE  name=anode    material=titanium  x.min=0     x.max=10    y.max=0
35. ELECTRODE  name=cathode  material=aluminum  y.min=182   y.max=184
36.
37. ## Doping Distribution
38.
39. ## Bulk Doping
40. DOPING  uniform  n.type  conc=3.8e15  REGION=2
41.
42. ## P+ Doping
43. DOPING  gauss  p.type  conc=1.e21  x.min=0   x.max=10   junc=2.0  rat=0.1
44.
45. ## P+ Field Rings
46. DOPING  gauss  p.type  conc=1.e20  x.min=11.00   x.max=12.00  junc=2.0  rat=0.1
47. DOPING  gauss  p.type  conc=1.e20  x.min=13.25   x.max=14.25  junc=2.0  rat=0.1
48. DOPING  gauss  p.type  conc=1.e20  x.min=15.50   x.max=16     junc=2.0  rat=0.1
49.
50. ## N+ Substrate Region Doping
51. DOPING  uniform  n.type  conc=1.e20   y.min=32    y.max=182
52.
53. SAVE  outf=PIN_Structure.str  master.out
54.
55. ##### STEADY STATE SIMULATION CIRCUIT #####
56.
57. GO ATLAS SIMFLAGS ="-V 5.18.3.R -P 32 -160"
58.
59. .BEGIN
60.
61. VPULSE      0    1    0
62. R_SERIES    1    2    2.68
63. ADIODE      2=anode   0=cathode     infile=PIN_Structure.str   WIDTH=1.e6
64.
65. .NODESET  v(1)=0  v(2)=0
66. .NUMERIC  imaxdc=100
67.
68. .DC   VPULSE     0.      -10.     -0.2
69. .DC   VPULSE    -10.     -50.     -5.
70. .DC   VPULSE    -50.     -100.    -10.
71. .DC   VPULSE    -100.    -3300.   -100.
72.
73. .LOG   outfile=PIN_DC_log
74. .SAVE   outfile=PIN_RLC_Bias
75. .OPTIONS  m2ln print noshift relpot
76.
77. .END
```

```
78.
79. ##### PHYSICS USED #####
80.
81. CONTACT   DEVICE=ADIODE   NAME=ANODE      EXT.ALPHA=10
82. CONTACT   DEVICE=ADIODE   NAME=CATHODE    EXT.ALPHA=10
83.
84. THERMCONTACT  DEVICE=ADIODE   num=3   x.min=0  x.max=16  y.min=-1.0  y.max=184
      alpha=10   ext.temp=300
85.
86. MATERIAL  DEVICE=ADIODE   material=4H-SiC  REGION=2  permittivity=9.76
      eg300=3.26   affinity=3.7   egalpha=3.3e-2   egbeta=1.e+5   nc300=1.7e+19
      nv300=2.5e+19  arichn=146  arichp=30  augn=3.e-29  augp=3.e-29  taun0=3.33e-6
      taup0=6.7e-7  nsrhn=3.e+17  nsrhp=3.e+17  edb=0.050  eab=0.20  tcon.polyn
      tc.a=0.137534   tc.b=0.00049662   tc.c=0.000000354   hc.a=2.35   hc.b=1.75e-3
      hc.c=1.e-9  hc.d=-6.6e4
87.
88. ## MODELS USED
89.
90. MODELS  DEVICE=ADIODE  REGION=2  MATERIAL=4H-SiC FERMIDIRAC ANALYTIC CONWELL
      SRH BGN AUGER INCOMPLETE LAT.TEMP  JOULE.HEAT GR.HEAT  PT.HEAT PRINT
91.
92. ## MOBILITY
93.
94. MOBILITY  DEVICE=ADIODE  material=4H-SiC REGION=2  vsatn=2.2e7  vsatp=2.2e7
      betan=1.2 betap=2  mu1n.caug=40  mu2n.caug=1136  ncritn.caug=2e17
      alphan.caug=-3  betan.caug=-3  gamman.caug=0.0  deltan.caug=0.76   mu1p.caug=20
      mu2p.caug=125  ncritp.caug=1.e19  alphap.caug=-3  betap.caug=-3
      gammap.caug=0.0 deltap.caug=0.5
95.
96. MOBILITY  DEVICE=ADIODE  material=4H-SiC REGION=2  n.canali  n.angle=90
      p.angle=90 vsatn=2.2e7  vsatp=2.2e7  betan=1.2 betap=2  mu1n.caug=5
      mu2n.caug=947  ncritn.caug=2e17  alphan.caug=-3  betan.caug=-3  gamman.caug=0.0
      deltan.caug=0.76  mu1p.caug=2.5  mu2p.caug=20  ncritp.caug=1.e19
      alphap.caug=-3  betap.caug=-3  gammap.caug=0.0  deltap.caug=0.5
97.
98. ## IMPACT IONIZATION
99.
100. IMPACT  DEVICE=ADIODE  REGION=2  ANISO  E.SIDE  SELB  SIC4H0001  an1=3.44e6
      an2=3.44e6  bn1=2.58e7  bn2=2.58e7  ap1=3.5e6  ap2=3.5e6  bp1=1.7e7  bp2=1.7e7
      opphe=0.106
101.
102. METHOD  BLOCK  climit=1.e-9  maxtraps=100  itlimit=100   max.temp=1000
      dvmax=1.e8  ir.tol=1.e-40  cr.tol=1.e-40  ix.tol=1.e-40  px.tol=1.e-30
      pr.tol=1.e-45  cx.tol=1.e-30
103.
104. ##### TRANSIENT SIMULATION CIRCUIT #####
105.
106. GO ATLAS SIMFLAGS ="-V 5.18.3.R -P 32 -160"
107.
108. .BEGIN
109.
110. VPULSE    0   1   -3300   PULSE  -3300 30  1us   50ns   50ns   2us   10us
111. R_SERIES  1   2   2.68
112. ADIODE    2=anode   0=cathode   infile=PIN_Structure.str   WIDTH=1.e6
113.
114. .NUMERIC imaxtr=100 dtmax=1.e-8
115. .OPTIONS m2ln.tr print noshift relpot  write=25
116.
117. .LOAD  infile=PIN_DC_Bias
118. .LOG   outfile=PIN_PULSING.log
```

```
119. .SAVE  master=PIN_PULSING_Transient
120. .SAVE  outfile=PIN_PULSING.str
121.
122. .TRAN  0.01us 5us
123.
124. .END
125.
126. ##### PHYSICS USED #####
127.
128. CONTACT  DEVICE=ADIODE  NAME=ANODE      EXT.ALPHA=10
129. CONTACT  DEVICE=ADIODE  NAME=CATHODE    EXT.ALPHA=10
130.
131. THERMCONTACT  DEVICE=ADIODE  num=3  x.min=0  x.max=16  y.min=-1.0  y.max=184
     alpha=10  ext.temp=300
132.
133. MATERIAL  DEVICE=ADIODE  material=4H-SiC  REGION=2  permittivity=9.76
     eg300=3.26  affinity=3.7  egalpha=3.3e-2  egbeta=1.e+5  nc300=1.7e+19
     nv300=2.5e+19  arichn=146  arichp=30  augn=3.e-29  augp=3.e-29  taun0=3.33e-6
     taup0=6.7e-7  nsrhn=3.e+17  nsrhp=3.e+17  edb=0.050  eab=0.200  tcon.polyn
     tc.a=0.137534  tc.b=0.00049662  tc.c=0.000000354  hc.a=2.35  hc.b=1.75e-3
     hc.c=1.e-9  hc.d=-6.6e4
134.
135. ## MODELS USED
136.
137. MODELS  DEVICE=ADIODE  REGION=2 MATERIAL=4H-SiC FERMIDIRAC ANALYTIC CONWELL SRH
     BGN AUGER INCOMPLETE LAT.TEMP  JOULE.HEAT  GR.HEAT  PT.HEAT PRINT
138.
139. ## MOBILITY
140.
141. MOBILITY  DEVICE=ADIODE  material=4H-SiC  REGION=2  vsatn=2.2e7  vsatp=2.2e7
     betan=1.2 betap=2  mu1n.caug=40  mu2n.caug=1136  ncritn.caug=2e17
     alphan.caug=-3  betan.caug=-3  gamman.caug=0.0  deltan.caug=0.76  mu1p.caug=20
     mu2p.caug=125  ncritp.caug=1.e19  alphap.caug=-3  betap.caug=-3
     gammap.caug=0.0  deltap.caug=0.5
142.
143. MOBILITY  DEVICE=ADIODE  material=4H-SiC  REGION=2  n.canali  n.angle=90
     p.angle=90 vsatn=2.2e7  vsatp=2.2e7  betan=1.2 betap=2  mu1n.caug=5
     mu2n.caug=947  ncritn.caug=2e17  alphan.caug=-3  betan.caug=-3  gamman.caug=0.0
     deltan.caug=0.76  mu1p.caug=2.5  mu2p.caug=20  ncritp.caug=1.e19
     alphap.caug=-3  betap.caug=-3  gammap.caug=0.0  deltap.caug=0.5
144.
145. ## IMPACT IONIZATION
146.
147. IMPACT  DEVICE=ADIODE  REGION=2  ANISO  E.SIDE  SELB  SIC4H0001  an1=3.44e6
     an2=3.44e6  bn1=2.58e7  bn2=2.58e7  ap1=3.5e6  ap2=3.5e6  bp1=1.7e7  bp2=1.7e7
     opphe=0.106
148.
149. OUTPUT  FLOWLINES  E.MOBILITY
150.
151. METHOD  BLOCK.TRAN  climit=1.e-9  maxtraps=100  itlimit=100   max.temp=1000
     dvmax=1.e8  ir.tol=1.e-35  cr.tol=1.e-35  ix.tol=1.e-35  px.tol=1.e-35
     pr.tol=1.e-45  cx.tol=1.e-35
152.
153. GO ATLAS SIMFLAGS ="-V 5.18.3.R -P 32 -160"
154.
155. QUIT
```

Table 5.　Code walkthrough: Planar junction p-i-n diode half-cell mixed-mode reverse recovery simulation.

Line No:	Functionality
1	Configure ATLAS simulator to use version 5.18.3.R, 160-bit extended precision and utilize 32 cores of the CPU if hardware resources are available.
5	Initialize device structure mesh information with width parameter.
7–25	X-axis and Y-axis mesh distribution.
29–30	Declare oxide and 4H-SiC as the material for the area of the semiconductor specified by the x and y coordinates.
34–35	Electrode specifications for the p-i-n diode (Titanium Anode and Aluminum Cathode).
37–51	Specify doping profile, type, and concentration for different areas of the p-i-n diode structure.
53	Save the device structure (*.str*) file on the local hard drive.
57	Initialize ATLAS simulator using GO ATLAS command (same as line 1).
59	Initialize the starting of SPICE-like code in Mixed-Mode steady-state simulation.
61–63	Reverse recovery test circuit description in SPICE-like format.
65	Declare the initial node voltage for the reverse recovery test circuit nodes.
66	Set the maximum number of mixed circuit-device iterations to be performed during steady-state analysis (*imaxdc*) to 100.
68–71	Ramp up DC voltage to attain steady-state condition, i.e. VPULSE = −3300 V. This can be split into multiple steps.
73	Save log file after steady-state simulation completion.
74	Save file with bias information which will be used for transient simulation.
75	Specify Mixed-Mode steady-state simulation conditions. Modified two-level Newton solution method (*m2ln*), disable the shift of voltage for ATLAS devices (*noshift*), and enable the use of relative convergence criteria for potential especially when large voltage biases are involved (*relpot*).
77	Initialize the ending of SPICE-like code in Mixed-Mode steady-state simulation.
81–82	Specify heat transfer coefficient (*ext.alpha*) for the anode and cathode contacts.
84	Specify the thermal boundary for the p-i-n diode. Parameters includes boundary dimensions, heat transfer coefficient (*alpha*), and temperature of the thermal boundary (*ext.temp*) which is typically at 300 K.
86	Specify material parameters for 4H-SiC.
90	Specify the various models to be included in the 4H-SiC PIN diode simulation.

(Continued)

Table 5. (*Continued*)

Line No:	Functionality
94	Specify parameters for mobility in 4H-SiC.
96	Specify parameters for anisotropic mobility in 4H-SiC.
100	Specify impact ionization parameters for 4H-SiC.
102	Specify the steady-state Block Newton solver type (***BLOCK***) and the tolerance values to be used during the simulation.
106	Initialize ATLAS simulator using GO ATLAS command (same as line 1) for steady-state bias point simulation.
108	Initialize the starting of SPICE-like code in Mixed-Mode transient simulation.
110–112	Reverse recovery test circuit description in SPICE-like format. The magnitude of DC voltage for the VPULSE source is initialized at −3300 V which is the result of the earlier steady-state simulation performed. Transient parameters have been added to the voltage source VPULSE to generate square wave.
114	Set the maximum number of mixed circuit-device iterations to be performed during transient analysis (***imaxtr***) to 100 and the maximum transient simulation time step (***dtmax***) to 10 ns.
115	Specify Mixed-Mode transient simulation conditions. Modified two-level Newton solution method for transient simulation (***m2ln.tr***), disable the shift of voltage for ATLAS devices (***noshift***), enable the use of relative convergence criteria for potential especially when large voltage biases are involved (***relpot***), and write structure file after every 25 time-step iterations.
117	Load the steady-state simulations results saved in line 74.
118	Save log file after the completion of transient simulation.
119	Save the structure file after every 25 time-step iterations specified in line 115.
120	Save the structure file after the completion of transient simulation.
122	Specify the initial time interval of 10 ns and total simulation time of 5 μs.
124	Initialize the ending of SPICE-like code in Mixed-Mode transient simulation.
126–147	Same as line 79 to line 100.
149	Include current flowlines (***FLOWLINES***) and Electron Mobility (***E.MOBILITY***) in the output structure file.
151	Specify the transient Block Newton solver type (***BLOCK.TRAN***) and the tolerance values to be used during the simulation.
153	Initialize ATLAS simulator using GO ATLAS command (same as line 1) for transient simulation.
155	Terminate the simulation.

6.4.3.6. *Mixed-mode transient simulation — reverse recovery results*

The reverse recovery simulation of planar junction p-i-n diode half-cell structure was carried out for varying values of negative rate of change of current density ($-dJ/dt$) during transition from forward conduction to reverse-blocking. In an actual clamped inductive switching circuit, dJ/dt of the diode is a function of the switching frequency of the MOSFET/IGBT. To replicate a similar effect, the voltage ramp down rate of the voltage source (**VPULSE**) during transition from +30 V to −3300 V was increased using the program code, thereby slowing down the voltage ramp down. This can be achieved by changing the **fall time** of the transient parameter **PULSE** which is used to define pulse waveform (details can be found in the Silvaco© ATLAS Manual Chapter "MixedMode: Mixed Circuit and Device Simulator"). In this simulation, voltage fall times of 50 ns, 100 ns, and 200 ns were used. The three different fall times, 50 ns, 100 ns, and 200 ns, used to control the negative rate of change of current density resulted in $-dJ/dt$ values of 245, 125, and 62 kA/cm$^2 \cdot \mu$s and peak reverse recovery current densities of 2500, 1650, and 1100 A/cm^2, respectively. This section will discuss the results pertaining to the maximum negative dJ/dt scenario (245 kA/cm$^2 \cdot \mu$s) followed by a summary of results for varying $-dJ/dt$.

The anode voltage and current density waveforms are shown in Fig. 38 and the power and energy density waveforms are shown in Fig. 39. The anode to cathode voltage across the diode during forward conduction is 3.1 V, which

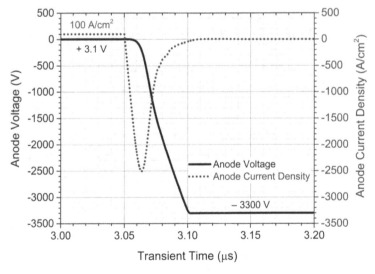

Fig. 38.   Anode voltage (solid) and current density (dotted) waveforms obtained during reverse recovery simulation corresponding to $-dJ/dt$ value of 245 kA/cm$^2 \cdot \mu$s.

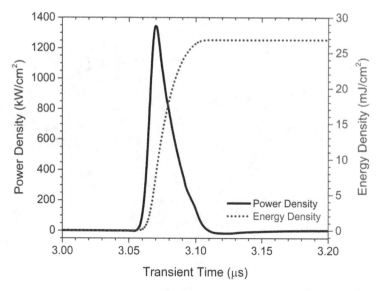

Fig. 39. Power density (solid) and energy density (dotted) waveforms obtained during reverse recovery simulation corresponding to $-dJ/dt$ value of $245\,\mathrm{kA/cm^2 \cdot \mu s}$.

coincides with the zero-mark due to the axis scale in Fig. 38. Peak reverse current density of $2500\,\mathrm{A/cm^2}$ was obtained during the simulation which corresponded to an instantaneous power dissipation of $1.34\,\mathrm{MW/cm^2}$ and energy density of $26.8\,\mathrm{mJ/cm^2}$ within the p-i-n diode.

The lattice temperature profiles of planar junction p-i-n diode half-cell structure for the maximum reverse current density scenario are shown in Figs. 40(a) and 40(b), respectively. Peak lattice temperature of $307\,\mathrm{K}$ was observed in the drift region closer to the P+/ N− interface. To further understand the various mechanisms involved during p-i-n diode reverse recovery, heat power and lattice temperature profiles were also recorded at the instant when the reverse current density was at its maximum magnitude.

The recombination rate and recombination heat power profiles at the instant of peak current density are shown in Figs. 41 and 42, respectively. Maximum carrier recombination occurs in the drift region during the reverse conduction process. The nearly identical contour plots indicate the direct dependence of carrier generation–recombination effects on the recombination heat power density.

The joule heat power and lattice temperature profiles at the instant of peak current density are shown in Figs. 43 and 44, respectively. The figures have been scaled to highlight the areas of interest. The joule heat power is due to high reverse current conduction along with the significant voltage drop across the diode (voltage and current density crossover shown in Fig. 38)

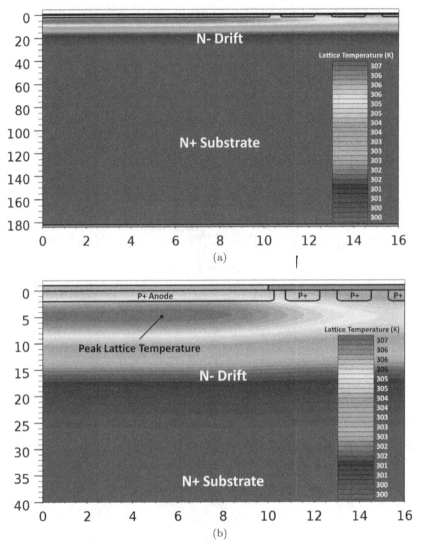

Fig. 40.   (a) Lattice temperature profile of planar junction p-i-n diode half-cell structure during reverse recovery simulation corresponding to $-dJ/dt$ value of $245\,\mathrm{kA/cm^2 \cdot \mu s}$. (b) Lattice temperature profile of planar junction p-i-n diode half-cell structure during reverse recovery simulation corresponding to $-dJ/dt$ value of $245\,\mathrm{kA/cm^2 \cdot \mu s}$ (zoomed-in view).

which initiates localized heating in the area closer to the edge of P+ region. The instantaneous lattice temperature profile shows the formation of thermal hot-spot at the edge of P+ region.

    The summary of p-i-n diode reverse recovery current density for varying $-dJ/dt$ is shown in Fig. 45. The magnitude of reverse current density

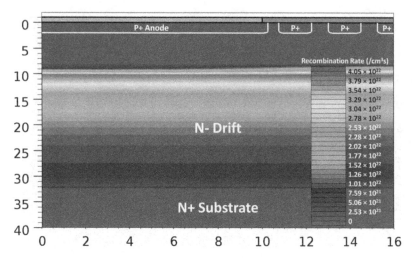

Fig. 41.   Recombination rate profile of planar junction p-i-n diode structure during reverse recovery simulation corresponding to $-dJ/dt$ value of $245\,\mathrm{kA/cm^2 \cdot \mu s}$ at maximum reverse current density instant.

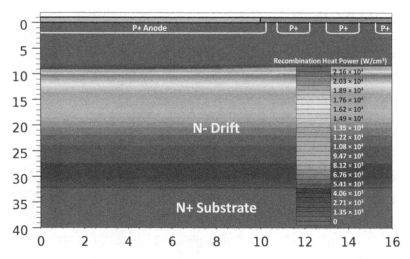

Fig. 42.   Recombination heat power profile of planar junction p-i-n diode structure during reverse recovery simulation corresponding to $-dJ/dt$ value of $245\,\mathrm{kA/cm^2 \cdot \mu s}$ at maximum reverse current density instant.

decreases with the negative rate of change of current density which places an upper limit on the switching frequency that can be used for power electronic systems employing SiC p-i-n diodes. The reverse recovery time obtained in these simulations is in the order of tens of nanoseconds, which is much lower than actual SiC p-i-n diodes. This is due to the simplified circuit which has

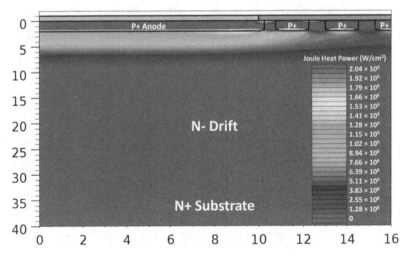

Fig. 43.   Joule heat power profile of planar junction p-i-n diode structure during reverse recovery simulation corresponding to $-dJ/dt$ value of $245\,\mathrm{kA/cm^2 \cdot \mu s}$ at maximum reverse current density instant.

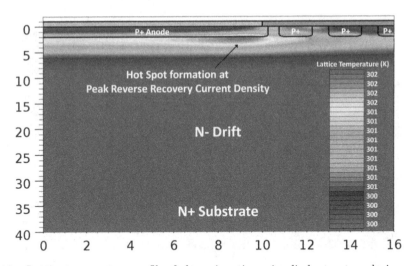

Fig. 44.   Lattice temperature profile of planar junction p-i-n diode structure during reverse recovery simulation corresponding to $-dJ/dt$ value of $245\,\mathrm{kA/cm^2 \cdot \mu s}$ at maximum reverse current density instant.

been used for TCAD simulation instead of the inductive clamped double-pulse circuit.

The summary of power dissipation density and lattice temperature is shown in Figs. 46 and 47, respectively. Maximum power dissipation of $1.34\,\mathrm{MW/cm^2}$ was obtained for a $-dJ/dt$ of $245\,\mathrm{kA/cm^2 \cdot \mu s}$ which

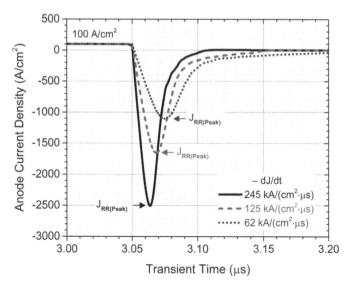

Fig. 45. Reverse recovery current density summary of planar junction SiC p-i-n diode half-cell structure for varying $-dJ/dt$.

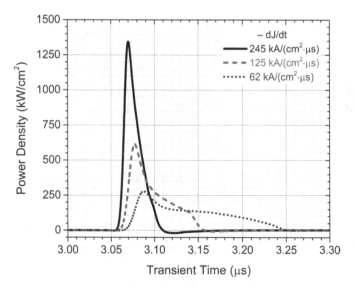

Fig. 46. Reverse recovery power dissipation density summary of the planar junction SiC p-i-n diode half-cell structure for varying $-dJ/dt$.

corresponded to a peak lattice temperature of 307 K. Reverse recovery waveforms corresponding to $-dJ/dt$ of 125 and 62 kA/cm^2 · μs yielded maximum power dissipation densities of 612 and 280 kW/cm^2 and peak lattice temperatures of 305.6 K and 304.6 K, respectively.

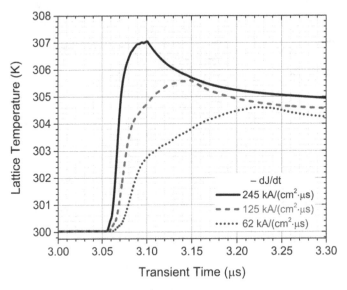

Fig. 47.   Reverse recovery lattice temperature summary of the planar junction SiC p-i-n diode half-cell structure for varying $-dJ/dt$.

 The quality of the reverse recovery waveforms obtained during p-i-n diode simulation is dependent on the structure of the device and mesh profile. The user may see significant noise in the waveform and it is advised to use a graphing/data analysis software to smooth out the data set.

6.4.4.   PIN diode structure with planar junction and floating field rings (Complete-cell)

In Section 6.4.3, a half-cell structure of p-i-n diode with planar junction was discussed. Even though a half-cell structure is a good representation of the actual device and provides a comparatively faster way to estimate device characteristics and performance, it is still not the best approximation to an actual device. In this p-i-n diode design, the P+ anode region had a junction depth of $2\,\mu m$ and was heavily doped with a peak acceptor concentration of $1.0 \times 10^{21}\,\text{cm}^{-3}$ using a Gaussian profile. The floating field rings also had a junction depth of $2\,\mu m$ and were heavily doped with a peak acceptor concentration of $1.0 \times 10^{20}\,\text{cm}^{-3}$ (slightly lower than the anode region) using a Gaussian profile. The N− epitaxial/drift region was $30\,\mu m$ thick with a doping concentration of $3.8 \times 10^{15}\,\text{cm}^{-3}$. The N+ substrate had a thickness

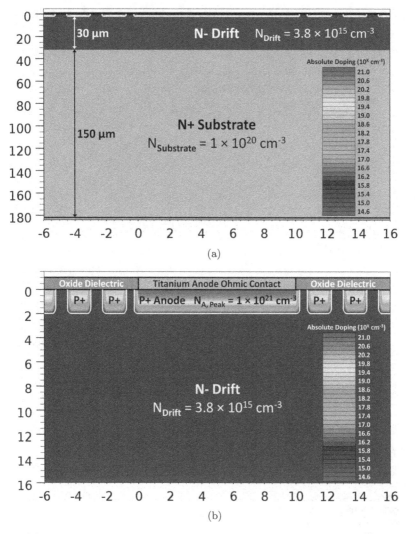

Fig. 48. (a) 3300 V SiC p-i-n diode planar junction complete-cell structure designed in Silvaco© ATLAS. (b) 3300 V SiC p-i-n diode planar junction complete-cell structure designed in Silvaco© ATLAS (zoomed-in view).

of $150\,\mu$m and doping concentration of 1.0×10^{20} cm^{-3}. Electron and hole lifetimes of $3.33\,\mu$s and $0.67\,\mu$s were selected based on research and literature review, respectively.[5–7] Titanium and aluminum were selected for the P+ anode and N+ cathode ohmic contacts, respectively.[8] In this complete-cell design, floating field rings are present on either side of the P+ anode region. The addition of field rings increased the cell pitch to $22\,\mu$m (as compared to $16\,\mu$m for the half-cell structure) with an active area of $10\,\mu$m^2 based on the

10 μm wide P+ anode region. A 1 μm thick oxide layer is used as the ILD over the floating field rings.

Due to the large substrate thickness as compared to the drift layer, the complete device structure designed using Silvaco© ATLAS has been split into Figs. 48(a) and 48(b), respectively. The Gaussian doping profile has been used for the P+ anode region and floating field rings, which can be seen in Fig. 48(b).

6.4.4.1. *Steady-state simulation*

This section will discuss the forward conduction and reverse breakdown current density versus anode voltage (J–V) characteristics at 27°C, 75°C, 125°C, and 175°C device temperature. The steady-state simulation code is similar to the one used for the planar junction half-cell diode except for change in device mesh profile.[7] The following code was used to simulate the complete-cell p-i-n diode J–V characteristics which includes forward conduction and reverse breakdown. A brief explanation of the steady-state simulation program is provided in the code walkthrough (Table 6).

```
Sample code: Planar junction SiC p-i-n diode complete-cell forward and breakdown J-V
characteristics @ 27°C

1.   GO ATLAS SIMFLAGS ="-V 5.18.3.R -P 32 -160"
2.
3.   ##### 3300V PLANAR JUNCTION PIN DIODE - COMPLETE CELL #####
4.
5.   MESH
6.
7.   ## X-MESH
8.
9.   X.MESH  loc=-6.0     spac=0.25
10.  X.MESH  loc=0.0      spac=0.25
11.  X.MESH  loc=1.0      spac=0.5
12.  X.MESH  loc=9.0      spac=0.5
13.  X.MESH  loc=10.0     spac=0.25
14.  X.MESH  loc=16.0     spac=0.25
15.
16.  ## Y-MESH
17.
18.  Y.MESH  loc=-1.0     spac=1.0
19.  Y.MESH  loc=0.0      spac=0.25
20.  Y.MESH  loc=2.1      spac=0.01
21.  Y.MESH  loc=30.0     spac=4.0
22.  Y.MESH  loc=32.1     spac=0.2
23.  Y.MESH  loc=33.0     spac=1.0
24.  Y.MESH  loc=34.0     spac=20
25.  Y.MESH  loc=180.0    spac=20
26.  Y.MESH  loc=182.0    spac=1.0
27.  Y.MESH  loc=184.0    spac=1.0
28.
29.  ## Defining Regions
```

```
30.
31. REGION   num=1   material=Oxide     y.max=0
32. REGION   num=2   material=4H-SiC    y.min=0   y.max=182
33.
34. ## Electrode
35.
36. ELECTRODE   name=anode     material=titanium   x.min=0.0   x.max=10   y.max=0
37. ELECTRODE   name=cathode   material=aluminum   y.min=182   y.max=184
38.
39. ## Bulk Doping
40. DOPING   uniform n.type conc=3.8e15   REGION=2
41.
42. ## P+ Doping
43. DOPING   gauss  p.type  conc=1.e21  x.min=0     x.max=10    junc=2.0   rat=0.1
44.
45. ## P+ Floating Field Rings
46.
47. DOPING   gauss  p.type  conc=1.e20  x.max=-5.50   junc=2.0      rat=0.1
48. DOPING   gauss  p.type  conc=1.e20  x.min=-4.25  x.max=-3.25  junc=2.0  rat=0.1
49. DOPING   gauss  p.type  conc=1.e20  x.min=-2.00  x.max=-1.00  junc=2.0  rat=0.1
50.
51. DOPING   gauss  p.type  conc=1.e20  x.min=11.00  x.max=12.00  junc=2.0  rat=0.1
52. DOPING   gauss  p.type  conc=1.e20  x.min=13.25  x.max=14.25  junc=2.0  rat=0.1
53. DOPING   gauss  p.type  conc=1.e20  x.min=15.50  x.max=16     junc=2.0  rat=0.1
54.
55. ## N+ Substrate Region Doping
56. DOPING   uniform n.type conc=1.e20   y.min=32   y.max=182
57.
58. SAVE   outf=PIN_Planar_FFR.str.str   master.out
59.
60. MATERIAL   material=4H-SiC  REGION=2  permittivity=9.76   eg300=3.26
    affinity=3.7  egalpha=3.3e-2  egbeta=1.e+5  nc300=1.7e+19  nv300=2.5e+19
    arichn=146  arichp=30  augn=3.e-29  augp=3.e-29  taun0=3.33e-6  taup0=6.7e-7
    nsrhn=3.e+17  nsrhp=3.e+17  edb=0.05  eab=0.200
61.
62. ## MODELS USED
63.
64. MODELS  REGION=2  MATERIAL=4H-SIC FERMIDIRAC ANALYTIC CONWELL INCOMPLETE SRH
    BGN AUGER TEMP=300 PRINT
65.
66. ## MOBILITY
67.
68. MOBILITY  material=4H-SiC  REGION=2  vsatn=2.2e7  vsatp=2.2e7  betan=1.2
    betap=2  mu1n.caug=40  mu2n.caug=1136  ncritn.caug=2e17  alphan.caug=-3
    betan.caug=-3  gamman.caug=0.0  deltan.caug=0.76   mu1p.caug=20  mu2p.caug=125
    ncritp.caug=1.e19  alphap.caug=-3  betap.caug=-3  gammap.caug=0.0
    deltap.caug=0.5
69.
70. IMPACT  REGION=2  ANISO  E.SIDE  SELB  SIC4H0001 an1=3.44e6  an2=3.44e6
    bn1=2.58e7  bn2=2.58e7  ap1=3.5e6  ap2=3.5e6  bp1=1.7e7  bp2=1.7e7 opphe=0.106
71.
72. METHOD  NEWTON AUTONR  climit=1.e-9  maxtraps=40  itlimit=40   dvmax=1.e8
    ir.tol=1.e-36  cr.tol=1.e-36  ix.tol=1.e-36  px.tol=1.e-30  pr.tol=1.e-45
    cx.tol=1.e-30
73.
74. OUTPUT  FLOWLINES
75.
76. LOG  outf=PIN_Forward_27C.log
77.
78. SOLVE  init
```

```
79. SOLVE   vanode=0.05  vstep=0.05  vfinal=2.6      name=anode
80. SOLVE   vstep=0.02               vfinal=3.2      name=anode
81. SOLVE   vstep=0.1                vfinal=4.0      name=anode
82.
83. SAVE  outf=PIN_Forward_27C.str
84.
85. LOG  outf=PIN_Reverse_27C.log
86.
87. SOLVE   init
88. SOLVE   vanode=-0.2   vstep=-0.2         vfinal=-2.0   name=anode
89. SOLVE   vstep=-2      vfinal=-20         name=anode
90. SOLVE   vstep=-5      vfinal=-100        name=anode
91. SOLVE   vstep=-10     vfinal=-1000       name=anode
92. SOLVE   vstep=-25     vfinal=-4000       name=anode
93. SOLVE   vstep=-10     vfinal=-4200       name=anode
94. SOLVE   vstep=-5      vfinal=-4500       name=anode    compl=1e-25  cname=anode
95.
96. SAVE  outf=PIN_Reverse_27C.str
97.
98. QUIT
```

Table 6. Code walkthrough: Planar junction P-I-N diode complete-cell forward and breakdown J–V characteristics.

Line No:	Functionality
1	Configure ATLAS simulator to use 160-bit extended precision and utilize 32 cores of the CPU if hardware resources are available. The version of ATLAS to be used by the simulator is set to 5.18.3.R using the -V option in the simflags command.
5	Initialize device structure mesh information.
7–27	X-axis and Y-axis mesh distribution.
31–32	Declare oxide and 4H-SiC as the material for the area of the semiconductor specified by the x and y coordinates.
36–37	Electrode specifications for the p-i-n diode (Anode and Cathode).
39–56	Specify doping profile, type, and concentration for different areas of the PIN diode structure. Code included to account for field rings on either side of P+ anode region.
58	Save the device structure (**.str**) file on the local hard drive. The device structure can be viewed by opening the file via **TonyPlot** to troubleshoot/optimize the structure.
60	Specify material parameters for 4H-SiC. Detailed description of these parameters is available in the Silvaco© ATLAS manual. The values for these parameters can either be obtained via material research or from literature.
64	Specify the various models to be included in the 4H-SiC p-i-n diode simulation.

(*Continued*)

Table 6. (*Continued*)

Line No:	Functionality
68	Specify mobility parameters for 4H-SiC. Detailed description of these parameters is available in the Silvaco© ATLAS manual. The values for these parameters can either be obtained via material research or from literature.
70	Specify impact ionization parameters for 4H-SiC. This statement is mandatory to obtain device breakdown characteristics.
72	Specify the solver type and the tolerance values to be used during the simulation. This is an extremely critical statement which can alter the simulation outcome.
74	Include current flowlines in the output structure file.
76	Save the forward-bias simulation log (*.log*) file on the local hard drive. The simulation results can be viewed by opening the file via **TonyPlot**.
78–81	Solve for the initial bias conditions for the simulation followed by positive sweep of anode voltage for steady-state forward characteristics.
83	Save the post-forward-bias simulation device structure (*.str*) file on the local hard drive. Saving the file at this stage of the simulation will enable the user to visualize the variation in various electrothermal parameters within the device structure introduced due to the particular simulation. For example in this simulation, the user can view the carrier concentration profile in the p-i-n diode during forward conduction.
85	Save the reverse-bias simulation log (*.log*) file on the local hard drive. The simulation results can be viewed by opening the file via **TonyPlot**.
87–94	Solve for the initial bias conditions for the simulation followed by negative sweep of anode voltage for steady-state reverse-bias characteristics. The compliance parameter (**compl**) in line 94 forces the simulator to proceed to the next line once the anode current reaches the specified compliance value. This is important, especially in breakdown simulation because once the device enters the breakdown regime, it is not necessary to run the simulation for higher magnitude of current since the breakdown voltage would have already been determined.
96	Save the post-reverse-bias simulation device structure (*.str*) file on the local hard drive. Saving the file at this stage of the simulation will enable the user to visualize the variation in various electrothermal parameters within the device structure introduced due to the particular simulation. For example in this simulation, the user can view the electric field profile in the p-i-n diode during avalanche breakdown.
98	Terminate the simulation.

6.4.4.2. *Steady-state simulation results*

The forward conduction J–V characteristics for the 3300 V planar junction SiC p-i-n diode complete-cell structure on a linear and semi-log scale are shown in Figs. 49(a) and 49(b), respectively. The inclusion of field rings in

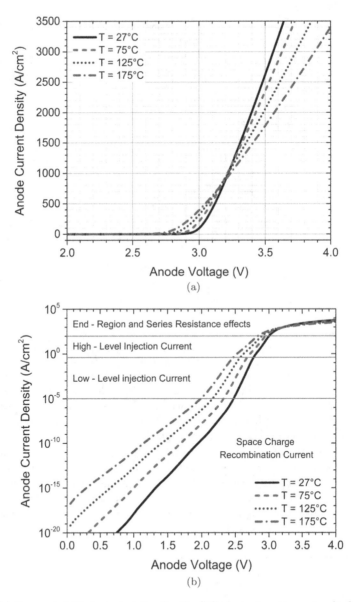

Fig. 49.   (a) Forward J–V characteristics for the SiC planar junction p-i-n diode complete-cell on a linear scale. (b) Forward J–V characteristics for the SiC planar junction p-i-n diode complete-cell on a semi-log scale.

a complete-cell structure did increase the simulation time due to a larger structure and increased mesh points; however, the increase in simulation time was reasonable and not painstakingly long. The simulations were carried out at varying lattice temperature values like the half-cell simulation. At an ON-state current density of $100\,\mathrm{A/cm^2}$, voltage drop of $3.00\,\mathrm{V}$ was observed across the diode at $27°\mathrm{C}$ device temperature. The various regions of p-i-n diode forward operation can be seen in the semi-log plot in Fig. 49(b).

The reverse-bias breakdown J–V characteristics for varying lattice temperature conditions are shown in Fig. 50. Breakdown voltage of $4254\,\mathrm{V}$ was obtained for the planar junction p-i-n diode structure with floating field rings at $27°\mathrm{C}$ device temperature. As seen in the case of half-cell diode structure, there is a progressive increase in the leakage current with lattice temperature.

The electric field distribution in the p-i-n diode complete-cell structure during breakdown is shown in the contour plot in Fig. 51(a) (Image has been scaled to highlight the area of interest). Maximum electric field of $2.65\,\mathrm{MV/cm}$ was observed at the point of breakdown. The presence of floating field rings on the either side of the active area aid in the distribution

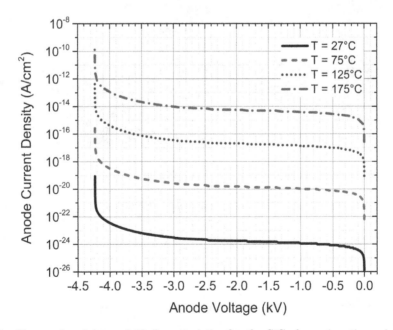

Fig. 50. Reverse breakdown J–V characteristics for the SiC planar junction p-i-n diode complete-cell structure on a semi-log scale.

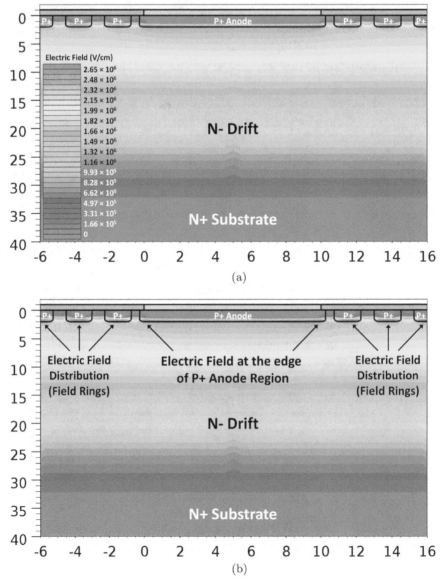

Fig. 51. (a) Electric field contour plot during reverse-bias breakdown in planar junction p-i-n diode complete-cell structure. (b) Electric field contour plot highlighting the distribution of electric field across the floating field rings during reverse-bias breakdown in a planar junction p-i-n diode complete-cell structure.

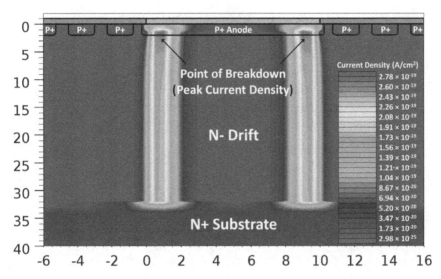

Fig. 52.   Conduction current density contour plot during reverse-bias breakdown in planar junction p-i-n diode complete-cell structure.

of the electric field (shown in Fig. 51(b)) and prevent premature breakdown at the edge of P+ anode region due to electric field enhancement.

The conduction current density contour plot during breakdown is shown in Fig. 52 (Image has been scaled to highlight the area of interest). It can be seen in Fig. 52 that avalanche breakdown occurs at the edges of the anode P+ region, which should be the case since floating field rings should not undergo breakdown.

1D electric field profile as a function of device depth is shown in Fig. 53(a). The plot has been scaled to highlight the region of interest. The electric field data was extracted for the following points: middle of the two field rings on the left side of P+ anode ($x = -3.5\,\mu$m and $x = -1.5\,\mu$m), edges of the active area P+ anode region where breakdown is occurring ($x = 0.2\,\mu$m and $x = 9.8\,\mu$m), and middle of the two field rings on the right side of P+ anode ($x = 11.5\,\mu$m and $x = 13.75\,\mu$m) using the ***cutline*** feature in ***TonyPlot***. Since it was known after the half-cell simulation that minimum electric field existed in the middle of the P+ anode region, the specific point has not been considered for electric field measurement in the complete-cell scenario. To have a closer look at the electric field distribution in the aforementioned points, individual electric field profiles are shown in Fig. 53(b), which is a zoomed-in version of Fig. 53(a). The electric field curves pertaining to breakdown are shown in bold in the graph legend.

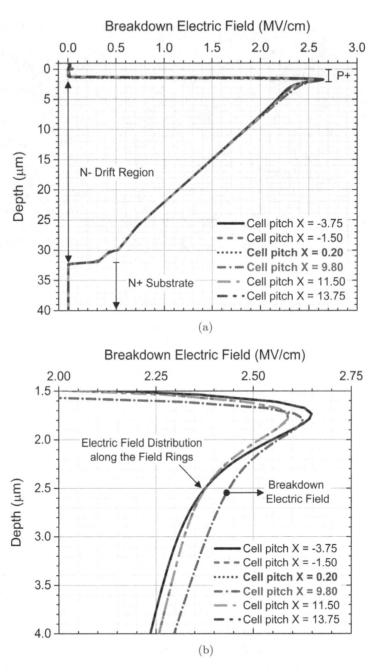

Fig. 53. (a) 1D electric field profile as a function of device depth at varying points across the diode active area/cell pitch. (b) 1D electric field profile as a function of device depth at varying points across the diode active area/cell pitch (zoomed-in view).

6.4.4.3. *Mixed-mode transient simulation — forward pulsing*

The forward pulsing Mixed-Mode transient simulation was performed using the RLC ring-down circuit shown in Fig. 10. The simulation code was similar to that used in the planar junction-i-n diode half-cell structure with changes pertaining to the complete-cell structure.[9,10] These changes include device mesh profile, inclusion of floating field rings on either side of the P+ anode region/active area, and dimensions of the thermal boundary using **Thermcontact** statement. The following code was used to simulate the p-i-n diode for a peak forward current density of $5000\,\mathrm{A/cm^2}$ under pulsed condition. A brief explanation of the Mixed-Mode simulation program is provided in the code walkthrough (Table 7).

```
Sample code: Planar junction SiC p-i-n diode complete-cell transient simulation

1.  GO ATLAS SIMFLAGS ="-V 5.18.3.R -P 32 -160"
2.
3.  ### 3300V PLANAR JUNCTION PIN DIODE - COMPLETE CELL RLC RINGDOWN PULSE 5000A/cm2 ###
4.
5.  MESH  WIDTH=1.2e6
6.
7.  ## X-MESH
8.
9.  X.MESH  loc=-6.0    spac=0.25
10. X.MESH  loc=0.0     spac=0.25
11. X.MESH  loc=1.0     spac=0.5
12. X.MESH  loc=9.0     spac=0.5
13. X.MESH  loc=10.0    spac=0.25
14. X.MESH  loc=16.0    spac=0.25
15.
16. ## Y-MESH
17.
18. Y.MESH  loc=-1.0    spac=1.0
19. Y.MESH  loc=0.0     spac=0.25
20. Y.MESH  loc=2.1     spac=0.01
21. Y.MESH  loc=30.0    spac=4.0
22. Y.MESH  loc=32.1    spac=0.2
23. Y.MESH  loc=33.0    spac=1.0
24. Y.MESH  loc=34.0    spac=20
25. Y.MESH  loc=180.0   spac=20
26. Y.MESH  loc=182.0   spac=1.0
27. Y.MESH  loc=184.0   spac=1.0
28.
29. ## Defining Regions
30.
31. REGION  num=1  material=Oxide    y.max=0
32. REGION  num=2  material=4H-SiC   y.min=0  y.max=182
33.
34. ## Electrode
35.
36. ELECTRODE  name=anode    material=titanium   x.min=0.0  x.max=10   y.max=0
37. ELECTRODE  name=cathode  material=aluminum   y.min=182  y.max=184
38.
39. ## Bulk Doping
```

```
40. DOPING  uniform  n.type  conc=3.8e15  REGION=2
41.
42. ## P+ Doping
43. DOPING  gauss  p.type  conc=1.e21  x.min=0    x.max=10    junc=2.0    rat=0.1
44.
45. ## P+ Field Rings
46.
47. DOPING  gauss  p.type  conc=1.e20  x.max=-5.50    junc=2.0    rat=0.1
48. DOPING  gauss  p.type  conc=1.e20  x.min=-4.25  x.max=-3.25  junc=2.0  rat=0.1
49. DOPING  gauss  p.type  conc=1.e20  x.min=-2.00  x.max=-1.00  junc=2.0  rat=0.1
50.
51. DOPING  gauss  p.type  conc=1.e20  x.min=11.00  x.max=12.00  junc=2.0  rat=0.1
52. DOPING  gauss  p.type  conc=1.e20  x.min=13.25  x.max=14.25  junc=2.0  rat=0.1
53. DOPING  gauss  p.type  conc=1.e20  x.min=15.50  x.max=16    junc=2.0    rat=0.1
54.
55. ## N+ Substrate Region Doping
56. DOPING  uniform  n.type   conc=1.e20   y.min=32    y.max=182
57.
58. SAVE  outf=PIN_Structure.str  master.out
59.
60. ##### STEADY STATE SIMULATION CIRCUIT #####
61.
62. GO ATLAS SIMFLAGS ="-V 5.18.3.R -P 32 -160"
63.
64. .BEGIN
65.
66. VDC          1    0    0
67. RSW          1    2    1.e-12
68. R_CHARGE    2    3    500
69. C_BANK      3    0    6u
70. R_SERIES    3    4    0.80
71. L_SERIES    4    5    500n
72. RSWITCH     5    6    1.e18
73. ADIODE       6=anode    0=cathode      infile=PIN_Structure.str    WIDTH=1.2e6
74.
75. .NODESET  v(1)=0  v(2)=0  v(3)=0  v(4)=0  v(5)=0  v(6)=0
76. .NUMERIC  imaxdc=100
77.
78. .DC    VDC   0.    10.    0.25
79. .DC    VDC   10.   100.   10.
80. .DC    VDC   100.  600.   25.
81.
82. .LOG   outfile=PIN_DC_log
83. .SAVE    outfile=PIN_RLC_Bias
84. .OPTIONS  m2ln print noshift relpot
85.
86. .END
87.
88. ##### PHYSICS USED #####
89.
90. CONTACT  DEVICE=ADIODE  NAME=ANODE       EXT.ALPHA=10
91. CONTACT  DEVICE=ADIODE  NAME=CATHODE     EXT.ALPHA=10
92.
93. THERMCONTACT DEVICE=ADIODE  num=3   x.min=-6   x.max=16   y.min=-1.0
    y.max=184   alpha=10   ext.temp=300
94.
95. MATERIAL  DEVICE=ADIODE  material=4H-SiC REGION=2  permittivity=9.76
    eg300=3.26   affinity=3.7   egalpha=3.3e-2   egbeta=1.e+5   nc300=1.7e+19
    nv300=2.5e+19  arichn=146  arichp=30  augn=3.e-29  augp=3.e-29  taun0=3.33e-6
    taup0=6.7e-7  nsrhn=3.e+17 nsrhp=3.e+17 edb=0.050  eab=0.20  tcon.polyn
```

```
        tc.a=0.137534    tc.b=0.00049662    tc.c=0.000000354   hc.a=2.35   hc.b=1.75e-3
        hc.c=1.e-9   hc.d=-6.6e4
96.
97. ## MODELS USED
98.
99. MODELS  DEVICE=ADIODE  REGION=2  MATERIAL=4H-SIC FERMIDIRAC ANALYTIC CONWELL
        SRH BGN AUGER INCOMPLETE LAT.TEMP   JOULE.HEAT GR.HEAT  PT.HEAT PRINT
100.
101. ## MOBILITY
102.
103. MOBILITY  DEVICE=ADIODE  material=4H-SiC  REGION=2  vsatn=2.2e7  vsatp=2.2e7
        betan=1.2 betap=2  mu1n.caug=40  mu2n.caug=1136  ncritn.caug=2e17
        alphan.caug=-3  betan.caug=-3  gamman.caug=0.0  deltan.caug=0.76   mu1p.caug=20
        mu2p.caug=125  ncritp.caug=1.e19  alphap.caug=-3  betap.caug=-3
        gammap.caug=0.0  deltap.caug=0.5
104.
105. MOBILITY  DEVICE=ADIODE  material=4H-SiC  REGION=2  n.canali  n.angle=90
        p.angle=90 vsatn=2.2e7  vsatp=2.2e7  betan=1.2 betap=2  mu1n.caug=5
        mu2n.caug=947  ncritn.caug=2e17  alphan.caug=-3  betan.caug=-3  gamman.caug=0.0
        deltan.caug=0.76   mu1p.caug=2.5  mu2p.caug=20  ncritp.caug=1.e19
        alphap.caug=-3  betap.caug=-3  gammap.caug=0.0  deltap.caug=0.5
106.
107. ## IMPACT IONIZATION
108.
109. IMPACT  DEVICE=ADIODE   REGION=2  ANISO  E.SIDE  SELB  SIC4H0001  an1=3.44e6
        an2=3.44e6  bn1=2.58e7  bn2=2.58e7  ap1=3.5e6  ap2=3.5e6  bp1=1.7e7  bp2=1.7e7
        opphe=0.106
110.
111. METHOD  BLOCK  climit=1.e-9  maxtraps=100  itlimit=100   max.temp=1000
        dvmax=1.e8  ir.tol=1.e-35  cr.tol=1.e-35  ix.tol=1.e-35  px.tol=1.e-30
        pr.tol=1.e-45  cx.tol=1.e-30
112.
113. ##### TRANSIENT SIMULATION CIRCUIT #####
114.
115. GO ATLAS SIMFLAGS ="-V 5.18.3.R -P 32 -160"
116.
117. .BEGIN
118.
119. VDC          1    0    600
120. RSW          1    2    1.e-12  PULSE  1.e-12  1.e18    5us   50ns   50ns   40us   80us
121. R_CHARGE     2    3    500
122. C_BANK       3    0    6u
123. R_SERIES     3    4    0.80
124. L_SERIES     4    5    500n
125. RSWITCH      5    6    1.e18   PULSE  1.e18   1.e-12  10us   50ns   50ns   40us   80us
126. ADIODE       6=anode     0=cathode      infile=PIN_Structure.str    WIDTH=1.2e6
127.
128. .NUMERIC  imaxtr=100  dtmax=5.e-8
129. .OPTIONS  m2ln.tr  print  noshift  relpot  write=10
130. .LOAD      infile=PIN_RLC_Bias
131. .SAVE      master=PIN_Transient
132. .LOG       outfile=PIN_RLC_Ringdown.log
133. .SAVE      outfile=PIN_RLC_Ringdown.str
134. .TRAN    0.01us  45us
135.
136. .END
137.
138. ##### PHYSICS USED #####
139.
140. CONTACT  device=ADIODE  NAME=ANODE       EXT.ALPHA=10
```

```
141. CONTACT  device=ADIODE  NAME=CATHODE    EXT.ALPHA=10
142.
143. THERMCONTACT  DEVICE=ADIODE    num=3    x.min=-6    x.max=16  y.min=-1.0
     y.max=184    alpha=10   ext.temp=300
144.
145. MATERIAL  DEVICE=ADIODE   material=4H-SiC  REGION=2  permittivity=9.76
     eg300=3.26   affinity=3.7   egalpha=3.3e-2  egbeta=1.e+5  nc300=1.7e+19
     nv300=2.5e+19  arichn=146  arichp=30  augn=3.e-29  augp=3.e-29  taun0=3.33e-6
     taup0=6.7e-7  nsrhn=3.e+17  nsrhp=3.e+17  edb=0.050  eab=0.200  tcon.polyn
     tc.a=0.137534   tc.b=0.00049662    tc.c=0.000000354  hc.a=2.35  hc.b=1.75e-3
     hc.c=1.e-9  hc.d=-6.6e4
146.
147. ## MODELS USED
148.
149. MODELS  DEVICE=ADIODE  REGION=2 MATERIAL=4H-SiC FERMIDIRAC ANALYTIC CONWELL SRH
     BGN AUGER INCOMPLETE LAT.TEMP  JOULE.HEAT  GR.HEAT  PT.HEAT PRINT
150.
151. ## MOBILITY
152.
153. MOBILITY  DEVICE=ADIODE  material=4H-SiC  REGION=2  vsatn=2.2e7  vsatp=2.2e7
     betan=1.2 betap=2  mu1n.caug=40  mu2n.caug=1136  ncritn.caug=2e17
     alphan.caug=-3  betan.caug=-3  gamman.caug=0.0  deltan.caug=0.76   mu1p.caug=20
     mu2p.caug=125  ncritp.caug=1.e19  alphap.caug=-3  betap.caug=-3
     gammap.caug=0.0  deltap.caug=0.5
154.
155. MOBILITY  DEVICE=ADIODE  material=4H-SiC  REGION=2  n.canali  n.angle=90
     p.angle=90 vsatn=2.2e7  vsatp=2.2e7  betan=1.2 betap=2  mu1n.caug=5
     mu2n.caug=947  ncritn.caug=2e17  alphan.caug=-3  betan.caug=-3  gamman.caug=0.0
     deltan.caug=0.76  mu1p.caug=2.5  mu2p.caug=20  ncritp.caug=1.e19
     alphap.caug=-3  betap.caug=-3  gammap.caug=0.0  deltap.caug=0.5
156.
157. ## IMPACT IONIZATION
158.
159. IMPACT  DEVICE=ADIODE  REGION=2  ANISO  E.SIDE  SELB  SIC4H0001  an1=3.44e6
     an2=3.44e6  bn1=2.58e7  bn2=2.58e7  ap1=3.5e6  ap2=3.5e6  bp1=1.7e7  bp2=1.7e7
     opphe=0.106
160.
161. OUTPUT  FLOWLINES  E.MOBILITY
162.
163. METHOD  BLOCK.TRAN  climit=1.e-9  maxtraps=100  itlimit=100   max.temp=1000
     dvmax=1.e8  ir.tol=1.e-25  cr.tol=1.e-25  ix.tol=1.e-30  px.tol=1.e-30
     pr.tol=1.e-36  cx.tol=1.e-30
164.
165. GO ATLAS SIMFLAGS ="-V 5.18.3.R -P 32 -128"
166.
167. QUIT
```

Table 7.   Code walkthrough: Planar junction p-i-n diode complete-cell Mixed-Mode forward pulsing simulation.

Line No:	Functionality
1	Configure ATLAS simulator to use version 5.18.3.R, 160-bit extended precision and utilize 32 cores of the CPU if hardware resources are available.
5	Initialize device structure mesh information with width parameter

(Continued)

Table 7. (*Continued*)

Line No:	Functionality
7–27	X-axis and Y-axis mesh distribution.
31–32	Declare oxide and 4H-SiC as the material for the area of the semiconductor specified by the x and y coordinates.
36–37	Electrode specifications for the p-i-n diode (Titanium Anode and Aluminum Cathode).
39–56	Specify doping profile, type, and concentration for different areas of the PIN diode structure. Code included to account for field rings on either side of P+ anode region.
58	Save the device structure (**.str**) file on the local hard drive.
62	Initialize ATLAS simulator using GO ATLAS command (same as line 1).
64	Initialize the starting of SPICE-like code in Mixed-Mode steady-state simulation.
66–73	RLC ring-down circuit description in SPICE-like format.
75	Declare the initial node voltage for the RLC ring-down circuit nodes.
76	Set the maximum number of mixed circuit-device iterations to be performed during steady-state analysis (**imaxdc**) to 100.
78–80	Ramp up DC voltage to attain steady-state condition, i.e. VDC = 600 V. This can be split into multiple steps.
82	Save log file after steady-state simulation completion.
83	Save file with bias information which will be used for transient simulation.
84	Specify Mixed-Mode steady-state simulation conditions. Modified two-level Newton solution method (**m2ln**), disable the shift of voltage for ATLAS devices (**noshift**), and enable the use of relative convergence criteria for potential especially when large voltage biases are involved (**relpot**).
86	Initialize the ending of SPICE-like code in Mixed-Mode steady-state simulation.
90–91	Specify heat transfer coefficient (**ext.alpha**) for the anode and cathode contacts.
93	Specify the thermal boundary for the p-i-n diode. Parameters includes boundary dimensions, heat transfer coefficient (**alpha**), and temperature of the thermal boundary (**ext.temp**) which is typically at 300 K.
95	Specify material parameters for 4H-SiC.
99	Specify the various models to be included in the 4H-SiC PIN diode simulation.
103	Specify parameters for mobility in 4H-SiC.
105	Specify parameters for anisotropic mobility in 4H-SiC.
109	Specify impact ionization parameters for 4H-SiC.

(*Continued*)

Table 7. (*Continued*)

Line No:	Functionality
111	Specify the steady-state Block Newton solver type (**BLOCK**) and the tolerance values to be used during the simulation.
115	Initialize ATLAS simulator using GO ATLAS command (same as line 1) for steady-state bias point simulation.
117	Initialize the starting of SPICE-like code in Mixed-Mode transient simulation.
119–126	RLC ring-down circuit description in SPICE-like format. The magnitude of DC voltage source is initialized at 600 V which is the result of the earlier steady-state simulation performed. Transient parameters have been added to the Resistor which is acting like a switch.
128	Set the maximum number of mixed circuit-device iterations to be performed during transient analysis (**imaxtr**) to 100 and the maximum transient simulation time step (**dtmax**) to 50 ns.
129	Specify Mixed-Mode transient simulation conditions. Modified two-level Newton solution method for transient simulation (**m2ln.tr**), disable the shift of voltage for ATLAS devices (**noshift**), enable the use of relative convergence criteria for potential especially when large voltage biases are involved (**relpot**), and write structure file after every 10 time-step iterations.
130	Load the steady-state simulations results saved in line 83.
131	Save the structure file after every 10 time-step iterations specified in line 129.
132	Save log file after the completion of transient simulation.
133	Save the structure file after the completion of transient simulation.
134	Specify the initial time interval of 10 ns and total simulation time of 45 μs.
136	Initialize the ending of SPICE-like code in Mixed-Mode transient simulation.
138–159	Same as line 88 to line 109.
161	Include current flowlines (**FLOWLINES**) and Electron Mobility (**E.MOBILITY**) in the output structure file.
163	Specify the transient Block Newton solver type (**BLOCK.TRAN**) and the tolerance values to be used during the simulation.
165	Initialize ATLAS simulator using GO ATLAS command (same as line 1) for transient simulation. A lower simulation precision of 128-bit has been used due to forward conduction mode of operation.
167	Terminate the simulation.

6.4.4.4. *Mixed-Mode transient simulation — forward pulsing results*

The forward pulsing transient simulation for the planar junction p-i-n diode complete-cell structure was carried out for varying magnitudes of peak current density ranging from $500\,\mathrm{A/cm^2}$ to $5000\,\mathrm{A/cm^2}$ in steps of 500 similar to the half-cell structure. The width parameter was used to change the peak current density through the diode without altering the waveform. In this section, results pertaining to the maximum current density scenario of $5000\,\mathrm{A/cm^2}$ will be discussed followed by a summary of all the other cases. The anode voltage and current density waveforms are shown in Fig. 54 and the power and energy density waveforms are shown in Fig. 55. There is a voltage overshoot that can be observed in the anode voltage waveform during the current ramp up phase in Fig. 54. This sudden rise in anode voltage is due to the finite time required for conductivity modulation to occur, also known as forward recovery. In the latter part of this section, a summary of anode voltage waveforms will be provided to explain the difference in the forward recovery voltage with varying peak pulsed current density.

Peak voltage drop of $5.42\,\mathrm{V}$ was observed across the p-i-n diode at peak current density of $5000\,\mathrm{A/cm^2}$, which corresponds to a peak power

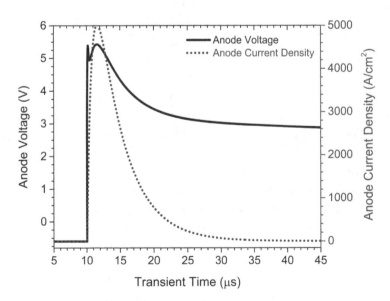

Fig. 54. Anode voltage (solid) and current density (dotted) waveforms pertaining to $5000\,\mathrm{A/cm^2}$ peak current density simulation.

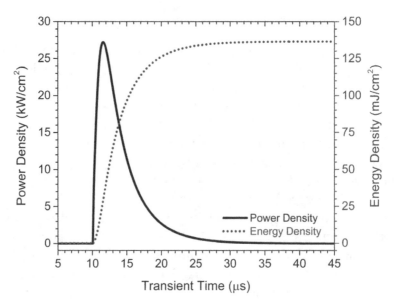

Fig. 55.   Power density (solid) and energy density (dotted) waveforms pertaining to 5000 A/cm^2 peak current density simulation.

dissipation density of 27.2 kW/cm^2. Integration of the power density waveform yielded an energy density of 136 mJ/cm^2. Peak lattice temperature of 302.5 K was observed in the p-i-n diode lattice during this pulsed operation. The variation of lattice temperature with power dissipation density and energy density during simulation is shown in Figs. 56 and 57, respectively. The simulation was run for only 45 μs, and hence does not show the complete decay of temperature waveform back to the ambient value. To identify the area of heat dissipation in the p-i-n diode structure, intermediate structure files were generated during the simulation. These structure files were manually scanned for the transient time instant which corresponds to the maximum lattice temperature.

The lattice temperature profile of the planar junction p-i-n diode structure recorded at the time instant corresponding to maximum temperature during high current density pulsed simulation are shown in Figs. 58(a) and 58(b). Maximum temperature of 302.5 K was observed in the P+ anode region.

Similar to the half-cell structure simulation, recombination heat power and joule heat power profiles were extracted from the structure file and are shown in Figs. 59 and 60, respectively (p–n junctions are marked in white). The heat power sources are expressed in W/cm^3 in **TonyPlot**, and the contour plots have been scaled to highlight the areas of interest. It can be

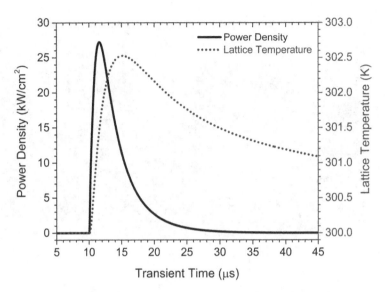

Fig. 56. Power density (solid) and lattice temperature (dotted) waveforms pertaining to 5000 A/cm^2 RLC ring-down simulation.

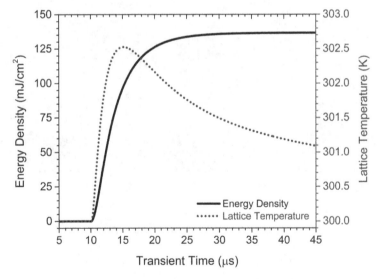

Fig. 57. Energy density (solid) and lattice temperature (dotted) waveforms pertaining to 5000 A/cm^2 RLC ring-down simulation.

seen from the heat power profiles that there is significant power dissipation in the P+ region due to carrier generation and recombination effects. The joule/resistive heat power dissipation is dominant only at the edges of P+ anode due to current crowding. This heat generation is due to the end region

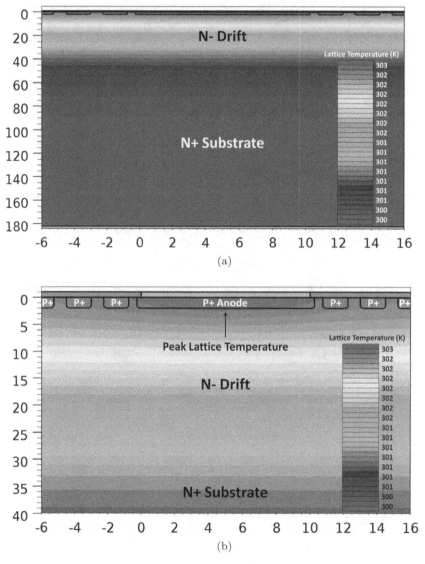

Fig. 58.   (a) Lattice temperature profile of planar junction p-i-n diode complete-cell structure during $5000\,\mathrm{A/cm^2}$ RLC ring-down simulation. (b) Lattice temperature profile of planar junction p-i-n diode complete-cell structure during $5000\,\mathrm{A/cm^2}$ RLC ring-down simulation (zoomed-in view).

recombination effects which increases the ON-state resistance, especially at higher current density forward operation.[11]

The summary of lattice temperature and anode voltage waveforms of the planar junction p-i-n diode complete-cell structure simulation for all the values of peak pulsed current density are shown in Figs. 61 and 62,

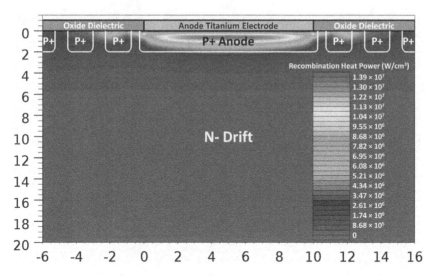

Fig. 59. Recombination heat power profile of planar junction p-i-n diode complete-cell structure during $5000 \, \text{A/cm}^2$ RLC ring-down simulation (zoomed-in view).

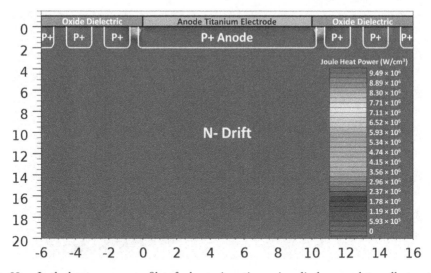

Fig. 60. Joule heat power profile of planar junction p-i-n diode complete-cell structure during $5000 \, \text{A/cm}^2$ RLC ring-down simulation (zoomed-in view).

respectively. To highlight the impact of forward recovery on the anode voltage, the anode voltage waveforms have been scaled to highlight the instant when the RLC ring-down circuit current density ramps up through the diode in Fig. 63.

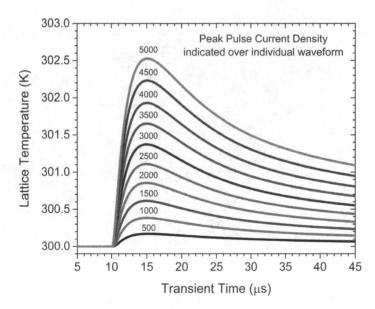

Fig. 61.   Lattice temperature summary of planar junction SiC p-i-n diode complete-cell structure during RLC ring-down simulation.

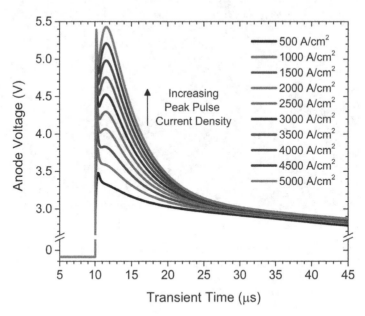

Fig. 62.   Anode voltage summary of planar junction SiC p-i-n diode complete-cell structure during RLC ring-down simulation.

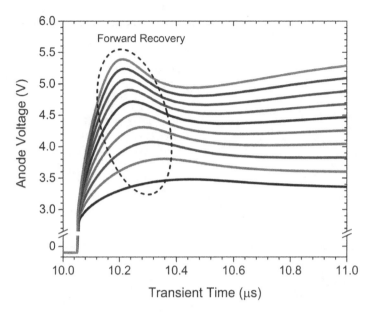

Fig. 63.   Anode voltage summary of planar junction SiC p-i-n diode complete-cell structure during RLC ring-down simulation with emphasis on the forward recovery process.

6.4.4.5.   *Mixed-Mode transient simulation — reverse recovery*

Reverse recovery simulation for the planar junction SiC p-i-n diode complete-cell structure was carried out using the circuit shown in Fig. 37. The following code was used to simulate the p-i-n diode for its reverse recovery characteristics, and a brief explanation of the Mixed-Mode simulation program is provided in the code walkthrough (Table 8).[9,12]

```
Sample code: Planar junction SiC p-i-n diode complete-cell structure reverse recovery
transient simulation

1. GO ATLAS SIMFLAGS ="-V 5.18.3.R -P 32 -160"
2.
3. ##### 3300V PLANAR JUNCTION PIN DIODE - COMPLETE CELL REVERSE RECOVERY ######
4.
5. MESH  WIDTH=1.2e6
6.
7. ## X-MESH
8.
9.  X.MESH  loc=-6.0    spac=0.25
10. X.MESH  loc=0.0     spac=0.25
11. X.MESH  loc=1.0     spac=0.5
12. X.MESH  loc=9.0     spac=0.5
13. X.MESH  loc=10.0    spac=0.25
14. X.MESH  loc=16.0    spac=0.25
15.
16. ## Y-MESH
17.
```

```
18. Y.MESH  loc=-1.0      spac=1.0
19. Y.MESH  loc=0.0       spac=0.25
20. Y.MESH  loc=2.1       spac=0.01
21. Y.MESH  loc=30.0      spac=4.0
22. Y.MESH  loc=32.1      spac=0.2
23. Y.MESH  loc=33.0      spac=1.0
24. Y.MESH  loc=34.0      spac=20
25. Y.MESH  loc=180.0     spac=20
26. Y.MESH  loc=182.0     spac=1.0
27. Y.MESH  loc=184.0     spac=1.0
28.
29. ## Defining Regions
30.
31. REGION  num=1 material=Oxide    y.max=0
32. REGION  num=2 material=4H-SiC   y.min=0  y.max=182
33.
34. ## Electrode
35.
36. ELECTRODE  name=anode    material=titanium  x.min=0   x.max=10   y.max=0
37. ELECTRODE  name=cathode  material=aluminum  y.min=182  y.max=184
38.
39. ## Bulk Doping
40. DOPING  uniform n.type  conc=3.8e15  REGION=2
41.
42. ## P+ Doping
43. DOPING  gauss p.type  conc=1.e21  x.min=0   x.max=10   junc=2.0  rat=0.1
44.
45. ## P+ Field Rings
46.
47. DOPING  gauss  p.type  conc=1.e20  x.max=-5.50            junc=2.0    rat=0.1
48. DOPING  gauss  p.type  conc=1.e20  x.min=-4.25  x.max=-3.25  junc=2.0  rat=0.1
49. DOPING  gauss  p.type  conc=1.e20  x.min=-2.00  x.max=-1.00  junc=2.0  rat=0.1
50.
51. DOPING  gauss  p.type  conc=1.e20  x.min=11.00  x.max=12.00  junc=2.0  rat=0.1
52. DOPING  gauss  p.type  conc=1.e20  x.min=13.25  x.max=14.25  junc=2.0  rat=0.1
53. DOPING  gauss  p.type  conc=1.e20  x.min=15.50  x.max=16    junc=2.0   rat=0.1
54.
55. ## N+ Substrate Region Doping
56. DOPING  uniform n.type   conc=1.e20  y.min=32    y.max=182
57.
58. SAVE  outf=PIN_Structure.str  master.out
59.
60. ##### STEADY STATE SIMULATION CIRCUIT #####
61.
62. GO ATLAS SIMFLAGS ="-V 5.18.3.R -P 32 -160"
63.
64. .BEGIN
65.
66. VPULSE     0    1    0
67. R_SERIES   1    2    2.68
68. ADIODE     2=anode   0=cathode      infile=PIN_Structure.str   WIDTH=1.e6
69.
70. .NODESET  v(1)=0  v(2)=0
71. .NUMERIC  imaxdc=100
72.
73. .DC   VPULSE    0.     -10.     -0.2
74. .DC   VPULSE   -10.    -50.     -5.
75. .DC   VPULSE   -50.   -100.    -10.
76. .DC   VPULSE  -100.  -3300.   -100.
77.
```

```
78. .LOG    outfile=PIN_DC_log
79. .SAVE   outfile=PIN_RLC_Bias
80. .OPTIONS  m2ln print noshift relpot
81.
82. .END
83.
84. ##### PHYSICS USED #####
85.
86. CONTACT  DEVICE=ADIODE  NAME=ANODE      EXT.ALPHA=10
87. CONTACT  DEVICE=ADIODE  NAME=CATHODE    EXT.ALPHA=10
88.
89. THERMCONTACT DEVICE=ADIODE   num=3   x.min=-6   x.max=16   y.min=-1.0
    y.max=182   alpha=10   ext.temp=300
90.
91. MATERIAL DEVICE=ADIODE  material=4H-SiC  REGION=2  permittivity=9.76
    eg300=3.26   affinity=3.7  egalpha=3.3e-2  egbeta=1.e+5  nc300=1.7e+19
    nv300=2.5e+19  arichn=146  arichp=30  augn=3.e-29  augp=3.e-29  taun0=3.33e-6
    taup0=6.7e-7  nsrhn=3.e+17  nsrhp=3.e+17  edb=0.050  eab=0.20  tcon.polyn
    tc.a=0.137534   tc.b=0.00049662    tc.c=0.000000354  hc.a=2.35  hc.b=1.75e-3
    hc.c=1.e-9  hc.d=-6.6e4
92.
93. ## MODELS USED
94.
95. MODELS DEVICE=ADIODE  REGION=2 MATERIAL=4H-SiC FERMIDIRAC ANALYTIC CONWELL SRH
    BGN AUGER INCOMPLETE LAT.TEMP  JOULE.HEAT GR.HEAT  PT.HEAT PRINT
96.
97. ## MOBILITY
98.
99. MOBILITY DEVICE=ADIODE  material=4H-SiC  REGION=2  vsatn=2.2e7  vsatp=2.2e7
    betan=1.2 betap=2  mu1n.caug=40  mu2n.caug=1136  ncritn.caug=2e17
    alphan.caug=-3  betan.caug=-3  gamman.caug=0.0  deltan.caug=0.76   mu1p.caug=20
    mu2p.caug=125  ncritp.caug=1.e19  alphap.caug=-3  betap.caug=-3
    gammap.caug=0.0  deltap.caug=0.5
100.
101. MOBILITY DEVICE=ADIODE  material=4H-SiC  REGION=2  n.canali  n.angle=90
     p.angle=90 vsatn=2.2e7  vsatp=2.2e7  betan=1.2 betap=2  mu1n.caug=5
     mu2n.caug=947  ncritn.caug=2e17  alphan.caug=-3  betan.caug=-3  gamman.caug=0.0
     deltan.caug=0.76   mu1p.caug=2.5  mu2p.caug=20  ncritp.caug=1.e19
     alphap.caug=-3  betap.caug=-3  gammap.caug=0.0  deltap.caug=0.5
102.
103. ## IMPACT IONIZATION
104.
105. IMPACT DEVICE=ADIODE  REGION=2 ANISO  E.SIDE  SELB  SIC4H0001  an1=3.44e6
     an2=3.44e6  bn1=2.58e7  bn2=2.58e7  ap1=3.5e6  ap2=3.5e6  bp1=1.7e7  bp2=1.7e7
     opphe=0.106
106.
107. METHOD  BLOCK climit=1.e-9  maxtraps=100  itlimit=100   max.temp=1000
     dvmax=1.e8  ir.tol=1.e-40  cr.tol=1.e-40  ix.tol=1.e-40  px.tol=1.e-30
     pr.tol=1.e-45  cx.tol=1.e-30
108.
109. ##### TRANSIENT SIMULATION CIRCUIT #####
110.
111. GO ATLAS SIMFLAGS ="-V 5.18.3.R -P 32 -160"
112.
113. .BEGIN
114.
115. VPULSE     0    1    -3300   PULSE -3300 30 1us    50ns    50ns   2us    10us
116. R_SERIES   1    2    2.68
117. ADIODE    2=anode    0=cathode   infile=PIN_Structure.str   WIDTH=1.e6
118.
```

```
119. .NUMERIC  imaxtr=100  dtmax=1.e-8
120. .OPTIONS  m2ln.tr print noshift relpot write=25
121.
122. .LOAD  infile=PIN_DC_Bias
123. .LOG   outfile=PIN_PULSING.log
124. .SAVE  master=PIN_PULSING_Transient
125. .SAVE  outfile=PIN_PULSING.str
126.
127. .TRAN  0.01us 5us
128.
129. .END
130.
131. ##### PHYSICS USED #####
132.
133. CONTACT  DEVICE=ADIODE  NAME=ANODE      EXT.ALPHA=10
134. CONTACT  DEVICE=ADIODE  NAME=CATHODE    EXT.ALPHA=10
135.
136. THERMCONTACT DEVICE=ADIODE   num=3   x.min=-6   x.max=16   y.min=-1.0
     y.max=182   alpha=10   ext.temp=300
137.
138. MATERIAL DEVICE=ADIODE MATERIAL=4H-SiC REGION=2  permittivity=9.76
     eg300=3.26  affinity=3.7  egalpha=3.3e-2  egbeta=1.e+5  nc300=1.7e+19
     nv300=2.5e+19  arichn=146  arichp=30  augn=3.e-29  augp=3.e-29  taun0=3.33e-6
     taup0=6.7e-7  nsrhn=3.e+17  nsrhp=3.e+17  edb=0.050  eab=0.200  tcon.polyn
     tc.a=0.137534  tc.b=0.00049662   tc.c=0.000000354  hc.a=2.35  hc.b=1.75e-3
     hc.c=1.e-9  hc.d=-6.6e4
139.
140. ## MODELS USED
141.
142. MODELS  DEVICE=ADIODE  REGION=2  MATERIAL=4H-SIC FERMIDIRAC ANALYTIC CONWELL
     SRH BGN AUGER INCOMPLETE LAT.TEMP  JOULE.HEAT  GR.HEAT  PT.HEAT PRINT
143.
144. ## MOBILITY
145.
146. MOBILITY  DEVICE=ADIODE  material=4H-SiC  REGION=2  vsatn=2.2e7  vsatp=2.2e7
     betan=1.2 betap=2  mu1n.caug=40  mu2n.caug=1136  ncritn.caug=2e17
     alphan.caug=-3  betan.caug=-3 gamman.caug=0.0 deltan.caug=0.76   mu1p.caug=20
     mu2p.caug=125  ncritp.caug=1.e19  alphap.caug=-3  betap.caug=-3
     gammap.caug=0.0  deltap.caug=0.5
147.
148. MOBILITY  DEVICE=ADIODE  material=4H-SiC REGION=2  n.canali  n.angle=90
     p.angle=90 vsatn=2.2e7  vsatp=2.2e7  betan=1.2 betap=2  mu1n.caug=5
     mu2n.caug=947  ncritn.caug=2e17  alphan.caug=-3  betan.caug=-3  gamman.caug=0.0
     deltan.caug=0.76   mu1p.caug=2.5  mu2p.caug=20  ncritp.caug=1.e19
     alphap.caug=-3  betap.caug=-3  gammap.caug=0.0  deltap.caug=0.5
149.
150. ## IMPACT IONIZATION
151.
152. IMPACT  DEVICE=ADIODE   REGION=2  ANISO  E.SIDE  SELB  SIC4H0001  an1=3.44e6
     an2=3.44e6  bn1=2.58e7  bn2=2.58e7  ap1=3.5e6  ap2=3.5e6  bp1=1.7e7  bp2=1.7e7
     opphe=0.106
153.
154. OUTPUT  FLOWLINES  E.MOBILITY
155.
156. METHOD  BLOCK.TRAN climit=1.e-9  maxtraps=100  itlimit=100   max.temp=1000
     dvmax=1.e8  ir.tol=1.e-35  cr.tol=1.e-35  ix.tol=1.e-35  px.tol=1.e-35
     pr.tol=1.e-45  cx.tol=1.e-35
157.
158. GO ATLAS SIMFLAGS ="-V 5.18.3.R -P 32 -160"
159.
160. QUIT
```

Table 8. Code walkthrough: Planar junction p-i-n diode complete-cell Mixed-Mode reverse recovery simulation.

Line No:	Functionality
1	Configure ATLAS simulator to use version 5.18.3.R, 160-bit extended precision and utilize 32 cores of the CPU if hardware resources are available.
5	Initialize device structure mesh information with width parameter.
7–27	X-axis and Y-axis mesh distribution.
31–32	Declare oxide and 4H-SiC as the material for the area of the semiconductor specified by the x and y coordinates.
36–37	Electrode specifications for the p-i-n diode (Titanium Anode and Aluminum Cathode).
39–56	Specify doping profile, type, and concentration for different areas of the p-i-n diode structure. Code included to account for field rings on either side of P+ anode region.
58	Save the device structure (**.str**) file on the local hard drive.
62	Initialize ATLAS simulator using GO ATLAS command (same as line 1).
64	Initialize the starting of SPICE-like code in Mixed-Mode steady-state simulation.
66–68	Reverse recovery test circuit description in SPICE-like format.
70	Declare the initial node voltage for the reverse recovery test circuit nodes.
71	Set the maximum number of mixed circuit-device iterations to be performed during steady-state analysis (**imaxdc**) to 100.
73–76	Ramp up DC voltage to attain steady-state condition, i.e. VPULSE = -3300 V. This can be split into multiple steps.
78	Save log file after steady-state simulation completion.
79	Save file with bias information which will be used for transient simulation.
80	Specify Mixed-Mode steady-state simulation conditions. Modified two-level Newton solution method (**m2ln**), disable the shift of voltage for ATLAS devices (**noshift**), and enable the use of relative convergence criteria for potential especially when large voltage biases are involved (**relpot**).
82	Initialize the ending of SPICE-like code in Mixed-Mode steady-state simulation.
86–87	Specify heat transfer coefficient (**ext.alpha**) for the anode and cathode contacts.
89	Specify the thermal boundary for the p-i-n diode. Parameters includes boundary dimensions, heat transfer coefficient (**alpha**), and temperature of the thermal boundary (**ext.temp**) which is typically at 300 K.
91	Specify material parameters for 4H-SiC.

(Continued)

Table 8. (*Continued*)

Line No:	Functionality
95	Specify the various models to be included in the 4H-SiC p-i-n diode simulation.
99	Specify parameters for mobility in 4H-SiC.
101	Specify parameters for anisotropic mobility in 4H-SiC.
105	Specify impact ionization parameters for 4H-SiC.
107	Specify the steady-state Block Newton solver type (**BLOCK**) and the tolerance values to be used during the simulation.
111	Initialize ATLAS simulator using GO ATLAS command (same as line 1) for steady-state bias point simulation.
113	Initialize the starting of SPICE-like code in Mixed-Mode transient simulation.
115–117	Reverse recovery test circuit description in SPICE-like format. The magnitude of DC voltage for the VPULSE source is initialized at −3300 V which is the result of the earlier steady-state simulation performed. Transient parameters have been added to the voltage source VPULSE to generate square wave.
119	Set the maximum number of mixed circuit-device iterations to be performed during transient analysis (**imaxtr**) to 100 and the maximum transient simulation time step (**dtmax**) to 10 ns.
120	Specify Mixed-Mode transient simulation conditions. Modified two-level Newton solution method for transient simulation (**m2ln.tr**), disable the shift of voltage for ATLAS devices (**noshift**), enable the use of relative convergence criteria for potential especially when large voltage biases are involved (**relpot**), and write structure file after every 25 time-step iterations.
122	Load the steady-state simulations results saved in line 79.
123	Save log file after the completion of transient simulation.
124	Save the structure file after every 25 time-step iterations specified in line 120.
125	Save the structure file after the completion of transient simulation.
127	Specify the initial time interval of 10 ns and total simulation time of 5 μs.
129	Initialize the ending of SPICE-like code in Mixed-Mode transient simulation.
131–152	Same as line 84 to line 105.
154	Include current flowlines (**FLOWLINES**) and Electron Mobility (**E.MOBILITY**) in the output structure file.
156	Specify the transient Block Newton solver type (**BLOCK.TRAN**) and the tolerance values to be used during the simulation.
158	Initialize ATLAS simulator using GO ATLAS command (same as line 1) for transient simulation.
160	Terminate the simulation.

6.4.4.6. *Mixed-Mode transient simulation — reverse recovery results*

The reverse recovery simulation of planar junction SiC p-i-n diode complete-cell structure was carried out for varying values of negative rate of change of current density $(-dJ/dt)$ during transition from forward conduction to reverse-blocking. Same as the half-cell simulation, voltage fall times of 50 ns, 100 ns, and 200 ns were used. The three different fall times, 50 ns, 100 ns, and 200 ns, used to control the negative rate of change of current density resulted in $-dJ/dt$ values of 245, 125, and 62 kA/cm$^2 \cdot \mu s$ and peak reverse recovery current densities of 2635, 1760, and 1166 A/cm^2, respectively.

This section will discuss the results pertaining to the maximum negative dJ/dt scenario (245 kA/cm$^2 \cdot \mu s$) followed by a summary of results for varying $-dJ/dt$. The anode voltage and current density waveforms are shown in Fig. 64, and the power and energy density waveforms are shown in Fig. 65. The anode to cathode voltage across the diode during forward conduction is 3.06 V, which coincides with the zero-mark due to the axis scale in Fig. 64. Peak reverse current density of 2635 A/cm^2 was obtained during the simulation, which corresponded to an instantaneous power dissipation of 1.47 MW/cm^2 and energy density of 29.6 mJ/cm^2 within the p-i-n diode.

The lattice temperature profiles of planar junction p-i-n diode complete-cell structure for the maximum reverse current density scenario are shown in Figs. 66(a) and 66(b), respectively. Peak lattice temperature of 305.7 K was

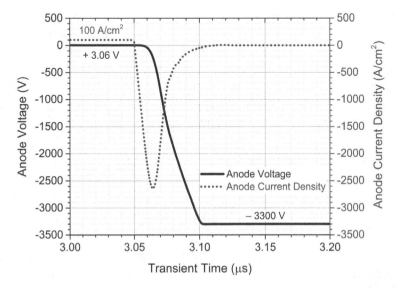

Fig. 64. Anode voltage (solid) and current density (dotted) waveforms obtained during reverse recovery simulation corresponding to $-dJ/dt$ value of 245 kA/cm$^2 \cdot \mu s$.

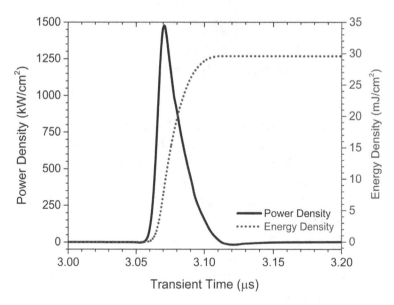

Fig. 65.   Power density (solid) and energy density (dotted) waveforms obtained during reverse recovery simulation corresponding to $-dJ/dt$ value of $245\,\mathrm{kA/cm^2 \cdot \mu s}$.

observed in the drift region closer to the P+/ N− interface. The heat power and lattice temperature profiles were also recorded at the instant when the reverse current density was at its maximum magnitude.

The recombination rate and recombination heat power profiles at the instant of peak current density are shown in Figs. 67 and 68 respectively. Maximum carrier recombination occurs in the drift region during the reverse conduction process. The nearly identical contour plots indicate the direct dependence of carrier generation–recombination effects on the recombination heat power density.

The joule heat power and lattice temperature profiles at the instant of peak current density are shown in Figs. 69 and 70, respectively. The figures have been scaled to highlight the areas of interest. The joule heat power is due to high reverse current conduction along with a significant voltage drop across the diode (voltage and current density crossover shown in Fig. 64) which initiates localized heating in the area closer to the edges of P+ region/active area. The instantaneous lattice temperature profile shows the formation of thermal hot-spot at the edges of P+ region.

The summary of p-i-n diode reverse recovery current density for varying $-dJ/dt$ is shown in Fig. 71. The magnitude of reverse current density decreases with the negative rate of change of current density and the reverse recovery time obtained in these simulations is in the order of tens

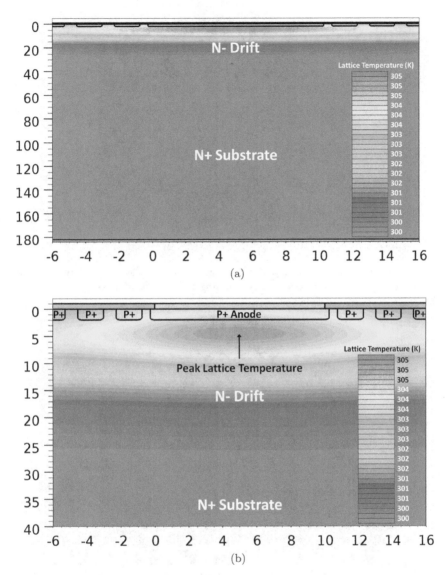

Fig. 66. (a) Lattice temperature profile of planar junction p-i-n diode complete-cell structure during reverse recovery simulation corresponding to $-dJ/dt$ value of $245\,\mathrm{kA/cm^2} \cdot \mu s$. (b) Lattice temperature profile of planar junction p-i-n diode complete-cell structure during reverse recovery simulation corresponding to $-dJ/dt$ value of $245\,\mathrm{kA/cm^2} \cdot \mu s$ (zoomed-in view).

of nanoseconds, which agrees with the results obtained during the half-cell simulation.

The summary of power dissipation density and lattice temperature is shown in Figs. 72 and 73, respectively. Maximum power dissipation of

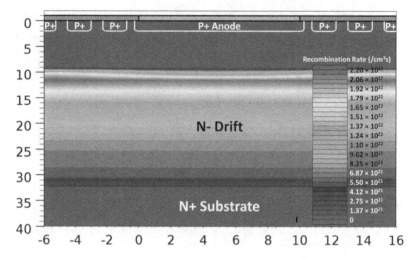

Fig. 67.   Recombination rate profile of planar junction p-i-n diode complete-cell structure during reverse recovery simulation corresponding to $-dJ/dt$ value of $245\,\mathrm{kA/cm^2} \cdot \mu s$ at maximum reverse current density instant.

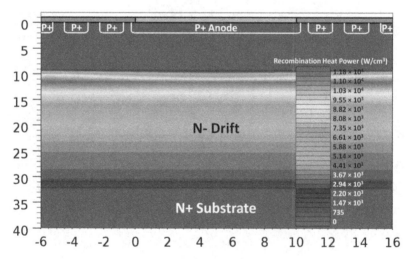

Fig. 68.   Recombination heat power profile of planar junction p-i-n diode complete-cell structure during reverse recovery simulation corresponding to $-dJ/dt$ value of $245\,\mathrm{kA/cm^2} \cdot \mu s$ at maximum reverse current density instant.

$1.47\,\mathrm{MW/cm^2}$ was obtained for a $-dJ/dt$ of $245\,\mathrm{kA/cm^2} \cdot \mu s$ which corresponded to a peak lattice temperature of $305.7\,\mathrm{K}$. Reverse recovery waveforms corresponding to $-dJ/dt$ of $125\,\mathrm{kA/cm^2} \cdot \mu s$ and $62\,\mathrm{kA/cm^2} \cdot \mu s$ yielded maximum power dissipation densities of $692\,\mathrm{kW/cm^2}$ and $307\,\mathrm{kW/cm^2}$ and peak lattice temperatures of $304.5\,\mathrm{K}$ and $303.6\,\mathrm{K}$ respectively.

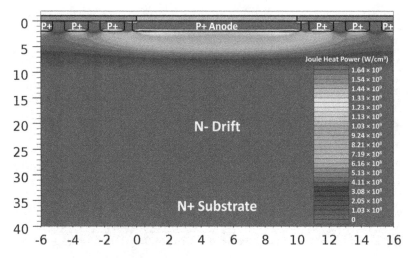

Fig. 69. Joule heat power profile of planar junction p-i-n diode complete-cell structure during reverse recovery simulation corresponding to $-dJ/dt$ value of $245\,\mathrm{kA/cm^2} \cdot \mu s$ at maximum reverse current density instant.

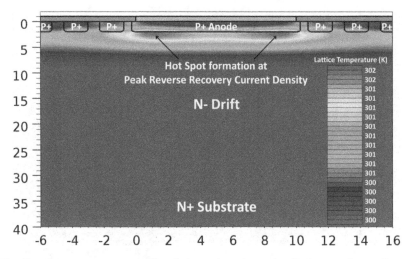

Fig. 70. Lattice temperature profile of planar junction p-i-n diode complete-cell structure during reverse recovery simulation corresponding to $-dJ/dt$ value of $245\,\mathrm{kA/cm^2} \cdot \mu s$ at maximum reverse current density instant.

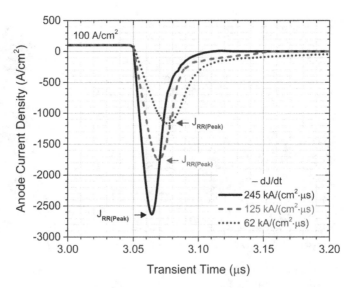

Fig. 71.   Reverse recovery current density summary of planar junction SiC p-i-n diode complete-cell structure for varying $-dJ/dt$.

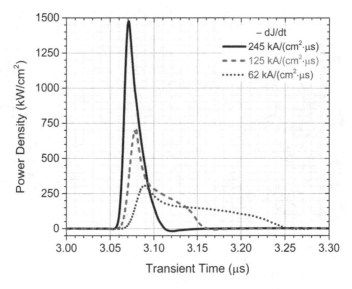

Fig. 72.   Reverse recovery power dissipation density summary of the planar junction SiC p-i-n diode complete-cell structure for varying $-dJ/dt$.

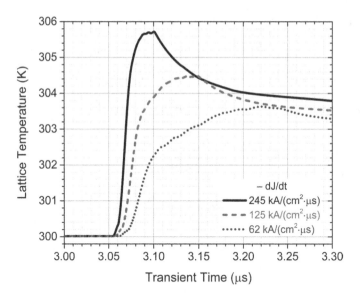

Fig. 73. Reverse recovery lattice temperature summary of the planar junction SiC p-i-n diode complete-cell structure for varying $-dJ/dt$.

References

1. T. B. Salah, C. Buttay, B. Allard, H. Morel, S. Ghedira and K. Besbes, Experimental analysis of punch-through conditions in power P-I-N diodes, *IEEE Transactions on Power Electronics*, Vol. 22, 2007, pp. 13–20.
2. B. Baliga, *Fundamentals of Power Semiconductor Devices*, New York, NY: Springer Verlag, 2008.
3. J. Lutz, H. Schlangenotto, U. Scheuermann and R. D. Doncker, *Semiconductor Power Device — Physics Characteristic Reliability*, New York, NY: Springer-Verlag, 2011.
4. *ATLAS User's Manual*, September 11, 2014, [online] Available at: www.silvaco.com.
5. A. A. Ogunniyi, H. K. O'Brien, M. Hinojosa, L. Cheng, C. J. Scozzie, B. N. Pushpakaran, S. Lacouture and B. S. Bayne, Analysis of carrier lifetime effects on HV SIC PiN diodes at elevated pulsed switching conditions, *2015 IEEE Pulsed Power Conference (PPC)*, Austin, TX, 2015, pp. 1–6.
6. M. J. Marinella, D. K. Schroder, C. Gilyong, M. J. Loboda, T. Isaacs-Smith and J. R. Williams, Carrier generation lifetimes in 4H-SiC MOS capacitors, *IEEE Transactions on Electron Devices*, 57, 2010, pp. 1910–1923.
7. M. E. Levinshtein, T. T. Mnatsakanov, P. Ivanov, J. W. Palmour, S. L. Rumyantsev, Ranbir Singh, S. N. Yurkov, Paradoxes of carrier lifetime measurements in high-voltage SiC diodes, *IEEE Transactions on Electron Devices* 48, 2001, pp. 1703–1710.
8. T. Kimoto and J. A. Cooper, *Fundamentals of Silicon Carbide Technology*, Singapore: Wiley, 2014.
9. B. Pushpakaran, S. Bayne and A. Ogunniyi, Silvaco-based electrothermal simulation of 10 kV 4H-SiC P-I-N diode under pulsed condition, *2017 IEEE 21st International Conference on Pulsed Power (PPC)*, Brighton, 2017, pp. 1–6.
10. B. N. Pushpakaran, S. B. Bayne and A. A. Ogunniyi, Electrothermal simulation-based comparison of 4H-SiC p-i-n, Schottky, and JBS diodes under high current density

pulsed operation, *IEEE Transactions on Plasma Science*, vol. 45, no. 1, Janurary 2017, pp. 68–75.

11. K. Kells, S. Müller, G. Wachutka and W. Fichtner, Simulation of self-heating effects in a power pin diode, *Proceedings of the 5th SISDEP Conference*, 1993, pp. 41–44.

12. B. N. Pushpakaran, S. B. Bayne and A. A. Ogunniyi, Physics-based simulation of 4H-SIC DMOSFET structure under inductive switching. *Journal of Computational Electronics*, 2015, pp. 1–9.

Chapter 7

Schottky Diode

The Schottky diode is a majority carrier device which inherently makes it a fast switching device suitable for high-frequency operation. The dependency of the diode characteristics on the Schottky contact properties enables the development of low ON-state voltage device, especially for wide bandgap material where the built-in potential is inherently high. A simplified cross-sectional structure of a Schottky diode is shown in Fig. 1. It consists of a lightly doped n-type region, also known as the drift or intrinsic region, which is electrically connected to metal anode to form the Schottky contact and a heavily doped n-type substrate which is electrically connected to the device cathode. The absence of conductivity modulation (i.e. injection of minority carrier injection into the drift region) in a Schottky diode limits the blocking voltage capability. The aforementioned aspects of a Schottky diode make it the device of choice for high-speed and low-voltage power electronics circuit. This section will discuss the basic operation of the Schottky diode and the governing equations used to model the device.

The Schottky contact is a metal to semiconductor contact where the metal has a workfunction that is given by Φ_M. The workfunction of a metal (Φ_M) is defined as the energy required to move an electron from the Fermi level to free space when operating in a vacuum. However, in a semiconductor, no electrons are located at the Fermi level; therefore, electron affinity (χ_S) is used. The electron affinity is defined as the energy required to move an electron from the bottom of the conduction band to free space. When a metal is brought in contact with a semiconductor, charge transfer occurs until thermal equilibrium is established (Fermi levels are aligned). For example, if the Fermi level is higher in the semiconductor than in the metal, electrons are transferred from the semiconductor to the metal.[1,2] The transfer of charge across the Schottky Barrier creates a depletion region with a width of W_0

Fig. 1.   Simplified cross-sectional image of power Schottky diode.

given by the following equation

$$W_0 = \sqrt{\frac{2\varepsilon_S V_{\text{bi}}}{q N_{\text{Drift}}}} \tag{1}$$

where ε_S is the semiconductor permittivity and N_{Drift} is the drift region doping concentration. A positive charge is created in the semiconductor because of the uncompensated donor ions. The difference between the workfunction of the metal and the semiconductor develops the equilibrium contact built-in potential V_{bi}. The built-in potential prevents electrons from further diffusing from the semiconductor into the metal. The Schottky barrier height (Φ_B), which plays a role in both forward-conduction and reverse-blocking operation of a Schottky diode is given by

$$\Phi_B = q V_{\text{bi}} + (E_C - E_{\text{FS}}) \tag{2}$$

where E_C is the energy at the conduction band and E_{FS} is the energy at the Fermi level. The barrier height can also be determined from the workfunction of the metal and the electron affinity of the semiconductor, as shown below.

$$\Phi_B = \Phi_M - \chi_S \tag{3}$$

7.1. Forward-bias Characteristics

Under forward-bias operation, there is current flow across the diode through the metal–semiconductor junction, mainly due to majority carriers. Since n-type Schottky diode will be discussed in this chapter, current flow mechanism will be analyzed with respect to electrons (majority carrier in n-type semiconductor). The energy barrier is reduced by the forward bias across the device followed by the transfer of electrons from the semiconductor over to the metal. This section will briefly discuss the forward conduction mechanism in a Schottky diode. Detailed discussion of the mechanism and derivation of equations is out of scope of this textbook. The forward conduction in a Schottky diode can occur by the following current transport mechanisms:

- **Thermionic emission current** — Thermionic emission current refers to the transport of electrons with energy greater than or equal to the conduction band energy barrier at the metal–semiconductor interface.

- **Tunneling current** — Transport of electrons through the conduction band energy barrier due to quantum mechanical tunneling process which considers the wave-nature of electrons, thereby allowing them to penetrate thin energy barriers.

- **Recombination current** — This component of current flow is due to the recombination of electrons and holes which gets transported into the space–charge/depletion region.

- **Minority carrier current** — Minority carrier current or hole-injection current is due to the transport of holes from the metal into the semiconductor followed by recombination.

Even though there are multiple mechanisms that could contribute to the forward-bias current flow, analysis have shown that there is only one dominant mechanism. Power Schottky rectifiers have a lightly doped drift region to support the large blocking voltage. This enables the spreading of the depletion region over a significant distance thereby preventing the formation of a sharp potential barrier which is necessary for quantum mechanical tunneling. The space–charge recombination current component is observable only at very low current density. The contribution of hole-injection current will be significant only when the Schottky barrier height is large; however, Schottky diodes are specifically designed with low barrier height for lower ON-state voltage drop. Under forward-bias condition, a relatively low potential barrier is seen by the electrons in the semiconductor which causes electron injection from the semiconductor into the metal, thereby leading to a large forward-bias current flow which increases exponentially with the forward-bias voltage across the device. This forward-bias current is due to thermionic emission, which is also the dominant current flow mechanism in a Schottky diode.[1,2] The forward current density (J_F) through the device is given by the following equation:

$$J_F = AT^2 e^{-\left(\frac{q\Phi_B}{kT}\right)} \cdot e^{\left(\frac{qV_F}{kT}\right)} \tag{4}$$

where A is the effective Richardson's constant, k is Boltzmann constant, V_F is the forward voltage applied, and T is the absolute temperature. The value of effective Richardson's constant for 4H-SiC is $146\,\text{A}\,\text{cm}^{-2}\,\text{K}^{-2}$. The first term in Eq. (4) is called the saturation current (J_S) of the diode which can be rewritten as

$$J_S = AT^2 e^{-\left(\frac{q\Phi_B}{kT}\right)} \tag{5}$$

The ON-state voltage drop for a Schottky diode is given by Eq. (6) which comprises of two components: Schottky voltage drop (V_{SCH}) and resistive voltage drop (V_{RES}). The Schottky component of voltage drop can be approximated to Eq. (7) at low forward current density which implies that an increase in lattice temperature would cause decrease in ON-state voltage drop due to the negative value of logarithmic term in Eq. (6). The resistive voltage drop is proportional to the total series specific resistance $R_{\text{S.SP}}$ which is the sum of contact $(R_{\text{Cont.SP}})$, drift region $(R_{\text{Drift.SP}})$, and substrate resistance $(R_{\text{Substrate.SP}})$ components as shown in Eq. (8). Unlike the p-i-n diode, there is no minority carrier injection in a Schottky diode to modulate and decrease the drift region resistance. From a design perspective, this places an upper limit on the blocking voltage to avoid ON-state losses at high current density.[1,2]

$$V_F = V_{\text{SCH}} + V_{\text{RES}} = \frac{kT}{q}\ln\left(\frac{J_F}{J_S}\right) + (R_{\text{S.SP}} \cdot J_F) \tag{6}$$

$$V_F \approx V_{\text{SCH}} = \Phi_B + \frac{kT}{q}\ln\left(\frac{J_F}{AT^2}\right) \tag{7}$$

$$R_{\text{S.SP}} = R_{\text{Cont.SP}} + R_{\text{Drift.SP}} + R_{\text{Substrate.SP}} \tag{8}$$

During blocking phase, negative bias voltage is applied to the Schottky metal with respect to the semiconductor, which increases the barrier height. The reverse-bias voltage is supported across the drift region of the diode with maximum electric field at the metal–semiconductor interface. The relationship between the drift region doping concentration (N_{Drift}) and depletion width (W_D) as a function of parallel plane breakdown voltage (BV_{PP}) is given by the following equations:[1]

$$N_{\text{Drift}} = 4.32 \times 10^{20}(BV_{PP})^{-\frac{4}{3}} \tag{9}$$

$$W_D = 1.6 \times 10^{-7}(BV_{PP})^{\frac{7}{6}} \tag{10}$$

7.2. Reverse-bias Characteristics

This section will briefly discuss the behavior of a Schottky diode under reverse-blocking phase. Besides thermionic emission, leakage current in a Schottky diode also comprises of reverse-bias hole diffusion current and generation–recombination current associated carrier generation in the depletion. However, due to the low Schottky barrier height, thermionic emission is the dominant mechanism responsible for reverse leakage current. During reverse bias, leakage current is given by Eq. (11) where V_R is the reverse-bias voltage. Since reverse-bias voltage is much higher than the thermal voltage (kT/q), Eq. (11) becomes equal and opposite to the saturation current J_S in Eq. (12).

$$J_L = AT^2 e^{-\left(\frac{q\Phi_B}{kT}\right)} \cdot \left(e^{-\left(\frac{qV_R}{kT}\right)} - 1\right) \tag{11}$$

$$J_L = -AT^2 e^{-\left(\frac{q\Phi_B}{kT}\right)} = -J_S \tag{12}$$

The saturation current is a strong function of the temperature and the barrier height. In order to reduce the leakage current, barrier height must be increased; however, an increase in barrier height will lead to an increase in the forward voltage of the diode. Another factor that affects the reverse-bias characteristics of a Schottky diode is a phenomenon known as Schottky barrier lowering which can degrade the performance of the Schottky diode during reverse-blocking by increasing the leakage current. Schottky barrier lowering refers to the reduction in the barrier height due to the influence of electric field at the metal–Semiconductor/Schottky interface.[1,2] The reduction in barrier height $(\Delta\Phi_B)$ is given by Eq. (13) where $E_{\max}$ is the maximum electric field at the Schottky interface.

$$\Delta\Phi_B = \sqrt{\frac{qE_{\max}}{4\pi\varepsilon_S}} \tag{13}$$

A complete analysis of the barrier lowering phenomenon can be found in the references. Another important parameter for the Schottky diode is the capacitance of the device. When the device is supporting reverse voltage, the depletion width is given by Eq. (14). The diode-specific capacitance

(capacitance per unit area) associated with the depletion width is given by Eq. (15).[1,2]

$$W_D = \sqrt{\frac{2\varepsilon_S}{qN_{\text{Drift}}}(V_R + V_{\text{bi}})} \tag{14}$$

$$C_{\text{SCH.SP}} = \frac{\varepsilon_S}{W_D} \tag{15}$$

7.3. Silvaco© ATLAS Modeling and Simulation

Irrespective of the device being simulated, it is highly recommended that the user starts off the modeling process by developing TCAD model for the most basic device design. This would not only streamline the overall modeling process by reducing the initial simulation time, enabling faster troubleshooting, and better understanding of the device model, but also helps in optimizing the more complex device design approach. In case of a Schottky diode, the most basic design consists of the parallel plane diode.

The following sections will discuss the modeling and simulation of a 3300 V SiC Schottky diode using parallel plane, half-cell and complete-cell structure designs. A detailed discussion of the design equations used for the Schottky diode is out of scope of this textbook. The simulations will consist of steady-state and transient characterization.

7.3.1. Simulation models

The physics-based models used for Schottky diode simulation accounted for Shockley–Read–Hall recombination (***SRH***), auger recombination (***AUGER***), bandgap narrowing (***BGN***), low-field mobility (***ANALYTIC***), mobility due to carrier–carrier scattering (***CONWELL***), incomplete ionization of dopants (***INCOMPLETE***), and impact ionization (***SELB***). The ***MODELS*** statement was used to implement these models in the deckbuild code. The temperature parameter (***TEMP***) can be used to change the steady-state lattice temperature of the simulation. For non-isothermal Mixed-Mode or transient simulation, in addition to the aforementioned models, lattice temperature model (***LAT.TEMP***) was included to account for the change in device lattice temperature during the course of simulation. The lattice temperature model was used in conjunction with models to account for heat generation due to joule heating (***JOULE.HEAT***), Carrier Generation and Recombination heating (***GR.HEAT***) and Peltier–Thomson heating (***PT.HEAT***). Performing non-isothermal simulations also require models and parameters to define thermal conductivity and heat capacity and its variation as a function of lattice temperature. The Schottky diode simulations discussed in this chapter use the polynomial function (***TCON.POLYN***) for thermal conductivity and the standard model for heat capacity.

The most important parameter for a Schottky diode is the barrier height which determines its forward and reverse characteristics. Therefore, it is crucial to select the appropriate Schottky metal for the device being modeled. The parameters which define the behavior of the Schottky interface are specified using the **CONTACT** statement. The user can either specify the Schottky metal to be used or the workfunction of the conductor. If a Schottky metal is specified out of the default library of metals, ATLAS will use the workfunction which is internally associated to the particular metal. When the user explicitly specifies the workfunction (***WORKFUNCTION***), ATLAS will associate that particular value to the conductor. In addition to specifying the Schottky metal workfunction, parameters need to be added to account for thermionic emission (***THERMION***) and parabolic field emission (***PARABOLIC***).[3-5]

 Even though it is not critical, user should check the Silvaco© manual for the latest parameter name based on the ATLAS version used for device simulation.

In SiC Schottky diode simulation, parabolic field emission defines current as a function of the applied bias voltage while factoring in the tunneling probability. Barrier lowering is an important phenomenon which is responsible for increasing the leakage current as a function of reverse-bias voltage; however, inclusion of models and parameters to account for barrier lowering would require accurate parameter values which can either be based on experimental work or literature review. Due to the simulation issues encountered with the addition of barrier lowering model/parameters, it has not been included in the Schottky diode simulations discussed in this chapter.

 The inclusion of Barrier lowering in a Schottky diode simulation without accurate parameters could lead to either convergence issues or incorrect simulation results.

7.3.2. Parallel plane Schottky diode

As discussed in the previous chapter, it is highly recommended to start off with the Schottky diode modeling using parallel plane approach due to its simplicity and relatively lower simulation time. The Schottky diode structure was designed for a rated current density of $100 \, \text{A/cm}^2$ and blocking voltage of $3300 \, \text{V}$. Since the rated blocking voltage is typically considered as 80% of the actual breakdown voltage, the diode was designed for a breakdown voltage of $4200 \, \text{V}$. The drift region was uniformly doped with a donor concentration of $3.8 \times 10^{15} \, \text{cm}^{-3}$ and the substrate was heavily doped with a donor concentration of $1.0 \times 10^{20} \text{cm}^{-3}$. In this model, n-type dopant is assumed to be nitrogen and a corresponding ionization energy of $50 \, \text{meV}$ was used in the incomplete ionization model parameter. The drift region thickness was calculated to be $30 \, \mu\text{m}$ based on the design equations. The anode Schottky metal was configured to be a conductor with a workfunction of $5.0 \, \text{eV}$ and aluminum was used for the cathode ohmic contact. The 2D Schottky diode cell was designed for an active area of $10 \, \mu\text{m}^2$ where the X-dimension is $10 \, \mu\text{m}$ and the default Z-dimension is $1 \, \mu\text{m}$. The parallel plane Schottky diode structure does not involve any field termination and assumes an ideal scenario. A simplified cross-sectional view of a parallel plane Schottky diode highlighting the critical regions and design parameters is shown in Fig. 2.

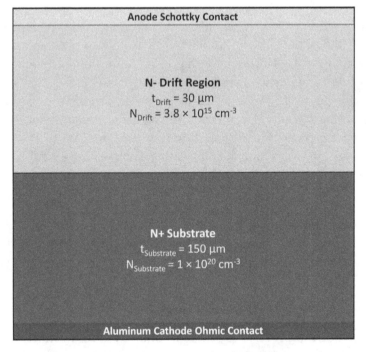

Fig. 2.   Cross-sectional view of parallel plane Schottky diode structure with design parameters (not drawn to scale).

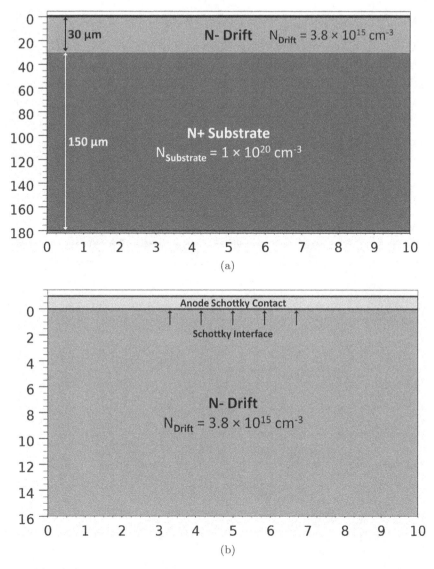

Fig. 3. (a) 3300 V SiC Schottky diode parallel plane structure designed in Silvaco© ATLAS. (b) 3300 V SiC Schottky diode parallel plane structure designed in Silvaco© ATLAS (zoomed-in view).

Due to the large substrate thickness as compared to the drift layer, the complete device structure designed using Silvaco© ATLAS does not clearly show the anode Schottky contact and cathode ohmic contact. Hence, device structure has been split into Figs. 3(a) and 3(b), respectively. Since there is no p-type region in a parallel plane Schottky diode structure, legends have not been included in Figs. 3(a) and 3(b).

7.3.2.1. *Steady-state simulation*

Steady-state/DC simulation helps in verifying the basic operation of the device model. This section will discuss the forward conduction and reverse breakdown current density versus anode voltage ($J-V$) characteristics at $27°C$, $75°C$, $125°C$, and $175°C$ device temperature. Steady-state simulations help the user to refine the device model which includes optimization of the mesh profile and adjustment of doping concentration to fine-tune the breakdown voltage. The following code was used to simulate the Schottky diode $J-V$ characteristics which includes forward-conduction and reverse-breakdown. A brief explanation of the steady-state simulation program is provided in the code walkthrough (Table 1).

```
Sample code: Parallel plane SiC Schottky diode forward and breakdown J-V characteristics
@ 27°C
────────────────────────────────────────────────────────────────────────────────────────
1.   GO ATLAS SIMFLAGS ="-V 5.18.3.R -P 32 -160"
2.
3.   ##### 3300V SCHOTTKY DIODE STEADY STATE @ 27C #####
4.
5.   MESH
6.
7.   ## X-MESH
8.
9.   X.MESH  loc=0.0      spac=0.25
10.  X.MESH  loc=10.0     spac=0.25
11.
12.  ## Y-MESH
13.
14.  Y.MESH  loc=-1.0     spac=1.0
15.  Y.MESH  loc=0.0      spac=0.2
16.  Y.MESH  loc=0.25     spac=0.1
17.  Y.MESH  loc=28.0     spac=10.0
18.  Y.MESH  loc=30.0     spac=0.2
19.  Y.MESH  loc=32.0     spac=20
20.  Y.MESH  loc=178.0    spac=20
21.  Y.MESH  loc=180.0    spac=1.0
22.  Y.MESH  loc=182.0    spac=1.0
23.
24.  ## DEFINING REGIONS
25.
26.  REGION  num=1  MATERIAL=4H-SiC  x.min=0  x.max=10  y.min=0  y.max=180
27.
28.  ## DEFINING ELECTRODES
29.
30.  ELECTRODE  name=anode    material=CONDUCTOR  x.min=0    x.max=10    y.max=0
31.  ELECTRODE  name=cathode  material=ALUMINUM   y.min=180  y.max=182
32.
33.  ## DOPING DISTRIBUTION
34.
35.  ## BULK DOPING
36.  DOPING  uniform  n.type  conc=3.8e15  REGION=1
37.
38.  ## N++ SUBSTRATE REGION DOPING
39.  DOPING  uniform  n.type  conc=1.e20   y.min=30    y.max=180
```

```
40.
41. SAVE  outf=Schottky_Parallel_Plane.str  master.out
42.
43. MATERIAL  material=4H-SiC REGION=1  permittivity=9.76 eg300=3.26
    affinity=3.7   egalpha=3.3e-2  egbeta=1.e+5  nc300=1.7e+19  nv300=2.5e+19
    arichn=146  arichp=30  augn=3.e-29  augp=3.e-29  taun0=3.33e-6  taup0=6.7e-7
    nsrhn=3.e+17  nsrhp=3.e+17  edb=0.05  eab=0.200
44.
45. CONTACT  NAME=ANODE  WORKFUNCTION=5.0  THERMION  PARABOLIC
46.
47. ## MODELS USED
48.
49. MODELS  REGION=1  MATERIAL=4H-SIC FERMIDIRAC ANALYTIC CONWELL SRH BGN AUGER
    TEMP=300 PRINT
50.
51. ## MOBILITY
52.
53. MOBILITY  material=4H-SiC REGION=1  vsatn=2.2e7  vsatp=2.2e7  betan=1.2 betap=2
    mu1n.caug=40  mu2n.caug=1136  ncritn.caug=2e17  alphan.caug=-3  betan.caug=-3
    gamman.caug=0.0  deltan.caug=0.76   mu1p.caug=20  mu2p.caug=125
    ncritp.caug=1.e19  alphap.caug=-3  betap.caug=-3  gammap.caug=0.0
    deltap.caug=0.5
54.
55. IMPACT  REGION=1  ANISO  E.SIDE  SELB  SIC4H0001 an1=3.44e6  an2=3.44e6
    bn1=2.58e7  bn2=2.58e7  ap1=3.5e6  ap2=3.5e6  bp1=1.7e7  bp2=1.7e7  opphe=0.106
56.
57. METHOD  NEWTON AUTONR  climit=1.e-9  maxtraps=150  itlimit=30   dvmax=1.e8
    ir.tol=1.e-35  cr.tol=1.e-35  ix.tol=1.e-35  px.tol=1.e-30  pr.tol=1.e-45  cx.tol=1.e-30
58.
59. OUTPUT  FLOWLINES
60.
61. LOG  outf=SCH_Forward_27C.log
62.
63. SOLVE  init
64. SOLVE  vanode=0.05 vstep=0.05 vfinal=2      name=anode
65. SOLVE  vstep=0.1              vfinal=4.0    name=anode
66.
67. SAVE  outf=SCH_Forward_27C.str
68.
69. LOG  outf=SCH_Reverse_27C.log
70.
71. SOLVE  init
72. SOLVE  vanode=-0.2  vstep=-0.2    vfinal=-2.0     name=anode
73. SOLVE  vstep=-2     vfinal=-20    name=anode
74. SOLVE  vstep=-5     vfinal=-100   name=anode
75. SOLVE  vstep=-10    vfinal=-1000  name=anode
76. SOLVE  vstep=-25    vfinal=-4000  name=anode
77. SOLVE  vstep=-10    vfinal=-4200  name=anode
78. SOLVE  vstep=-2     vfinal=-4500  name=anode  compl=1e-14 cname=anode previous
79.
80. SAVE  outf=SCH_Reverse_27C.str
81.
82. QUIT
```

Table 1.   Code walkthrough: Parallel plane Schottky diode forward and breakdown $J-V$ characteristics.

Line No:	Functionality
1	Configure ATLAS simulator to use 160-bit extended precision and utilize 32 cores of the CPU if hardware resources are available. The version of ATLAS to be used by the simulator is set to 5.18.3.R using the -V option in the simflags command.
5	Initialize device structure mesh information.
7–22	X-axis and Y-axis mesh distribution.
26	Declare 4H-SiC as the material for the area of the semiconductor specified by the x and y coordinates.
30–31	Electrode specifications for the Schottky diode (metal conductor Anode and aluminum Cathode).
35–39	Specify doping profile, type and concentration for different areas of the Schottky diode structure.
41	Save the device structure (**.str**) file on the local hard drive. The device structure can be viewed by opening the file via **TonyPlot** to troubleshoot/optimize the structure.
43	Specify material parameters for 4H-SiC. Detailed description of these parameters are available in the Silvaco© ATLAS manual. The values for these parameters can either be obtained via material research or from literature.
45	Specify Schottky metal workfunction and model/parameters for thermionic emission and parabolic field emission using **Contact** statement.
49	Specify the various models to be included in the 4H-SiC Schottky diode simulation.
53	Specify mobility parameters for 4H-SiC. Detailed description of these parameters are available in the Silvaco© ATLAS manual. The values for these parameters can either be obtained via material research or from literature.
55	Specify Impact Ionization parameters for 4H-SiC. This statement is mandatory to obtain device breakdown characteristics.
57	Specify the solver type and the tolerance values to be used during the simulation. This is an extremely critical statement which can alter the simulation outcome.
59	Include current flowlines in the output structure file.
61	Save the simulation log (**.log**) file on the local hard drive. The simulation results can be viewed by opening the file via **TonyPlot**.
63–65	Solve for the initial bias conditions for the simulation followed by positive sweep of anode voltage for steady-state forward characteristics.
67	Save the post-forward-bias simulation device structure (**.str**) file on the local hard drive. Saving the file at this stage of the simulation will enable the user to visualize the variation in various electrothermal parameters within the device structure introduced due to the particular simulation.

(Continued)

Table 1. (*Continued*)

Line No:	Functionality
69	Save the reverse-bias simulation log (**.log**) file on the local hard drive. The simulation results can be viewed by opening the file via **TonyPlot**.
71–78	Use solve statement to increment the negative anode voltage in discrete steps. The compliance parameter (**compl**) in line 78 forces the simulator to proceed to the next line once the anode current reaches the specified compliance value. This is important, especially in breakdown simulation because once the device enters the breakdown regime, it is not necessary to run the simulation for higher magnitude of current since the breakdown voltage would have already been determined.
80	Save the post-reverse-bias simulation device structure (**.str**) file on the local hard drive. Saving the file at this stage of the simulation will enable the user to visualize the variation in various electrothermal parameters within the device structure introduced due to the particular simulation.
82	Terminate the simulation.

7.3.2.2. *Steady-state simulation results*

The forward conduction $J-V$ characteristics for the $3300\,\text{V}$ SiC Schottky diode on a linear and semi-log scale are shown in Figs. 4(a) and 4(b), respectively. It can be seen from Fig. 4(a) that there is a steady decrease in the diode turn-ON voltage as the lattice temperature increases from $27°\text{C}$ to $175°\text{C}$. This reduced ON-state voltage drop at low current density can be attributed to the reduction in Schottky barrier height with increase in lattice temperature. However, since Schottky diode is a majority carrier device, the degradation in the bulk mobility at elevated temperature increases the ON-state resistance, thereby leading to higher ON-state losses. At an ON-state current density of $100\,\text{A/cm}^2$, voltage drop of 1.45 V was observed across the Schottky diode at $27°\text{C}$ device temperature.

The reverse-bias breakdown $J-V$ characteristics are shown in Fig. 5. Breakdown voltage of 4314 V was obtained for the parallel plane Schottky diode at $27°\text{C}$ device temperature. There is a progressive increase in the leakage current with device temperature without any change in the breakdown voltage. The breakdown characteristics are dependent on the impact ionization coefficients (*line 55 in the simulation code*), and it is up to the user to specify them based on experimental data or literature review.

The electric field distribution in a parallel plane Schottky diode structure during breakdown is shown in the contour plot in Fig. 6. The contour plot has been scaled to focus on the electric field in the critical regions of the

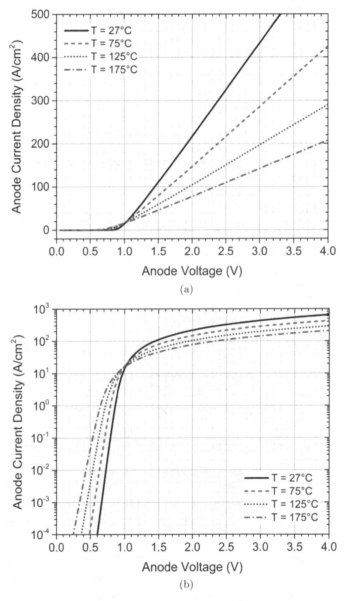

Fig. 4.   (a) Forward $J-V$ characteristics for the SiC parallel plane Schottky diode on a linear scale. (b) Forward $J-V$ characteristics for the SiC parallel plane Schottky diode on a semi-log scale.

device, i.e. Schottky interface. A maximum electric field of 2.49 MV/cm was observed at the Schottky interface and gradually decreases towards the N–drift/N+ substrate junction. Due to the parallel plane design, peak electric field is uniform across the diode active area at the Schottky interface. The

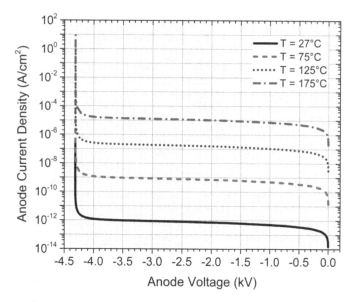

Fig. 5. Reverse breakdown $J-V$ characteristics for the SiC parallel plane Schottky diode on a semi-log scale.

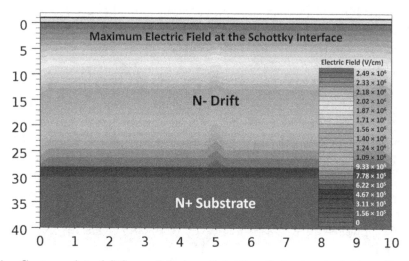

Fig. 6. Contour plot of SiC parallel plane Schottky diode electric field profile during reverse breakdown.

magnitude of electric field in the substrate is approximately zero, hence only a segment of the substrate width is shown in Fig. 6. Using the **cutline** feature in **TonyPlot**, 1D electric field profile as a function of device depth was generated and is shown in Fig. 7. The electric field profiles were generated for three points along the cell pitch/active area: $x = 2.5\,\mu\text{m}$, $x = 5.0\,\mu\text{m}$, and

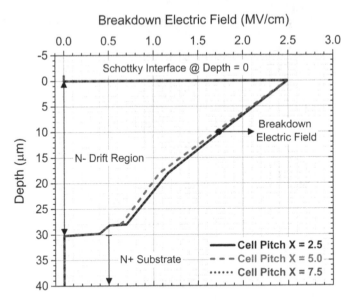

Fig. 7. 1D electric field profile in a parallel plane SiC Schottky diode as a function of device depth.

$x = 7.5\,\mu$m. Ideally, for a parallel plane structure, the electric field profiles should be overlapping; however, in Fig. 7, there is slight difference in the profile at $x = 5.0\,\mu$m due to the merger of mesh from the left and right halves of the complete structure.

As observed in Figs. 6 and 7, the Schottky interface is exposed to high electric field which results in the lowering of the Schottky barrier height thereby increasing the reverse-bias leakage current. Hence, it is critical to protect/shield the Schottky interface from high electric field to improve the reverse-blocking characteristics.

7.3.2.3.   *Mixed-Mode transient simulation*

Transient simulation of the Schottky diode model helps in predicting the behavior of the device in an actual circuit. This section will discuss the transient simulation of a parallel plane SiC Schottky diode using the Mixed-Mode circuit simulator. An RLC ring-down circuit was used to simulate the Schottky diode structure under high current density pulsed operation.[6] The working of an RLC ring-down circuit has already been discussed in the previous chapters. The circuit was designed to generate a current pulse with pulse-width of $5\,\mu$s and the peak current was varied using the **width** parameter in the deckbuild code. The following code was used to simulate the Schottky diode for a peak current density of $5000\,\text{A/cm}^2$ under pulsed condition. A brief explanation of the Mixed-Mode simulation program is provided in the code walkthrough (Table 2).

```
Sample code: Parallel plane SiC Schottky diode transient simulation

1.   GO ATLAS SIMFLAGS ="-V 5.18.3.R -P 32 -160"
2.
3.   ##### PARALLEL PLANE SCHOTTKY DIODE RLC RINGDOWN PULSE 5000A/cm2 #####
4.
5.   MESH  WIDTH=1.2e6
6.
7.   ## X-MESH
8.
9.   X.MESH  loc=0.0      spac=0.25
10.  X.MESH  loc=10.0     spac=0.25
11.
12.  ## Y-MESH
13.
14.  Y.MESH  loc=-1.0     spac=1.0
15.  Y.MESH  loc=0.0      spac=0.2
16.  Y.MESH  loc=0.25     spac=0.1
17.  Y.MESH  loc=28.0     spac=10.0
18.  Y.MESH  loc=30.0     spac=0.2
19.  Y.MESH  loc=32.0     spac=20
20.  Y.MESH  loc=178.0    spac=20
21.  Y.MESH  loc=180.0    spac=1.0
22.  Y.MESH  loc=182.0    spac=1.0
23.
24.  ## DEFINING REGIONS
25.
26.  REGION  num=1  MATERIAL=4H-SiC   x.min=0   x.max=10   y.min=0  y.max=180
27.
28.  ## DEFINING ELECTRODES
29.
30.  ELECTRODE  name=anode    material=CONDUCTOR   x.min=0    x.max=10    y.max=0
31.  ELECTRODE  name=cathode  material=ALUMINUM    y.min=180   y.max=182
32.
33.  ## DOPING DISTRIBUTION
34.
35.  ## BULK DOPING
36.  DOPING  uniform  n.type   conc=3.8e15  REGION=1
37.
38.  ## N++ SUBSTRATE REGION DOPING
39.  DOPING  uniform  n.type   conc=1.e20   y.min=30     y.max=180
40.
41.  SAVE  outf=SCH_Structure.str  master.out
42.
43.  ##### STEADY STATE SIMULATION CIRCUIT #####
44.
45.  GO ATLAS SIMFLAGS ="-V 5.18.3.R -P 32 -160"
46.
47.  .BEGIN
48.
49.  VDC          1     0     0
50.  RSW          1     2     1.e-12
51.  R_CHARGE     2     3     500
52.  C_BANK       3     0     6u
53.  R_SERIES     3     4     0.80
54.  L_SERIES     4     5     500n
55.  RSWITCH      5     6     1.e18
```

```
56. ADIODE        6=anode    0=cathode    infile=SCH_Structure.str    width=1.2e6
57.
58. .NODESET  v(1)=0  v(2)=0  v(3)=0  v(4)=0  v(5)=0  v(6)=0
59. .NUMERIC  imaxdc=100
60.
61. .DC    VDC  0.    10.   0.25
62. .DC    VDC  10.   100.  5.
63. .DC    VDC  100.  600.  10.
64.
65. .LOG  outfile=SCH_DC_log
66. .SAVE  outfile=SCH_RLC_Bias
67. .OPTIONS  m2ln print noshift relpot
68.
69. .END
70.
71. ##### PHYSICS USED #####
72.
73. CONTACT  DEVICE=ADIODE  NAME=ANODE  WORKFUNCTION=5.0 THERMION  PARABOLIC
    EXT.ALPHA=10
74. CONTACT  DEVICE=ADIODE  NAME=CATHODE    EXT.ALPHA=10
75.
76. THERMCONTACT  DEVICE=ADIODE    num=3    x.min=0    x.max=10  y.min=-1.0  y.max=182
    alpha=10   ext.temp=300
77.
78. MATERIAL  material=4H-SiC  REGION=1  permittivity=9.76    eg300=3.26
    affinity=3.7    egalpha=3.3e-2    egbeta=1.e+5  nc300=1.7e+19  nv300=2.5e+19
    arichn=146  arichp=30  augn=3.e-29  augp=3.e-29  taun0=3.33e-6  taup0=6.7e-7
    nsrhn=3.e+17  nsrhp=3.e+17  edb=0.05  eab=0.20  tcon.polyn  tc.a=0.137534
    tc.b=0.00049662    tc.c=0.000000354  hc.a=2.35  hc.b=1.75e-3  hc.c=1.e-9
    hc.d=-6.6e4
79.
80. ## MODELS USED
81.
82. MODELS  DEVICE=ADIODE   REGION=1 MATERIAL=4H-SiC FERMIDIRAC ANALYTIC CONWELL
    SRH BGN AUGER INCOMPLETE LAT.TEMP  JOULE.HEAT GR.HEAT  PT.HEAT  PRINT
83.
84. ## MOBILITY
85.
86. MOBILITY  DEVICE=ADIODE  material=4H-SiC REGION=1  vsatn=2.2e7  vsatp=2.2e7
    betan=1.2 betap=2  mu1n.caug=40  mu2n.caug=1136  ncritn.caug=2e17
    alphan.caug=-3  betan.caug=-3  gamman.caug=0.0  deltan.caug=0.76    mu1p.caug=20
    mu2p.caug=125  ncritp.caug=1.e19  alphap.caug=-3  betap.caug=-3
    gammap.caug=0.0  deltap.caug=0.5
87.
88. MOBILITY  DEVICE=ADIODE material=4H-SiC REGION=1  n.canali  n.angle=90
    p.angle=90 vsatn=2.2e7  vsatp=2.2e7  betan=1.2 betap=2  mu1n.caug=5
    mu2n.caug=947  ncritn.caug=2e17  alphan.caug=-3  betan.caug=-3  gamman.caug=0.0
    deltan.caug=0.76    mu1p.caug=2.5 mu2p.caug=20  ncritp.caug=1.e19
    alphap.caug=-3  betap.caug=-3  gammap.caug=0.0  deltap.caug=0.5
89.
90. ## Impact Ionization
91.
92. IMPACT  DEVICE=ADIODE   REGION=1  ANISO  E.SIDE  SELB  SIC4H0001  an1=3.44e6
    an2=3.44e6  bn1=2.58e7  bn2=2.58e7  ap1=3.5e6  ap2=3.5e6  bp1=1.7e7
    bp2=1.7e7 opphe=0.106
93.
94. METHOD BLOCK climit=1.e-9 maxtraps=100 itlimit=100   max.temp=1000
    dvmax=1.e8  ir.tol=1.e-35  cr.tol=1.e-35  ix.tol=1.e-35  px.tol=1.e-30
    pr.tol=1.e-45  cx.tol=1.e-30
95.
```

```
96. GO ATLAS SIMFLAGS ="-V 5.18.3.R -P 32 -160"
97.
98. ##### TRANSIENT SIMULATION CIRCUIT #####
99.
100. .BEGIN
101.
102. VDC        1   0    600
103. RSW        1   2    1.e-12  PULSE 1.e-12  1.e18  5us  100ns  100ns  40us  80us
104. R_CHARGE   2   3    500
105. C_BANK     3   0    6u
106. R_SERIES   3   4    0.80
107. L_SERIES   4   5    500n
108. RSWITCH    5   6    1.e18   PULSE 1.e18  1.e-12  10us  100ns  100ns  40us  80us
109. ADIODE     6=anode     0=cathode      infile=SCH_Structure.str     width=1.2e6
110.
111. .NUMERIC   imaxtr=100  dtmax=5.e-8
112. .OPTIONS   m2ln.tr  print  noshift  relpot  write=20
113. .LOAD      infile=SCH_RLC_Bias
114. .SAVE      master=SCH_Transient
115. .LOG       outfile=SCH_Ringdown_5000.log
116. .SAVE      outfile=SCH_Ringdown_5000.str
117.
118. .TRAN  0.01us  45us
119.
120. .END
121.
122. ##### PHYSICS USED #####
123.
124. CONTACT  DEVICE=ADIODE  NAME=ANODE   WORKFUNCTION=5.0  THERMION  PARABOLIC
     EXT.ALPHA=10
125. CONTACT  DEVICE=ADIODE  NAME=CATHODE   EXT.ALPHA=10
126.
127. THERMCONTACT  DEVICE=ADIODE   num=3   x.min=0   x.max=10  y.min=-1.0  y.max=180
     alpha=10   ext.temp=300
128.
129. MATERIAL  material=4H-SiC  REGION=1  permittivity=9.76   eg300=3.26
     affinity=3.7   egalpha=3.3e-2   egbeta=1.e+5  nc300=1.7e+19  nv300=2.5e+19
     arichn=146  arichp=30  augn=3.e-29  augp=3.e-29  taun0=3.33e-6  taup0=6.7e-7
     nsrhn=3.e+17  nsrhp=3.e+17  edb=0.05  eab=0.20  tcon.polyn  tc.a=0.137534
     tc.b=0.00049662   tc.c=0.000000354  hc.a=2.35  hc.b=1.75e-3  hc.c=1.e-9
     hc.d=-6.6e4
130.
131. ## MODELS USED
132.
133. MODELS  DEVICE=ADIODE   REGION=1 MATERIAL=4H-SIC FERMIDIRAC ANALYTIC CONWELL
     SRH BGN AUGER INCOMPLETE LAT.TEMP  JOULE.HEAT GR.HEAT  PT.HEAT  PRINT
134.
135. ## MOBILITY
136.
137. MOBILITY  DEVICE=ADIODE  material=4H-SiC REGION=1  vsatn=2.2e7  vsatp=2.2e7
     betan=1.2 betap=2  mu1n.caug=40  mu2n.caug=1136  ncritn.caug=2e17
     alphan.caug=-3  betan.caug=-3  gamman.caug=0.0  deltan.caug=0.76  mu1p.caug=20
     mu2p.caug=125  ncritp.caug=1.e19  alphap.caug=-3  betap.caug=-3 gammap.caug=0.0
     deltap.caug=0.5
138.
139. MOBILITY  DEVICE=ADIODE  material=4H-SiC REGION=1  n.canali  n.angle=90
     p.angle=90 vsatn=2.2e7  vsatp=2.2e7  betan=1.2 betap=2  mu1n.caug=5
     mu2n.caug=947  ncritn.caug=2e17  alphan.caug=-3  betan.caug=-3  gamman.caug=0.0
     deltan.caug=0.76  mu1p.caug=2.5  mu2p.caug=20  ncritp.caug=1.e19
     alphap.caug=-3  betap.caug=-3  gammap.caug=0.0  deltap.caug=0.5
```

```
140.
141. ## Impact Ionization
142.
143. IMPACT DEVICE=ADIODE   REGION=1  ANISO  E.SIDE  SELB  SIC4H0001  an1=3.44e6
     an2=3.44e6  bn1=2.58e7  bn2=2.58e7  ap1=3.5e6  ap2=3.5e6  bp1=1.7e7  bp2=1.7e7
     opphe=0.106
144.
145. OUTPUT  FLOWLINES  E.MOBILITY
146.
147. METHOD  BLOCK.TRAN climit=1.e-9  maxtraps=100  itlimit=100   max.temp=1000
     dvmax=1.e8  ir.tol=1.e-25  cr.tol=1.e-25  ix.tol=1.e-30  px.tol=1.e-30
     pr.tol=1.e-36  cx.tol=1.e-30
148.
149. GO ATLAS SIMFLAGS ="-V 5.18.3.R -P 32 -128"
150.
151. QUIT
```

Table 2. Code walkthrough: Parallel plane Schottky diode Mixed-Mode simulation.

Line No:	Functionality
1	Configure ATLAS simulator to use version 5.18.3.R, 160-bit extended precision and utilize 32 cores of the CPU if hardware resources are available.
5	Initialize device structure mesh information with width parameter.
7–22	X-axis and Y-axis mesh distribution.
26	Declare 4H-SiC as the material for the area of the semiconductor specified by the x and y coordinates.
30–31	Electrode specifications for the Schottky diode (metal conductor Anode and aluminum Cathode).
35–39	Specify doping profile, type and concentration for different areas of the Schottky diode structure.
41	Save the device structure (*.str*) file on the local hard drive.
45	Initialize ATLAS simulator using GO ATLAS command (same as line 1).
47	Initialize the starting of SPICE-like code in Mixed-Mode steady-state, simulation.
49–56	RLC ring-down circuit description in SPICE-like format
58	Declare the initial node voltage for the RLC ring-down circuit nodes.
59	Set the maximum number of mixed circuit-device iterations to be performed during steady-state analysis (*imaxdc*) to 100.
61–63	Ramp up DC voltage to attain steady state condition, i.e. VDC = 600 V. This can be split into multiple steps.
65	Save log file after steady-state simulation completion.
66	Save file with bias information which will be used for transient simulation.

(Continued)

Table 2. (*Continued*)

Line No:	Functionality
67	Specify Mixed-Mode steady-state simulation conditions. Modified two-level Newton solution method (**m2ln**), disable the shift of voltage for ATLAS devices (**noshift**), and enable the use of relative convergence criteria for potential especially when large voltage biases are involved (**relpot**).
69	Initialize the ending of SPICE-like code in Mixed-Mode steady-state simulation.
73–74	Specify heat transfer coefficient (**ext.alpha**) for the anode and cathode contacts.
76	Specify the thermal boundary for the Schottky diode. Parameters includes boundary dimensions, heat transfer coefficient (**alpha**), and temperature of the thermal boundary (**ext.temp**) which is typically at 300 K.
78	Specify material parameters for 4H-SiC.
82	Specify the various models to be included in the 4H-SiC Schottky diode simulation.
86	Specify parameters for mobility in 4H-SiC.
88	Specify parameters for anisotropic mobility in 4H-SiC.
92	Specify impact ionization parameters for 4H-SiC.
94	Specify the steady-state Block Newton solver type (**BLOCK**) and the tolerance values to be used during the simulation.
96	Initialize ATLAS simulator using GO ATLAS command (same as line 1) for steady-state bias point simulation.
100	Initialize the starting of SPICE-like code in Mixed-Mode transient simulation.
102–109	RLC ring-down circuit description in SPICE-like format. The magnitude of DC voltage source is initialized at 600 V, result of the steady-state simulation performed earlier. Transient parameters have been added to the Resistor which is acting like a switch.
111	Set the maximum number of mixed circuit-device iterations to be performed during transient analysis (**imaxtr**) to 100 and the maximum transient simulation time step (**dtmax**) to 50 ns.
112	Specify Mixed-Mode transient simulation conditions. Modified two-level Newton solution method for transient simulation (**m2ln.tr**), disable the shift of voltage for ATLAS devices (**noshift**), enable the use of relative convergence criteria for potential especially when large voltage biases are involved (**relpot**), and write structure file after every 20 time-step iterations.
113	Load the steady-state simulations results saved in line 66.
114	Save the structure file after every 20 time-step iterations specified in line 112.

(*Continued*)

Table 2.   (*Continued*)

Line No:	Functionality
115	Save log file after the completion of transient simulation.
116	Save the structure file after the completion of transient simulation.
118	Specify the initial time interval of 10 ns and total simulation time of 45 μs.
120	Initialize the ending of SPICE-like code in Mixed-Mode transient simulation.
122–143	Same as line 71 to line 92.
145	Include current flowlines (***FLOWLINES***) and Electron Mobility (***E.MOBILITY***) in the output structure file.
147	Specify the transient Block Newton solver type (***BLOCK.TRAN***) and the tolerance values to be used during the simulation.
149	Initialize ATLAS simulator using GO ATLAS command (same as line 1) for transient simulation. A lower simulation precision of 128-bit has been used due to forward conduction mode of operation.
151	Terminate the simulation.

7.3.2.4.   *Mixed-Mode transient simulation results*

The transient simulation for the parallel plane Schottky diode was carried out for varying magnitudes of peak current density ranging from 500 A/cm^2 to 5000 A/cm^2 in steps of 500. The width parameter was used to change the peak current density through the diode without altering the waveform. In this section, the results pertaining to the maximum current density scenario of 5000 A/cm^2 will be discussed followed by a summary of all the other cases. The anode voltage and current density waveforms are shown in Fig. 8, and the power and energy density waveforms are shown in Fig. 9. The absence of anode voltage overshoot and close overlap between the anode voltage and current density validates the inherently fast switching capability of a Schottky diode as compared to a p-i-n diode. However, due to the absence of conductivity modulation, the ON-state voltage is significantly high, which also reduced the peak current density through the device. At the peak anode current density of 4800 A/cm^2, ON-state voltage drop of 35.8 V was observed across the diode.

This product of anode voltage and current density resulted in a peak power dissipation density of 170 kW/cm^2, and the integration of power density waveform yielded an energy density of 712 mJ/cm^2. Peak lattice temperature of 353 K was observed in the Schottky diode structure during this pulsed operation. The variation of lattice temperature with power

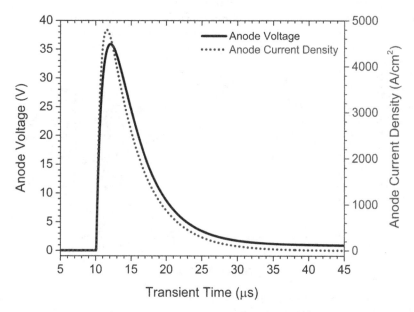

Fig. 8.   Anode voltage (solid) and current density (dotted) waveforms pertaining to 5000 A/cm² peak current density simulation.

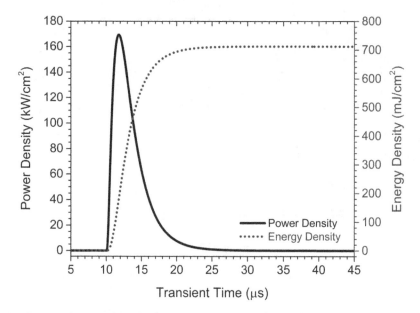

Fig. 9.   Power density (solid) and energy density (dotted) waveforms pertaining to 5000 A/cm² peak current density simulation.

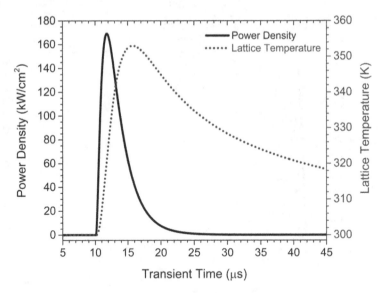

Fig. 10.   Power Density (solid) and lattice temperature (dotted) waveforms pertaining to 5000 A/cm^2 RLC ring-down simulation.

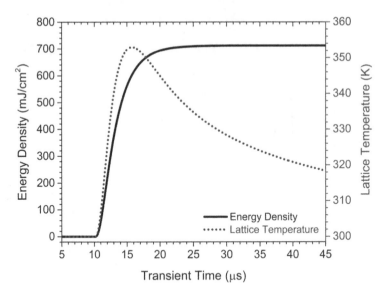

Fig. 11.   Energy density (solid) and lattice temperature (dotted) waveforms pertaining to 5000 A/cm^2 RLC ring-down simulation.

dissipation density and energy density during simulation is shown in Figs. 10 and 11, respectively. The simulation was run for only 45 μs, and hence does not show the complete decay of temperature waveform back to the ambient value. To identify the area of heat dissipation in the Schottky diode structure, intermediate structure files were generated during the simulation (in this scenario, a structure file was generated every 20 time-step iterations). These structure files were manually scanned for the transient time instant which corresponds to the maximum lattice temperature.

The lattice temperature profile of the Schottky diode structure recorded at the time instant corresponding to maximum temperature during RLC ring-down simulation is shown in Figs. 12(a) and 12(b). A maximum

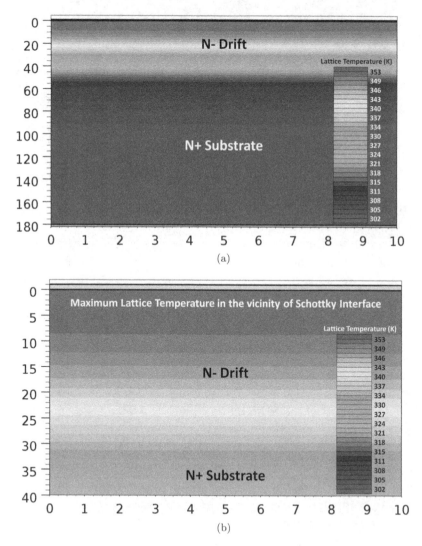

Fig. 12. (a) Lattice temperature profile of parallel plane Schottky diode structure during 5000 A/cm^2 RLC ring-down simulation. (b) Lattice temperature profile of parallel plane Schottky diode structure during 5000 A/cm^2 RLC ring-down simulation (zoomed-in view).

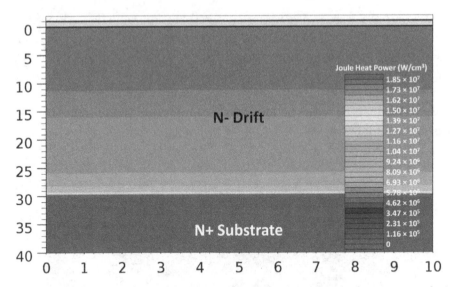

Fig. 13. Joule heat power profile of parallel plane Schottky diode structure during $5000 \, \text{A}/\text{cm}^2$ RLC ring-down simulation (zoomed-in view).

temperature of $353 \, \text{K}$ was observed at the metal–semiconductor/Schottky interface.

To investigate the heat dissipation source, joule heat power profile was extracted from the structure file and is shown in Fig. 13. Since Schottky diodes are majority carrier devices, power dissipation due to carrier generation–recombination is negligible. There is significant heat dissipation in the drift region due to resistive losses, which is in accordance with the lattice temperature profiles shown in Figs. 12(a) and 12(b). The heat power sources are expressed in W/cm^3 in **TonyPlot**, and the contour plot has been scaled to highlight the areas of interest.

The summary of lattice temperature and anode voltage waveforms for the parallel plane Schottky diode for all the values of peak pulsed current density are shown in Figs. 14 and 15, respectively. From the lattice temperature and anode voltage waveforms, it can be inferred that high-voltage SiC Schottky diodes have significantly higher losses at high current density as compared to the p-i-n diode; however, Schottky diodes have negligible/zero reverse recovery as compared to p-i-n diodes, which makes it suitable for high-frequency switching applications.

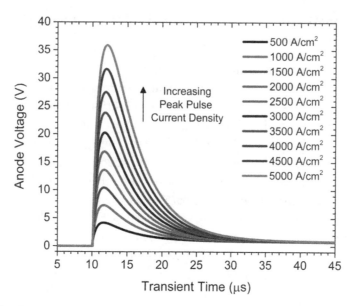

Fig. 14.   Lattice temperature summary of parallel plane SiC Schottky diode structure during RLC ring-down simulation.

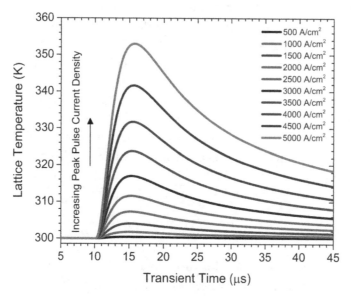

Fig. 15.   Anode voltage summary of parallel plane SiC Schottky diode structure during RLC ring-down simulation.

7.3.3.   Schottky diode structure with planar junction termination (half-cell)

Parallel plane structure is an ideal design which is good for simulation and basic understanding of device performance. However, it is not a practical design that can be fabricated into a production device. Almost ideal breakdown voltage can be obtained using a parallel plane structure, whereas the planar junction has a lower breakdown voltage due to electric field enhancement at the edge of the cylindrical junction. *The Schottky diode structure discussed in this section uses a field termination design which is based on a field termination scheme known as Hybrid Junction Termination Extension (Hybrid JTE) designed and developed by W. Sung and B. J. Baliga.*[7,8] A detailed description of this termination technique can be found in the literature review. In this Schottky diode design, the P+ field JTE had a junction depth of $2\,\mu$m and was doped with a peak acceptor concentration of $1.0 \times 10^{18}\,\text{cm}^{-3}$ using a Gaussian profile. The floating field rings within the JTE had a junction depth of $1\,\mu$m and were heavily doped with a peak acceptor concentration of $1.0 \times 10^{20}\,\text{cm}^{-3}$ using a Gaussian profile. The N− epitaxial/drift region was $30\,\mu$m thick with a doping concentration of $3.2 \times 10^{15}\,\text{cm}^{-3}$. The N+ substrate had a thickness of $150\,\mu$m and doping concentration of $1.0 \times 10^{20}\,\text{cm}^{-3}$. The anode Schottky metal was configured to be a conductor with a workfunction of $5.0\,\text{eV}$ and aluminum was used for the cathode ohmic contact. Due to the presence of the Hybrid JTE, the 2D device structure had a cell pitch of $16\,\mu$m and an active area of $10\,\mu\text{m}^2$ based on the $10\,\mu$m wide Schottky anode region. A $1\,\mu$m thick oxide layer is used as the Inter-Layer Dielectric (ILD) over the JTE area.

Due to the large substrate thickness as compared to the drift layer, the complete device structure designed using Silvaco© ATLAS has been split into Figs. 16(a) and 16(b), respectively. The Gaussian doping profile has been used for the Hybrid JTE scheme which can be seen in Fig. 16(b).

7.3.3.1.   *Steady-state simulation*

This section will discuss the forward conduction and reverse breakdown current density versus anode voltage $(J{-}V)$ characteristics at 27°C, 75°C, 125°C, and 175°C device temperature. The steady-state simulation code is similar to the one used for the parallel plane diode except for change in device mesh profile and the inclusion of oxide material. The following code was used to simulate the Schottky diode $J{-}V$ characteristics which includes forward

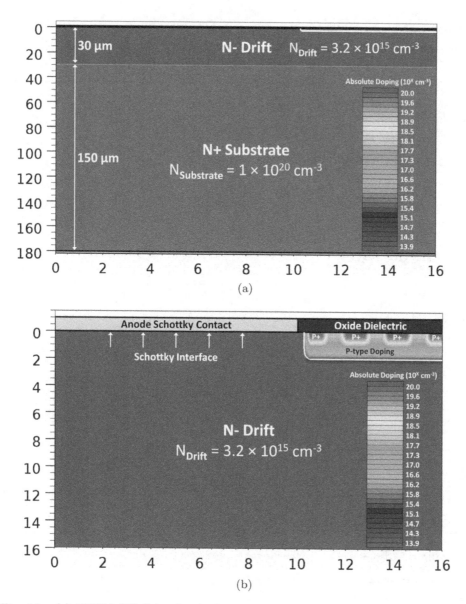

Fig. 16. (a) 3300 V SiC Schottky diode planar junction half-cell structure designed in Silvaco© ATLAS. (b) 3300 V SiC Schottky diode planar junction half-cell structure designed in Silvaco© ATLAS (zoomed-in view).

conduction and reverse breakdown. A brief explanation of the steady-state simulation program is provided in the code walkthrough (Table 3).

```
Sample code: Planar junction SiC Schottky diode forward and breakdown J-V characteristics
@ 27°C

1.   GO ATLAS SIMFLAGS ="-V 5.18.3.R -P 32 -160"
2.
3.   ##### 3300V PLANAR JUNCTION SCHOTTKY DIODE - HALF CELL @ 27C #####
4.
5.   MESH
6.
7.   ## X-MESH
8.
9.   X.MESH  loc=0.0    spac=0.5
10.  X.MESH  loc=9.0    spac=0.5
11.  X.MESH  loc=10.0   spac=0.25
12.  X.MESH  loc=16.0   spac=0.25
13.
14.  ## Y-MESH
15.
16.  Y.MESH  loc=-1.0   spac=0.25
17.  Y.MESH  loc=0.0    spac=0.25
18.  Y.MESH  loc=0.25   spac=0.1
19.  Y.MESH  loc=2.1    spac=0.01
20.  Y.MESH  loc=28.0   spac=10.0
21.  Y.MESH  loc=30.1   spac=0.2
22.  Y.MESH  loc=31.0   spac=1.0
23.  Y.MESH  loc=32.0   spac=20
24.  Y.MESH  loc=178.0  spac=20
25.  Y.MESH  loc=180.0  spac=1.0
26.  Y.MESH  loc=182.0  spac=1.0
27.
28.  ## Defining 4H-SiC and Oxide Region
29.
30.  REGION  num=1  material=OXIDE   y.max=0
31.  REGION  num=2  material=4H-SiC  x.min=0  x.max=16  y.min=0  y.max=180
32.
33.  ## Electrode
34.
35.  ELECTRODE  name=anode    material=CONDUCTOR  x.min=0   x.max=10  y.max=0
36.  ELECTRODE  name=cathode  material=ALUMINUM   y.min=180  y.max=182
37.
38.  ## Doping Distribution
39.
40.  ## Bulk Doping
41.  DOPING  uniform  n.type  conc=3.2e15  REGION=2
42.
43.  ## P+ JTE and Field Rings
44.  DOPING  gauss p.type conc=1.e18  x.min=10.50  junc=2.0       rat=0.1
45.  DOPING  gauss p.type conc=1.e20  x.min=10.50  x.max=11.00  junc=1.0  rat=0.1
46.  DOPING  gauss p.type conc=1.e20  x.min=12.00  x.max=12.75  junc=1.0  rat=0.1
47.  DOPING  gauss p.type conc=1.e20  x.min=13.75  x.max=14.50  junc=1.0  rat=0.1
48.  DOPING  gauss p.type conc=1.e20  x.min=15.50  x.max=16     junc=1.0  rat=0.1
49.
50.  ## N+ Substrate Region Doping
51.  DOPING  uniform  n.type  conc=1.e20  y.min=30  y.max=180
```

```
52.
53. SAVE  outf=Schottky_Planar_FFR_27C.str  master.out
54.
55. MATERIAL  material=4H-SiC REGION=2 permittivity=9.76  eg300=3.26
    affinity=3.7  egalpha=3.3e-2  egbeta=1.e+5  nc300=1.7e+19  nv300=2.5e+19
    arichn=146  arichp=30  augn=3.e-29  augp=3.e-29  taun0=3.33e-6  taup0=6.7e-7
    nsrhn=3.e+17  nsrhp=3.e+17  edb=0.05  eab=0.20
56.
57. CONTACT  NAME=ANODE   WORKFUNCTION=5.0   THERMION  PARABOLIC
58.
59. ## MODELS USED
60.
61. MODELS  REGION=2  MATERIAL=4H-SIC FERMIDIRAC ANALYTIC CONWELL INCOMPLETE
    SRH BGN AUGER TEMP=300 PRINT
62.
63. ## MOBILITY
64.
65. MOBILITY  material=4H-SiC REGION=2 vsatn=2.2e7 vsatp=2.2e7 betan=1.2
    betap=2 mu1n.caug=40 mu2n.caug=1136 ncritn.caug=2e17 alphan.caug=-3
    betan.caug=-3 gamman.caug=0.0 deltan.caug=0.76  mu1p.caug=20 mu2p.caug=125
    ncritp.caug=1.e19 alphap.caug=-3 betap.caug=-3 gammap.caug=0.0
    deltap.caug=0.5
66.
67. IMPACT  REGION=2 ANISO E.SIDE SELB SIC4H0001 an1=3.44e6  an2=3.44e6
    bn1=2.58e7 bn2=2.58e7 ap1=3.5e6 ap2=3.5e6 bp1=1.7e7  bp2=1.7e7 opphe=0.106
68.
69. METHOD  NEWTON AUTONR  climit=1.e-9 maxtraps=40 itlimit=40   dvmax=1.e8
    ir.tol=1.e-35  cr.tol=1.e-35  ix.tol=1.e-35  px.tol=1.e-30  pr.tol=1.e-45
    cx.tol=1.e-30
70.
71. OUTPUT  FLOWLINES
72.
73. LOG  outf=SCH_Forward_27C.log
74.
75. SOLVE init
76. SOLVE vanode=0.05  vstep=0.05  vfinal=2.0     name=anode
77. SOLVE vstep=0.1                vfinal=4.0     name=anode
78.
79. SAVE  outf=SCH_Forward_27C.str
80.
81. LOG  outf=SCH_Reverse_27C.log
82.
83. SOLVE  init
84. SOLVE  vanode=-0.2  vstep=-0.2    vfinal=-2.0    name=anode
85. SOLVE  vstep=-2     vfinal=-20    name=anode
86. SOLVE  vstep=-5     vfinal=-100   name=anode
87. SOLVE  vstep=-10    vfinal=-1000  name=anode
88. SOLVE  vstep=-25    vfinal=-4000  name=anode
89. SOLVE  vstep=-10    vfinal=-4200  name=anode
90. SOLVE  vstep=-2     vfinal=-4240  name=anode
91. SOLVE  vstep=-0.5   vfinal=-4400  name=anode  compl=1e-16 cname=anode  previous
92.
93. SAVE  outf=SCH_Reverse_27C.str
94.
95. QUIT
```

Table 3. Code walkthrough: Planar junction Schottky diode half-cell forward and breakdown $J-V$ characteristics.

Line No:	Functionality
1	Configure ATLAS simulator to use 160-bit extended precision and utilize 32 cores of the CPU if hardware resources are available. The version of ATLAS to be used by the simulator is set to 5.18.3.R using the -V option in the simflags command.
5	Initialize device structure mesh information.
7–26	X-axis and Y-axis mesh distribution.
30–31	Declare Oxide and 4H-SiC as the material for the area of the semiconductor specified by the x and y coordinates.
35–36	Electrode specifications for the Schottky diode (metal conductor Anode and aluminum Cathode).
40–51	Specify doping profile, type, and concentration for different areas of the Schottky diode structure.
53	Save the device structure (**.str**) file on the local hard drive. The device structure can be viewed by opening the file via **TonyPlot** to troubleshoot/optimize the structure.
55	Specify material parameters for 4H-SiC. Detailed description of these parameters is available in the Silvaco© ATLAS manual. The values for these parameters can either be obtained via material research or from literature.
57	Specify Schottky metal workfunction and model/parameters for thermionic emission and parabolic field emission using **Contact** statement.
61	Specify the various models to be included in the 4H-SiC Schottky diode simulation.
65	Specify mobility parameters for 4H-SiC. Detailed description of these parameters is available in the Silvaco© ATLAS manual. The values for these parameters can either be obtained via material research or from literature.
67	Specify Impact Ionization parameters for 4H-SiC. This statement is mandatory to obtain device breakdown characteristics.
69	Specify the solver type and the tolerance values to be used during the simulation. This is an extremely critical statement which can alter the simulation outcome.
71	Include current flowlines in the output structure file.
73	Save the simulation log (**.log**) file on the local hard drive. The simulation results can be viewed by opening the file via **TonyPlot**.
75–77	Solve for the initial bias conditions for the simulation followed by positive sweep of anode voltage for steady-state forward characteristics.

(Continued)

Table 3. (*Continued*)

Line No:	Functionality
79	Save the post-forward-bias simulation device structure (*.str*) file on the local hard drive. Saving the file at this stage of the simulation will enable the user to visualize the variation in various electrothermal parameters within the device structure introduced due to the particular simulation.
81	Save the reverse-bias simulation log (*.log*) file on the local hard drive. The simulation results can be viewed by opening the file via **TonyPlot**.
83–91	Use solve statement to increment the negative anode voltage in discrete steps. The compliance parameter (**compl**) in line 91 forces the simulator to proceed to the next line once the anode current reaches the specified compliance value. This is important, especially in breakdown simulation because once the device enters the breakdown regime, it is not necessary to run the simulation for higher magnitude of current since the breakdown voltage would have already been determined.
93	Save the post-reverse-bias simulation device structure (*.str*) file on the local hard drive. Saving the file at this stage of the simulation will enable the user to visualize the variation in various electrothermal parameters within the device structure introduced due to the particular simulation.
95	Terminate the simulation.

7.3.3.2. *Steady-state simulation results*

The forward conduction $J-V$ characteristics for the 3300 V SiC Schottky diode with planar junction termination on a linear and semi-log scale are shown in Figs. 17(a) and 17(b), respectively. The simulations were carried out at varying lattice temperature values like the parallel plane diode simulation. At an ON-state current density of 100 A/cm^2, voltage drop of 1.37 V was observed across the diode at 27°C device temperature, which is lower than voltage drop obtained for the parallel plane structure at the same current density. This is due to the wider cell pitch which helps in reducing the ON-state resistance despite having the same active area.

The reverse-bias breakdown $J-V$ characteristics for varying lattice temperature conditions are shown in Fig. 18. Breakdown voltage of 4315 V was obtained for the Schottky diode structure with planar junction termination at 27°C device temperature.

The electric field distribution in the Schottky diode structure during breakdown are shown in the contour plot in Figs. 19(a) and 19(b) (Images have been scaled to highlight the area of interest). Maximum electric field of 2.76 MV/cm was observed at the edge of the junction termination in Fig. 19(b), which is also the point of breakdown. The presence of the Hybrid

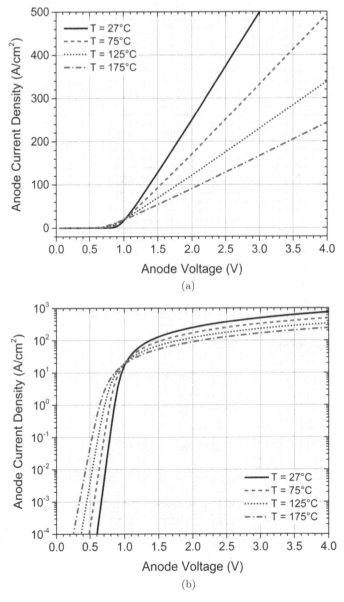

Fig. 17. (a) Forward $J-V$ characteristics for the SiC planar junction Schottky diode half-cell structure on a linear scale. (b) Forward $J-V$ characteristics for the SiC planar junction Schottky diode half-cell structure on a semi-log scale.

JTE scheme helps in the distribution of electric field and diverts the electric field away from the Schottky interface. From a practical design standpoint, device breakdown should not occur through the junction termination/field rings. However, obtaining diode breakdown through the Schottky contact

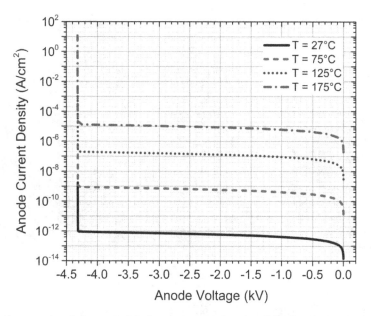

Fig. 18. Reverse breakdown $J-V$ characteristics for the SiC planar junction Schottky diode half-cell structure on a semi-log scale.

in a non-parallel plane diode structure is extremely difficult in a TCAD simulation due to localized field enhancement at the edges of the p-type region which is generally used for junction termination/floating field rings. Since device breakdown is occurring at the p–n junction, there is an abrupt increase in the diode current in case of a planar junction structure (Fig. 18) as compared to a gradual increase in the diode current in a parallel plane structure (Fig. 5).

 The magnitude of device current post-breakdown is dependent on the area of electrode available for current conduction. This is important especially for Schottky diode structures where breakdown occurs through the termination instead of the active area. A smaller electrode area would result in extremely high current density which causes the simulator to re-iterate through the same voltage bias point due to non-convergence.

1D electric field profile as a function of device depth is shown in Figs. 20(a) and 20(b). The plot has been scaled to highlight the region of interest. The electric field data was extracted for the following points: anode

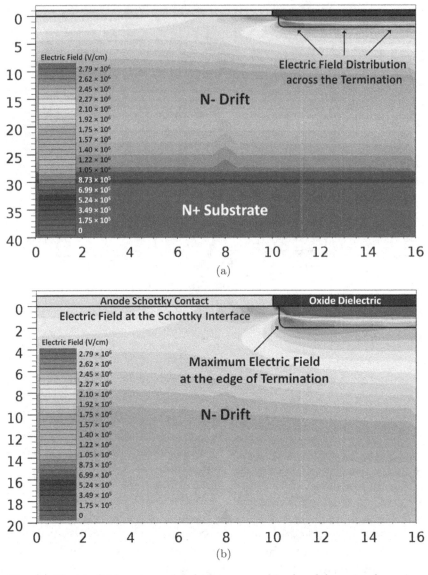

Fig. 19.   (a) Electric field contour plot during reverse-bias breakdown in planar junction Schottky diode half-cell structure. (b) Electric field contour plot during reverse-bias breakdown in planar junction Schottky diode half-cell structure (zoomed-in view).

Schottky contact active area ($x = 2.5\,\mu\mathrm{m}$, $x = 5\,\mu\mathrm{m}$, and $x = 7.5\,\mu\mathrm{m}$), edge of the active area Hybrid JTE region which is also the point of breakdown ($x = 10.5\,\mu\mathrm{m}$), and extension of the Hybrid JTE region ($x = 12.5\,\mu\mathrm{m}$ and $x = 15\,\mu\mathrm{m}$) using the **cutline** feature in **TonyPlot**. To have a closer look at the electric field distribution in the aforementioned points, individual

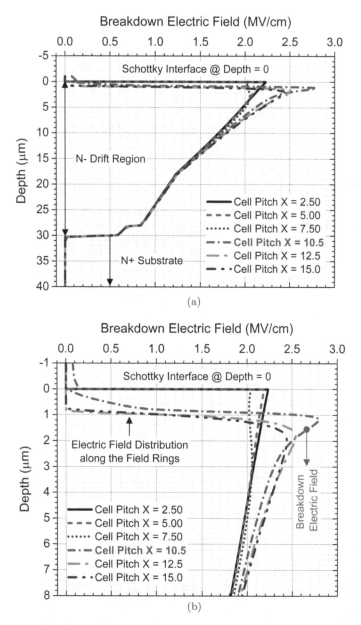

Fig. 20. (a) 1D electric field profile as a function of device depth at varying points across the diode active area/cell pitch. (b) 1D electric field profile as a function of device depth at varying points across the diode active area/cell pitch (zoomed-in view).

electric field profiles are shown in Fig. 20(b), which is a zoomed-in version of Fig. 20(a). It can be seen from Fig. 20(a) and 20(b) that even though there is a reduction in the magnitude of electric field at the Schottky interface, it is still not far away from the breakdown electric field.

7.3.3.3.   *Mixed-Mode transient simulation*

The Mixed-Mode transient simulation was performed using the RLC ring-down circuit.[6] The simulation code was similar to that used in the parallel plane diode structure with changes pertaining to the planar junction structure. These changes include device mesh profile, inclusion of floating field rings, and dimensions of the thermal boundary using **_Thermcontact_** statement. The following code was used to simulate the Schottky diode for a peak forward current density of $2000\,\text{A}/\text{cm}^2$ under pulsed condition. A brief explanation of the Mixed-Mode simulation program is provided in the code walkthrough (Table 4).

```
Sample code: Planar junction SiC Schottky diode half-cell transient simulation

1.   GO ATLAS SIMFLAGS ="-V 5.18.3.R -P 32 -160"
2.
3.   ##### 3300V PLANAR JUNCTION SCHOTTKY DIODE RLC RINGDOWN PULSE 2000A/cm2 #####
4.
5.   MESH  WIDTH=3.e6
6.
7.   ## X-MESH
8.
9.   X.MESH  loc=0.0   spac=0.5
10.  X.MESH  loc=9.0   spac=0.5
11.  X.MESH  loc=10.0  spac=0.25
12.  X.MESH  loc=16.0  spac=0.25
13.
14.  ## Y-MESH
15.
16.  Y.MESH  loc=-1.0     spac=0.25
17.  Y.MESH  loc=0.0      spac=0.25
18.  Y.MESH  loc=0.25     spac=0.1
19.  Y.MESH  loc=2.1      spac=0.01
20.  Y.MESH  loc=28.0     spac=10.0
21.  Y.MESH  loc=30.1     spac=0.2
22.  Y.MESH  loc=31.0     spac=1.0
23.  Y.MESH  loc=32.0     spac=20
24.  Y.MESH  loc=178.0    spac=20
25.  Y.MESH  loc=180.0    spac=1.0
26.  Y.MESH  loc=182.0    spac=1.0
27.
28.  ## Defining 4H-SiC and Oxide Regions
29.
30.  REGION  num=1  material=OXIDE    y.max=0
31.  REGION  num=2  material=4H-SiC   x.min=0   x.max=16   y.min=0   y.max=180
32.
33.  ## Electrode
34.
35.  ELECTRODE  name=anode    material=CONDUCTOR   x.min=0    x.max=10    y.max=0
36.  ELECTRODE  name=cathode  material=ALUMINUM    y.min=180  y.max=182
37.
38.  ## Doping Distribution
39.
40.  ## Bulk Doping
41.  DOPING  uniform  n.type  conc=3.2e15  REGION=2
42.
```

```
43. ## P+ Field Rings
44. DOPING  gauss p.type conc=1.e18  x.min=10.50  junc=2.0   rat=0.1
45. DOPING  gauss p.type conc=1.e20  x.min=10.50  x.max=11.00   junc=1.0  rat=0.1
46. DOPING  gauss p.type conc=1.e20  x.min=12.00  x.max=12.75   junc=1.0  rat=0.1
47. DOPING  gauss p.type conc=1.e20  x.min=13.75  x.max=14.50   junc=1.0  rat=0.1
48. DOPING  gauss p.type conc=1.e20  x.min=15.50  x.max=16      junc=1.0  rat=0.1
49.
50. ## N+ Substrate Region Doping
51. DOPING  uniform  n.type   conc=1.e20   y.min=30    y.max=180
52.
53. SAVE outf=SCH_Structure.str  master.out
54.
55. ##### STEADY STATE SIMULATION CIRCUIT #####
56.
57. GO ATLAS SIMFLAGS ="-V 5.18.3.R -P 32 -160"
58.
59. .BEGIN
60.
61. VDC           1    0    0
62. RSW           1    2    1.e-12
63. R_CHARGE      2    3    500
64. C_BANK        3    0    6u
65. R_SERIES      3    4    0.80
66. L_SERIES      4    5    500n
67. RSWITCH       5    6    1.e18
68. ADIODE        6=anode   0=cathode    infile=SCH_Structure.str    width=3.e6
69.
70. .NODESET  v(1)=0  v(2)=0  v(3)=0  v(4)=0  v(5)=0   v(6)=0
71. .NUMERIC  imaxdc=100
72.
73. .DC   VDC   0.   10.   0.25
74. .DC   VDC   10.  100.  5.
75. .DC   VDC   100. 600.  20.
76.
77. .LOG  outfile=SCH_DC_log
78. .SAVE outfile=SCH_RLC_Bias
79. .OPTIONS m2ln print noshift relpot
80.
81. .END
82.
83. ##### PHYSICS USED #####
84.
85. CONTACT  DEVICE=ADIODE  NAME=ANODE   WORKFUNCTION=5.0  THERMION  PARABOLIC
    EXT.ALPHA=10
86. CONTACT  DEVICE=ADIODE  NAME=CATHODE   EXT.ALPHA=10
87.
88. THERMCONTACT  DEVICE=ADIODE  num=3   x.min=0  x.max=16  y.min=-1.0  y.max=182
    alpha=10   ext.temp=300
89.
90. MATERIAL  material=4H-SiC  REGION=2  permittivity=9.76   eg300=3.26
    affinity=3.7  egalpha=3.3e-2  egbeta=1.e+5  nc300=1.7e+19  nv300=2.5e+19
    arichn=146  arichp=30  augn=3.e-29  augp=3.e-29  taun0=3.33e-6  taup0=6.7e-7
    nsrhn=3.e+17  nsrhp=3.e+17  edb=0.05  eab=0.20  tcon.polyn  tc.a=0.137534
    tc.b=0.00049662   tc.c=0.000000354  hc.a=2.35  hc.b=1.75e-3  hc.c=1.e-9
    hc.d=-6.6e4
91.
92. ## MODELS USED
93.
94. MODELS  DEVICE=ADIODE   REGION=2 MATERIAL=4H-SiC FERMIDIRAC ANALYTIC CONWELL
    SRH BGN AUGER INCOMPLETE LAT.TEMP  JOULE.HEAT GR.HEAT  PT.HEAT   PRINT
```

```
95.
96. ## MOBILITY
97.
98. MOBILITY  DEVICE=ADIODE  material=4H-SiC REGION=2  vsatn=2.2e7  vsatp=2.2e7
      betan=1.2 betap=2  mu1n.caug=40  mu2n.caug=1136  ncritn.caug=2e17
      alphan.caug=-3  betan.caug=-3  gamman.caug=0.0  deltan.caug=0.76  mu1p.caug=20
      mu2p.caug=125  ncritp.caug=1.e19  alphap.caug=-3  betap.caug=-3 gammap.caug=0.0
      deltap.caug=0.5
99.
100. MOBILITY  DEVICE=ADIODE  material=4H-SiC REGION=2  n.canali  n.angle=90
      p.angle=90 vsatn=2.2e7  vsatp=2.2e7  betan=1.2 betap=2  mu1n.caug=5
      mu2n.caug=947  ncritn.caug=2e17  alphan.caug=-3  betan.caug=-3  gamman.caug=0.0
      deltan.caug=0.76  mu1p.caug=2.5  mu2p.caug=20  ncritp.caug=1.e19
      alphap.caug=-3  betap.caug=-3  gammap.caug=0.0  deltap.caug=0.5
101.
102. ## Impact Ionization
103.
104. IMPACT  DEVICE=ADIODE   REGION=2  ANISO  E.SIDE  SELB  SIC4H0001  an1=3.44e6
      an2=3.44e6  bn1=2.58e7  bn2=2.58e7  ap1=3.5e6  ap2=3.5e6  bp1=1.7e7  bp2=1.7e7
      opphe=0.106
105.
106. METHOD  BLOCK climit=1.e-9  maxtraps=100  itlimit=100   max.temp=1000
      dvmax=1.e8  ir.tol=1.e-35  cr.tol=1.e-35  ix.tol=1.e-35  px.tol=1.e-30
      pr.tol=1.e-45  cx.tol=1.e-30
107.
108. GO ATLAS SIMFLAGS ="-V 5.18.3.R -P 32 -160"
109.
110. ##### TRANSIENT SIMULATION CIRCUIT #####
111.
112. .BEGIN
113.
114. VDC       1   0   600
115. RSW       1   2   1.e-12  PULSE   1.e-12  1.e18  5us  100ns  100ns  40us  80us
116. R_CHARGE  2   3   500
117. C_BANK    3   0   6u
118. R_SERIES  3   4   0.80
119. L_SERIES  4   5   500n
120. RSWITCH   5   6   1.e18  PULSE  1.e18  1.e-12  10us  100ns  100ns  40us  80us
121. ADIODE    6=anode   0=cathode    infile=SCH_Structure.str    width=3.e6
122.
123. .NUMERIC  imaxtr=100  dtmax=1.e-7
124. .OPTIONS  m2ln.tr  print  noshift  relpot  write=50
125. .LOAD     infile=SCH_RLC_Bias
126. .SAVE     master=SCH_Transient
127. .LOG      outfile=SCH_Ringdown_2000.log
128. .SAVE     outfile=SCH_Ringdown_2000.str
129.
130. .TRAN  0.01us 45us
131.
132. .END
133.
134. ##### PHYSICS USED #####
135.
136. CONTACT DEVICE=ADIODE NAME=ANODE   WORKFUNCTION=5.0  THERMION  PARABOLIC
      EXT.ALPHA=10
137. CONTACT DEVICE=ADIODE NAME=CATHODE   EXT.ALPHA=10
138.
139. THERMCONTACT DEVICE=ADIODE   num=3   x.min=0   x.max=16  y.min=-1.0  y.max=182
      alpha=10   ext.temp=300
140.
```

```
141. MATERIAL  material=4H-SiC  REGION=2  permittivity=9.76    eg300=3.26
     affinity=3.7    egalpha=3.3e-2  egbeta=1.e+5  nc300=1.7e+19  nv300=2.5e+19
     arichn=146  arichp=30  augn=3.e-29  augp=3.e-29  taun0=3.33e-6  taup0=6.7e-7
     nsrhn=3.e+17  nsrhp=3.e+17  edb=0.05  eab=0.20  tcon.polyn  tc.a=0.137534
     tc.b=0.00049662    tc.c=0.000000354  hc.a=2.35  hc.b=1.75e-3  hc.c=1.e-9
     hc.d=-6.6e4
142.
143. ## MODELS USED
144.
145. MODELS  DEVICE=ADIODE   REGION=2  MATERIAL=4H-SiC  FERMIDIRAC  ANALYTIC  CONWELL
     SRH  BGN  AUGER  INCOMPLETE  LAT.TEMP  JOULE.HEAT  GR.HEAT  PT.HEAT  PRINT
146.
147. ## MOBILITY
148.
149. MOBILITY  DEVICE=ADIODE  material=4H-SiC  REGION=2   vsatn=2.2e7  vsatp=2.2e7
     betan=1.2  betap=2  mu1n.caug=40  mu2n.caug=1136  ncritn.caug=2e17
     alphan.caug=-3  betan.caug=-3  gamman.caug=0.0  deltan.caug=0.76   mu1p.caug=20
     mu2p.caug=125  ncritp.caug=1.e19  alphap.caug=-3  betap.caug=-3
     gammap.caug=0.0  deltap.caug=0.5
150.
151. MOBILITY  DEVICE=ADIODE  material=4H-SiC  REGION=2  n.canali  n.angle=90
     p.angle=90  vsatn=2.2e7  vsatp=2.2e7  betan=1.2  betap=2  mu1n.caug=5
     mu2n.caug=947  ncritn.caug=2e17  alphan.caug=-3  betan.caug=-3  gamman.caug=0.0
     deltan.caug=0.76   mu1p.caug=2.5  mu2p.caug=20  ncritp.caug=1.e19
     alphap.caug=-3  betap.caug=-3  gammap.caug=0.0  deltap.caug=0.5
152.
153. ## Impact Ionization
154.
155. IMPACT  DEVICE=ADIODE  REGION=2  ANISO  E.SIDE  SELB  SIC4H0001  an1=3.44e6
     an2=3.44e6  bn1=2.58e7  bn2=2.58e7  ap1=3.5e6  ap2=3.5e6  bp1=1.7e7  bp2=1.7e7
     opphe=0.106
156.
157. OUTPUT  FLOWLINES  E.MOBILITY
158.
159. METHOD  BLOCK.TRAN  climit=1.e-9  maxtraps=100  itlimit=100   max.temp=1000
     dvmax=1.e8  ir.tol=1.e-25  cr.tol=1.e-25  ix.tol=1.e-30  px.tol=1.e-30
     pr.tol=1.e-36  cx.tol=1.e-30
160.
161. GO ATLAS SIMFLAGS ="-V 5.18.3.R -P 32 -128"
162.
163. QUIT
```

Table 4. Code walkthrough: Planar junction Schottky diode half-cell Mixed-Mode simulation.

Line No:	Functionality
1	Configure ATLAS simulator to use version 5.18.3.R, 160-bit extended precision and utilize 32 cores of the CPU if hardware resources are available.
5	Initialize device structure mesh information with width parameter.
7–26	X-axis and Y-axis mesh distribution.
30–31	Declare Oxide and 4H-SiC as the material for the area of the semiconductor specified by the x and y coordinates.

(*Continued*)

Table 4.   (*Continued*)

Line No:	Functionality
35–36	Electrode specifications for the Schottky diode (metal conductor anode and aluminum Cathode).
40–51	Specify doping profile, type, and concentration for different areas of the Schottky diode structure.
53	Save the device structure (**.str**) file on the local hard drive.
57	Initialize ATLAS simulator using GO ATLAS command (same as line 1).
59	Initialize the starting of SPICE-like code in Mixed-Mode steady-state simulation.
61–68	RLC ring-down circuit description in SPICE-like format.
70	Declare the initial node voltage for the RLC ring-down circuit nodes.
71	Set the maximum number of mixed circuit-device iterations to be performed during steady-state analysis (**imaxdc**) to 100.
73–75	Ramp up DC voltage to attain steady-state condition, i.e. VDC = 600 V. This can be split into multiple steps.
77	Save log file after steady-state simulation completion.
78	Save file with bias information which will be used for transient simulation.
79	Specify Mixed-Mode steady-state simulation conditions. Modified two-level Newton solution method (**m2ln**), disable the shift of voltage for ATLAS devices (**noshift**), and enable the use of relative convergence criteria for potential especially when large voltage biases are involved (**relpot**).
81	Initialize the ending of SPICE-like code in Mixed-Mode steady-state simulation.
85–86	Specify heat transfer coefficient (**ext.alpha**) for the anode and cathode contacts.
88	Specify the thermal boundary for the Schottky diode. Parameters includes boundary dimensions, heat transfer coefficient (**alpha**), and temperature of the thermal boundary (**ext.temp**) which is typically at 300 K.
90	Specify material parameters for 4H-SiC.
94	Specify the various models to be included in the 4H-SiC Schottky diode simulation.
98	Specify parameters for mobility in 4H-SiC.
100	Specify parameters for anisotropic mobility in 4H-SiC.
104	Specify impact ionization parameters for 4H-SiC.
106	Specify the steady-state Block Newton solver type (**BLOCK**) and the tolerance values to be used during the simulation.
108	Initialize ATLAS simulator using GO ATLAS command (same as line 1) for steady-state bias point simulation.

(*Continued*)

Table 4. (*Continued*)

Line No:	Functionality
112	Initialize the starting of SPICE-like code in Mixed-Mode transient simulation.
114–121	RLC ring-down circuit description in SPICE-like format. The magnitude of DC voltage source is initialized at 600 V, result of the steady-state simulation performed earlier. Transient parameters have been added to the Resistor which is acting like a switch.
123	Set the maximum number of mixed circuit-device iterations to be performed during transient analysis (*imaxtr*) to 100 and the maximum transient simulation time step (*dtmax*) to 100 ns.
124	Specify Mixed-Mode transient simulation conditions. Modified two-level Newton solution method for transient simulation (*m2ln.tr*), disable the shift of voltage for ATLAS devices (*noshift*), enable the use of relative convergence criteria for potential especially when large voltage biases are involved (*relpot*), and write structure file after every 50 time-step iterations.
125	Load the steady-state simulations results saved in line 78.
126	Save the structure file after every 50 time-step iterations specified in line 124.
127	Save log file after the completion of transient simulation.
128	Save the structure file after the completion of transient simulation.
130	Specify the initial time interval of 10 ns and total simulation time of 45 μs.
132	Initialize the ending of SPICE-like code in Mixed-Mode transient simulation.
136–155	Same as line 85 to line 104.
157	Include current flowlines (*FLOWLINES*) and Electron Mobility (*E.MOBILITY*) in the output structure file.
159	Specify the transient Block Newton solver type (*BLOCK.TRAN*) and the tolerance values to be used during the simulation.
161	Initialize ATLAS simulator using GO ATLAS command (same as line 1) for transient simulation. A lower simulation precision of 128-bit has been used due to forward conduction mode of operation.
163	Terminate the simulation.

7.3.3.4. *Mixed-Mode transient simulation results*

The transient simulation for the planar junction Schottky diode half-cell structure was carried out for varying magnitudes of peak current density ranging from $500\,\text{A/cm}^2$ to $2000\,\text{A/cm}^2$ in steps of 500. The reason behind limiting the peak pulse current density to $2000\,\text{A/cm}^2$ will be discussed at the end of this chapter. The width parameter was used to change the peak current density through the diode without altering the waveform. In this

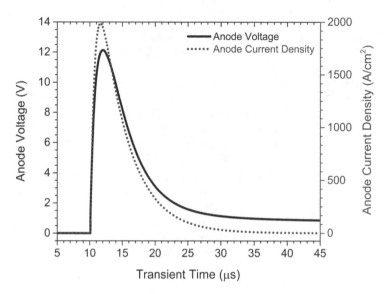

Fig. 21. Anode voltage (solid) and current density (dotted) waveforms pertaining to $2000 \, \text{A/cm}^2$ peak current density simulation.

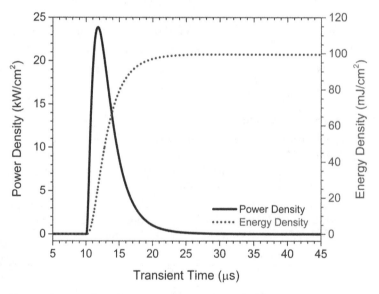

Fig. 22. Power density (solid) and energy density (dotted) waveforms pertaining to $2000 \, \text{A/cm}^2$ peak current density simulation.

section, the results pertaining to the maximum current density scenario of $2000 \, \text{A/cm}^2$ will be discussed followed by a summary of all the other cases. The anode voltage and current density waveforms are shown in Fig. 21, and the power and energy density waveforms are shown in Fig. 22.

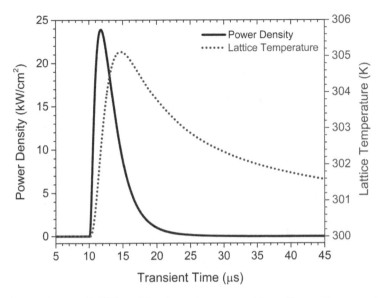

Fig. 23. Power density (solid) and lattice temperature (dotted) waveforms pertaining to 2000 A/cm² peak current density simulation.

Peak voltage drop of 12.1 V was observed across the Schottky diode at peak current density of 2000 A/cm², which corresponds to a peak power dissipation density of 23.8 kW/cm². Integration of the power density waveform yielded an energy density of 99.4 mJ/cm². Peak lattice temperature of 305.1 K was observed in the Schottky diode structure during this pulsed operation. The variation of lattice temperature with power dissipation density and energy density during simulation is shown in Figs. 23 and 24, respectively. The simulation was run for only 45 μs, and hence does not show the complete decay of temperature waveform back to the ambient value. To identify the area of heat dissipation in the Schottky diode structure, intermediate structure files were generated during the simulation. These structure files were manually scanned for the transient time instant which corresponds to the maximum lattice temperature.

The lattice temperature profile of the planar junction Schottky diode structure recorded at the time instant corresponding to maximum temperature during high current density pulsed simulation are shown in Fig. 25(a) and 25(b). Maximum temperature of 305.1 K was observed at the Schottky interface away from the junction termination. To investigate the heat dissipation source, joule heat power profile was extracted from same structure file and is shown in Figs. 26 (p–n junction is shown in white). The heat power sources are expressed in W/cm³ in **TonyPlot**, and the contour plots have been scaled to highlight the areas of interest.

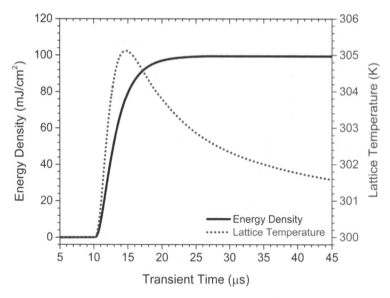

Fig. 24.   Energy density (solid) and lattice temperature (dotted) waveforms pertaining to 2000 A/cm^2 peak current density simulation.

It can be seen from the joule heat power profile that there is significant power dissipation due to resistive loss in the vicinity of the Schottky interface away from the junction termination. To understand the reason behind the specific heat power profile, the conduction current density profile was extracted at the same time instant when the lattice temperature was at its maximum value. The current density distribution within the device at peak lattice temperature is shown in Fig. 27. The current density profile shows that the depletion region formed at the p–n junction of the JTE region and drift region is forcing the diode current into a narrower path, thereby resulting in a peak current density of 2450 A/cm^2.

The same effect can be seen in the current density contour plot (shown in Fig. 28) extracted at the time instant when the anode current density waveform is at its peak value of 2000 A/cm^2. Even though the circuit was designed for 2000 A/cm^2 peak current density, the actual current density in the device is close to 3150 A/cm^2 due to the reduction in active area. The formation of depletion region can be validated through the electron concentration contour plot captured at the maximum anode current density time instant shown in Fig. 29. It can be speculated that the resistive voltage drop across the Schottky diode is increasing the reverse-bias voltage across the p–n junction formed by the JTE region and drift region, thereby leading to the formation of a depletion/space–charge region.

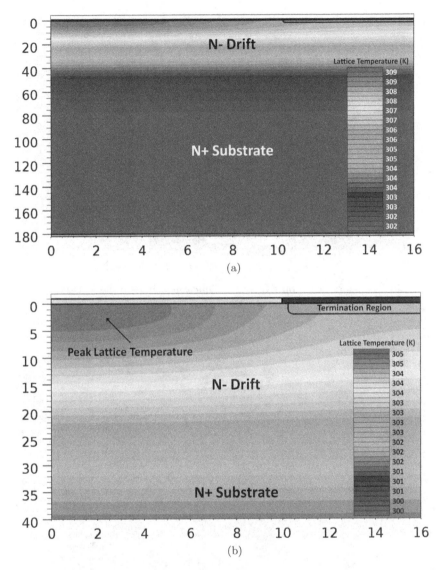

Fig. 25. (a) Lattice temperature profile of planar junction Schottky diode half-cell structure during 2000 A/cm² RLC ring-down simulation. (b) Lattice temperature profile of planar junction Schottky diode half-cell structure during 2000 A/cm² RLC ring-down simulation (zoomed-in view).

The summary of lattice temperature and anode voltage waveforms for the Schottky diode structure with planar junction termination for all the values of peak pulsed current density are shown in Figs. 30 and 31, respectively. The summary of lattice temperature and anode voltage is similar to the results obtained for the parallel plane design except for the difference induced due

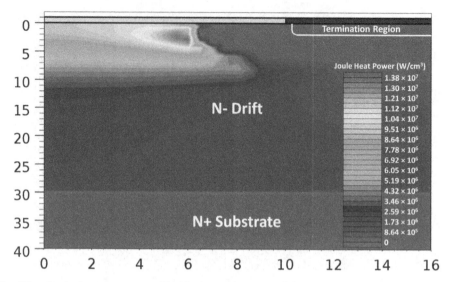

Fig. 26.   Joule heat power profile of planar junction Schottky diode half-cell structure during 2000 A/cm² RLC ring-down simulation (zoomed-in view).

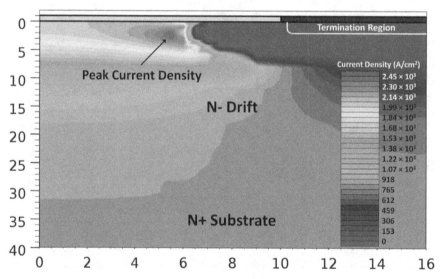

Fig. 27.   Conduction current density profile of planar junction Schottky diode half-cell structure during 2000 A/cm² RLC ring-down simulation (zoomed-in view).

to the change in cell structure/pitch. The increase in cell pitch reduces the ON-state resistance and increases the area of the thermal boundary which reduces the ON-state power dissipation and increases the heat dissipation area, thereby resulting in lower lattice temperature rise.

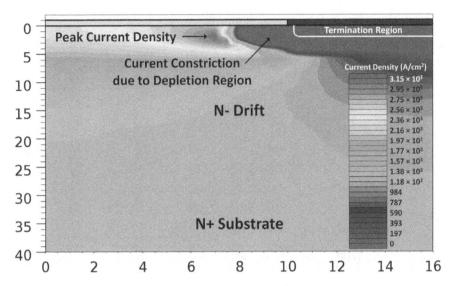

Fig. 28. Conduction current density profile of planar junction Schottky diode half-cell structure during 2000 A/cm² RLC ring-down simulation at peak current density time instant (zoomed-in view).

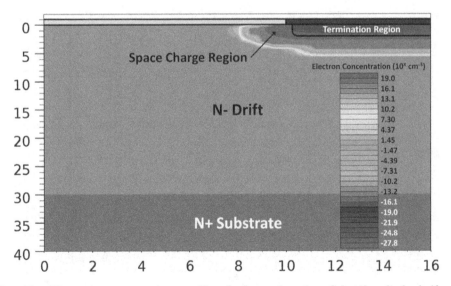

Fig. 29. Electron concentration profile of planar junction Schottky diode half-cell structure during 2000 A/cm² RLC ring-down simulation at peak current density time instant (zoomed-in view).

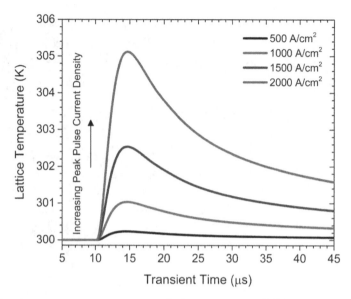

Fig. 30.   Lattice temperature summary of planar junction SiC Schottky diode half-cell structure during RLC ring-down simulation.

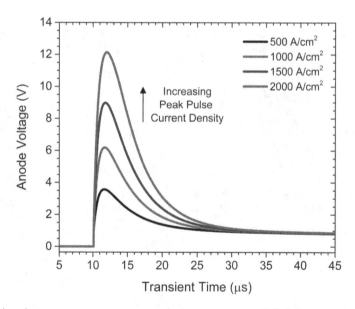

Fig. 31.   Anode temperature summary of planar junction SiC Schottky diode half-cell structure during RLC ring-down simulation.

7.3.4. Schottky diode structure with planar junction termination (complete-cell)

In Section 7.3.3, a half-cell structure of Schottky diode with planar junction termination was discussed. Even though a half-cell structure is a good representation of the actual device and provides a comparatively faster way to estimate device characteristics and performance, it is still not the best approximation to an actual device. In this section, a complete-cell structure of the Schottky diode design will be discussed, which is an extension of the

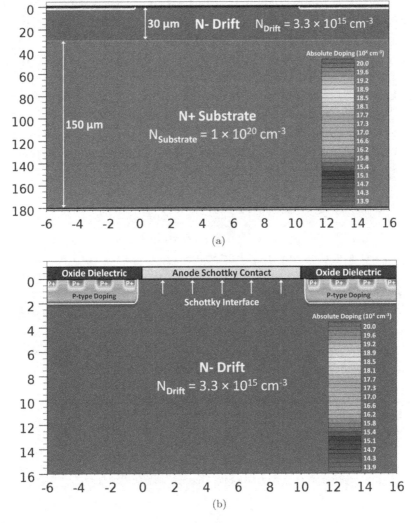

Fig. 32. (a) 3300 V SiC Schottky diode planar junction complete-cell structure designed in Silvaco© ATLAS. (b) 3300 V SiC Schottky diode planar junction complete-cell structure designed in Silvaco© ATLAS (zoomed-in view).

design discussed earlier. The P+ field JTE had a junction depth of $2\,\mu$m and was doped with a peak acceptor concentration of 1.0×10^{18} cm^{-3} using a Gaussian profile. The floating field rings within the JTE had a junction depth of $1\,\mu$m and were heavily doped with a peak acceptor concentration of 1.0×10^{20} cm^{-3} using a Gaussian profile. The N− epitaxial/drift region was $30\,\mu$m thick with a doping concentration of 3.3×10^{15} cm^{-3}. The doping concentration had to be slightly increased as compared to the half-cell structure to obtain similar breakdown voltage range due to the presence of field termination on either side of the active area.[7,8] The N+ substrate had a thickness of $150\,\mu$m and doping concentration of 1.0×10^{20} cm^{-3}. The anode Schottky metal was configured to be a conductor with a workfunction of 5.0 eV and aluminum was used for the cathode ohmic contact. Due to the presence of the Hybrid JTE on either side of the active area, the 2D device structure had a cell pitch of $22\,\mu$m and an active area of $10\,\mu$m^2 based on the $10\,\mu$m wide Schottky anode region. A $1\,\mu$m thick oxide layer is used as the ILD over the hybrid JTE area.

Due to the large substrate thickness as compared to the drift layer, the complete device structure designed using Silvaco© ATLAS has been split into Figs. 32(a) and 32(b), respectively. The Gaussian doping profile has been used for the Hybrid JTE scheme which can be seen in Fig. 32(a).

7.3.4.1. *Steady-State simulation*

This section will discuss the forward conduction and reverse breakdown current density versus anode voltage $(J-V)$ characteristics at 27°C, 75°C, 125°C, and 175°C device temperature. The Steady-State simulation code is like the one used for the planar junction half-cell structure except for changes in device mesh profile. The following code was used to simulate the complete-cell Schottky diode $J-V$ characteristics which includes forward conduction and reverse breakdown. A brief explanation of the Steady-State simulation program is provided in the code walkthrough (Table 5)

```
Sample code: Planar junction SiC Schottky diode complete-cell forward and breakdown J-V
characteristics @ 27°C

1.   GO ATLAS SIMFLAGS ="-V 5.18.3.R -P 32 -160"
2.
3.   ##### 3300V PLANAR JUNCTION SCHOTTKY DIODE - COMPLETE CELL @ 27C #####
4.
5.   MESH
6.
7.   ## X-MESH
8.
```

```
9.  X.MESH   loc=-6.0    spac=0.25
10. X.MESH   loc=0.0     spac=0.25
11. X.MESH   loc=1.0     spac=0.5
12. X.MESH   loc=9.0     spac=0.5
13. X.MESH   loc=10.0    spac=0.25
14. X.MESH   loc=16.0    spac=0.25
15.
16. ## Y-MESH
17.
18. Y.MESH   loc=-1.0    spac=0.25
19. Y.MESH   loc=0.0     spac=0.25
20. Y.MESH   loc=0.25    spac=0.1
21. Y.MESH   loc=2.1     spac=0.01
22. Y.MESH   loc=28.0    spac=10.0
23. Y.MESH   loc=30.1    spac=0.2
24. Y.MESH   loc=31.0    spac=1.0
25. Y.MESH   loc=32.0    spac=20
26. Y.MESH   loc=178.0   spac=20
27. Y.MESH   loc=180.0   spac=1.0
28. Y.MESH   loc=182.0   spac=1.0
29.
30. ## Defining 4H-SiC and Oxide Region
31.
32. REGION   num=1  material=OXIDE    y.max=0
33. REGION   num=2  material=4H-SiC   x.min=-6   x.max=16   y.min=0   y.max=180
34.
35. ## Electrode
36.
37. ELECTRODE  name=anode    material=CONDUCTOR  x.min=0    x.max=10   y.max=0
38. ELECTRODE  name=cathode  material=ALUMINUM   y.min=180  y.max=182
39.
40. ## Doping Distribution
41.
42. ## Bulk Doping
43. DOPING  uniform n.type conc=3.3e15  REGION=2
44.
45. ## P+ Field Rings
46. DOPING  gauss p.type conc=1.e18  x.max=-0.50  junc=2.0  rat=0.1
47. DOPING  gauss p.type conc=1.e20  x.min=-1.00  x.max=-0.50  junc=1.0  rat=0.1
48. DOPING  gauss p.type conc=1.e20  x.min=-2.75  x.max=-2.00  junc=1.0  rat=0.1
49. DOPING  gauss p.type conc=1.e20  x.min=-4.50  x.max=-3.75  junc=1.0  rat=0.1
50. DOPING  gauss p.type conc=1.e20  x.min=-6.00  x.max=-5.50  junc=1.0  rat=0.1
51.
52. DOPING  gauss p.type conc=1.e18  x.min=10.50  junc=2.0  rat=0.1
53. DOPING  gauss p.type conc=1.e20  x.min=10.50  x.max=11.00  junc=1.0  rat=0.1
54. DOPING  gauss p.type conc=1.e20  x.min=12.00  x.max=12.75  junc=1.0  rat=0.1
55. DOPING  gauss p.type conc=1.e20  x.min=13.75  x.max=14.50  junc=1.0  rat=0.1
56. DOPING  gauss p.type conc=1.e20  x.min=15.50  x.max=16    junc=1.0  rat=0.1
57.
58. ## N+ Substrate Region Doping
59. DOPING  uniform n.type   conc=1.e20   y.min=30   y.max=180
60.
61. SAVE  outf=Schottky_Planar_FFR_27C.str  master.out
62.
63. MATERIAL  material=4H-SiC REGION=2  permittivity=9.76   eg300=3.26
       affinity=3.7  egalpha=3.3e-2  egbeta=1.e+5  nc300=1.7e+19  nv300=2.5e+19
       arichn=146  arichp=30  augn=3.e-29  augp=3.e-29  taun0=3.33e-6  taup0=6.7e-7
       nsrhn=3.e+17  nsrhp=3.e+17  edb=0.05  eab=0.20
64.
```

```
65. CONTACT  NAME=ANODE   WORKFUNCTION=5.0   THERMION  PARABOLIC
66.
67. ## MODELS USED
68.
69. MODELS  REGION=2 MATERIAL=4H-SIC FERMIDIRAC ANALYTIC CONWELL INCOMPLETE SRH BGN
    AUGER TEMP=300 PRINT
70.
71. ## MOBILITY
72.
73. MOBILITY  material=4H-SiC  REGION=2  vsatn=2.2e7  vsatp=2.2e7  betan=1.2
    betap=2  mu1n.caug=40  mu2n.caug=1136  ncritn.caug=2e17  alphan.caug=-3
    betan.caug=-3  gamman.caug=0.0  deltan.caug=0.76   mu1p.caug=20  mu2p.caug=125
    ncritp.caug=1.e19  alphap.caug=-3  betap.caug=-3  gammap.caug=0.0
    deltap.caug=0.5
74.
75. IMPACT  REGION=2  ANISO  E.SIDE  SELB  SIC4H0001  an1=3.44e6  an2=3.44e6
    bn1=2.58e7  bn2=2.58e7  ap1=3.5e6  ap2=3.5e6  bp1=1.7e7  bp2=1.7e7  opphe=0.106
76.
77. METHOD  NEWTON AUTONR  climit=1.e-9  maxtraps=40  itlimit=40  dvmax=1.e8
    ir.tol=1.e-35  cr.tol=1.e-35  ix.tol=1.e-35  px.tol=1.e-30  pr.tol=1.e-45
    cx.tol=1.e-30
78.
79. OUTPUT  FLOWLINES
80.
81. LOG  outf=SCH_Forward_27C.log
82.
83. SOLVE  init
84. SOLVE  vanode=0.05  vstep=0.05  vfinal=2      name=anode
85. SOLVE  vstep=0.1              vfinal=4.0     name=anode
86.
87. SAVE  outf=SCH_Forward_27C.str
88.
89. LOG  outf=SCH_Reverse_27C.log
90.
91. SOLVE  init
92. SOLVE  vanode=-0.2  vstep=-0.2   vfinal=-2.0   name=anode
93. SOLVE  vstep=-2     vfinal=-20    name=anode
94. SOLVE  vstep=-5     vfinal=-100   name=anode
95. SOLVE  vstep=-10    vfinal=-1000  name=anode
96. SOLVE  vstep=-25    vfinal=-4000  name=anode
97. SOLVE  vstep=-10    vfinal=-4200  name=anode
98. SOLVE  vstep=-2     vfinal=-4240  name=anode
99. SOLVE  vstep=-0.5   vfinal=-4400  name=anode  compl=1e-16  cname=anode previous
100.
101. SAVE  outf=SCH_Reverse_27C.str
102.
103. QUIT
```

Table 5.   Code walkthrough: Planar junction Schottky diode complete-cell forward and breakdown $J-V$ characteristics.

Line No:	Functionality
1	Configure ATLAS simulator to use 160-bit extended precision and utilize 32 cores of the CPU if hardware resources are available. The version of ATLAS to be used by the simulator is set to 5.18.3.R using the $-V$ option in the simflags command.

(Continued)

Table 5. (*Continued*)

Line No:	Functionality
5	Initialize device structure mesh information.
7–28	X-axis and Y-axis mesh distribution.
32–33	Declare Oxide and 4H-SiC as the material for the area of the semiconductor specified by the x and y coordinates.
37–38	Electrode specifications for the Schottky diode (metal conductor anode and aluminum Cathode).
42–59	Specify doping profile, type, and concentration for different areas of the Schottky diode structure.
61	Save the device structure (**.str**) file on the local hard drive. The device structure can be viewed by opening the file via **TonyPlot** to troubleshoot/optimize the structure.
63	Specify material parameters for 4H-SiC. Detailed description of these parameters is available in the Silvaco© ATLAS manual. The values for these parameters can either be obtained via material research or from literature.
65	Specify Schottky metal workfunction and model/parameters for thermionic emission and parabolic field emission using **Contact** statement.
69	Specify the various models to be included in the 4H-SiC Schottky diode simulation.
73	Specify mobility parameters for 4H-SiC. Detailed description of these parameters is available in the Silvaco© ATLAS manual. The values for these parameters can either be obtained via material research or from literature.
75	Specify Impact Ionization parameters for 4H-SiC. This statement is mandatory to obtain device breakdown characteristics.
77	Specify the solver type and the tolerance values to be used during the simulation. This is an extremely critical statement which can alter the simulation outcome.
79	Include current flowlines in the output structure file.
81	Save the simulation log (**.log**) file on the local hard drive. The simulation results can be viewed by opening the file via **TonyPlot**.
83–85	Solve for the initial bias conditions for the simulation followed by positive sweep of anode voltage for steady-state forward characteristics.
87	Save the post-forward-bias simulation device structure (**.str**) file on the local hard drive. Saving the file at this stage of the simulation will enable the user to visualize the variation in various electrothermal parameters within the device structure introduced due to the particular simulation.
89	Save the reverse-bias simulation log (**.log**) file on the local hard drive. The simulation results can be viewed by opening the file via **TonyPlot**.

(*Continued*)

Table 5.   (*Continued*)

Line No:	Functionality
91–99	Use solve statement to increment the negative anode voltage in discrete steps. The compliance parameter (**compl**) in line 99 forces the simulator to proceed to the next line once the anode current reaches the specified compliance value. This is important, especially in breakdown simulation because once the device enters the breakdown regime, it is not necessary to run the simulation for higher magnitude of current since the breakdown voltage would have already been determined.
101	Save the post-reverse-bias simulation device structure (**.str**) file on the local hard drive. Saving the file at this stage of the simulation will enable the user to visualize the variation in various electrothermal parameters within the device structure introduced due to the particular simulation.
103	Terminate the simulation.

7.3.4.2.   *Steady-state simulation results*

The forward conduction $J-V$ characteristics for the 3300 V SiC Schottky diode complete-cell structure with planar junction termination on a linear and semi-log scale are shown in Figs. 33(a) and 33(b), respectively. The simulations were carried out at varying lattice temperature values like the previous Schottky diode simulations. At an ON-state current density of $100 \, \text{A/cm}^2$, voltage drop of 1.3 V was observed across the diode at 27°C device temperature, which is lower than the voltage drop obtained for the planar junction half-cell structure at the same current density. This is due to the wider cell pitch which helps in reducing the ON-state resistance despite having the same active area.

The reverse-bias breakdown $J-V$ characteristics for varying lattice temperature conditions are shown in Fig. 34. Breakdown voltage of 4329 V was obtained for the planar junction Schottky diode complete-cell structure with hybrid JTE at 27°C device temperature. As seen in the case of half-cell diode structure, there is a progressive increase in the leakage current with lattice temperature.

The electric field distribution in the Schottky diode structure during breakdown is shown in the contour plot in Figs. 35(a) and 35(b) (Images have been scaled to highlight the area of interest). Maximum electric field of $2.76 \, \text{MV/cm}$ was observed at both the edge of the junction termination in Fig. 35(b), which is also the point of breakdown. As discussed in the previous section, device breakdown should not occur through the junction

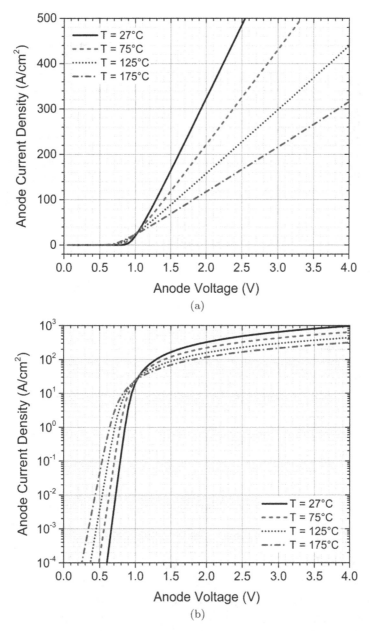

Fig. 33. (a) Forward $J-V$ characteristics for the SiC planar junction Schottky diode complete-cell on a linear scale. (b) Forward $J-V$ characteristics for the SiC planar junction Schottky diode complete-cell on a semi-log scale.

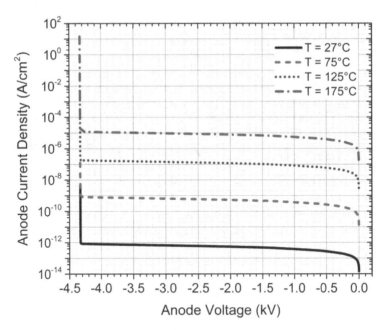

Fig. 34.   Reverse breakdown J–V characteristics for the SiC planar junction Schottky diode complete-cell structure on a semi-log scale.

termination/field rings. However, obtaining diode breakdown through the Schottky contact in a non-parallel plane diode structure is extremely difficult in a TCAD simulation due to localized field enhancement at the edges of the p-type region which is generally used for junction termination/floating field rings.

For the complete-cell structure, 1D electric field profile as a function of device depth is shown in Figs. 36 and 37. Figure 36 shows the electric field distribution across the hybrid JTE structure (including point of breakdown), whereas Figs. 37(a) and 37(b) focus on the electric field distribution in the active area (including point of breakdown). The plot has been scaled to highlight the region of interest. The electric field data was extracted for the following points: extension of the Hybrid JTE region on the left side of the active area ($x = -4\,\mu$m and $x = -2\,\mu$m), edge of the left Hybrid JTE region which is also the point of breakdown ($x = -0.6\,\mu$m), anode Schottky contact active area ($x = 2\,\mu$m, $x = 5\,\mu$m, and $x = 8\,\mu$m), edge of the right Hybrid JTE region which is also the point of breakdown ($x = 10.6\,\mu$m), and extension of the Hybrid JTE region on the right side of the active area ($x = 12\,\mu$m and $x = 14\,\mu$m) using the **cutline** feature in **TonyPlot**.

To have a closer look at the electric field distribution across the Schottky interface in the active area, electric field profiles are shown in Figs. 37(a)

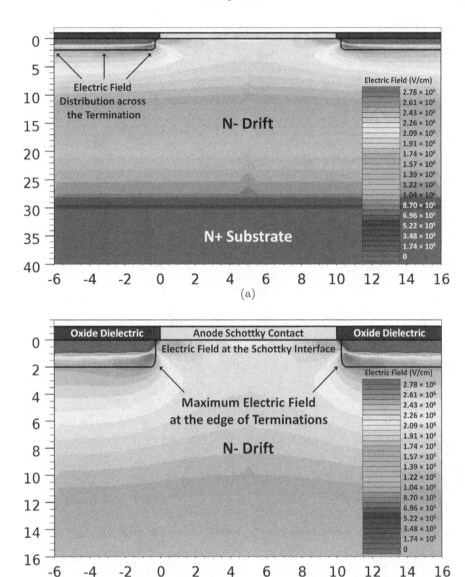

Fig. 35.   (a) Electric field contour plot during reverse-bias breakdown in planar junction Schottky diode complete-cell structure. (b) Electric field contour plot during reverse-bias breakdown in planar junction Schottky diode complete-cell structure (zoomed-in view).

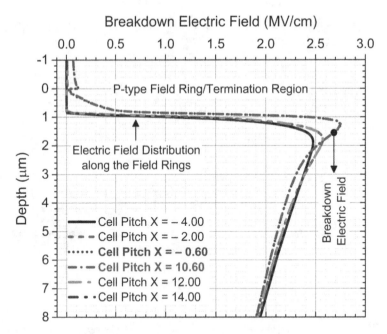

Fig. 36.   1D electric field profile as a function of device depth at varying points across the diode active area/cell pitch in the termination regions.

and 37(b) where Fig. 37(b) is a zoomed-in version of Fig. 37(a). The point of breakdown has been indicated in bold in the graph legend. It can be seen from Fig. 37(b) that even though there is a reduction in the magnitude of electric field at the Schottky interface, it is still not far away from the breakdown electric field.

7.3.4.3.   *Mixed-mode transient simulation*

The Mixed-Mode transient simulation was performed using the RLC ring-down circuit.[6] The simulation code was similar to that used in the half-cell structure with changes pertaining to the complete-cell structure. These changes include device mesh profile, inclusion of hybrid JTE on either side of the active area, and dimensions of the thermal boundary using **Thermcontact** statement. The following code was used to simulate the Schottky diode for a peak forward current density of $2000\,A/cm^2$ under pulsed condition. A brief explanation of the Mixed-Mode simulation program is provided in the code walkthrough (Table 6).

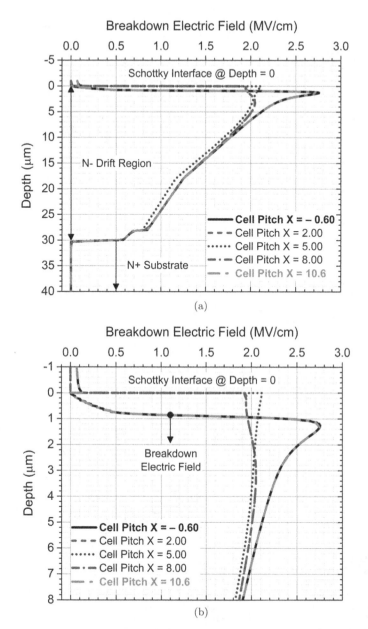

Fig. 37. (a) 1D electric field profile as a function of device depth at varying points across the diode active area/cell pitch focusing on the Schottky interface. (b) 1D electric field profile as a function of device depth at varying points across the diode active area/cell pitch focusing on the Schottky interface (zoomed-in view).

```
Sample code: Planar junction SiC Schottky diode complete-cell transient simulation

1.   GO ATLAS SIMFLAGS ="-V 5.18.3.R -P 32 -160"
2.
3.   ##### 3300V PLANAR JUNCTION SCHOTTKY DIODE COMPLETE-CELL RLC RINGDOWN PULSE 2000A/cm2 #####
4.
5.   MESH  WIDTH=3.e6
6.
7.   ## X-MESH
8.
9.   X.MESH  loc=-6.0  spac=0.25
10.  X.MESH  loc=0.0   spac=0.25
11.  X.MESH  loc=1.0   spac=0.5
12.  X.MESH  loc=9.0   spac=0.5
13.  X.MESH  loc=10.0  spac=0.25
14.  X.MESH  loc=16.0  spac=0.25
15.
16.  ## Y-MESH
17.
18.  Y.MESH  loc=-1.0     spac=0.25
19.  Y.MESH  loc=0.0      spac=0.25
20.  Y.MESH  loc=0.25     spac=0.1
21.  Y.MESH  loc=2.1      spac=0.01
22.  Y.MESH  loc=28.0     spac=10.0
23.  Y.MESH  loc=30.1     spac=0.2
24.  Y.MESH  loc=31.0     spac=1.0
25.  Y.MESH  loc=32.0     spac=20
26.  Y.MESH  loc=178.0    spac=20
27.  Y.MESH  loc=180.0    spac=1.0
28.  Y.MESH  loc=182.0    spac=1.0
29.
30.  ## Defining 4H-SiC AND Oxide Region
31.
32.  REGION  num=1 material=OXIDE    y.max=0
33.  REGION  num=2 material=4H-SiC   x.min=-6   x.max=16   y.min=0   y.max=180
34.
35.  ## Electrode
36.
37.  ELECTRODE  name=anode    material=CONDUCTOR   x.min=0    x.max=10   y.max=0
38.  ELECTRODE  name=cathode  material=ALUMINUM    y.min=180  y.max=182
39.
40.  ## Doping Distribution
41.
42.  ## Bulk Doping
43.  DOPING  uniform  n.type  conc=3.3e15  REGION=2
44.
45.  ## P+ Field Rings
46.  DOPING  gauss p.type conc=1.e18  x.max=-0.50  junc=2.0   rat=0.1
47.  DOPING  gauss p.type conc=1.e20  x.min=-1.00  x.max=-0.50   junc=1.0  rat=0.1
48.  DOPING  gauss p.type conc=1.e20  x.min=-2.75  x.max=-2.00   junc=1.0  rat=0.1
49.  DOPING  gauss p.type conc=1.e20  x.min=-4.50  x.max=-3.75   junc=1.0  rat=0.1
50.  DOPING  gauss p.type conc=1.e20  x.min=-6.00  x.max=-5.50   junc=1.0  rat=0.1
51.
52.  DOPING  gauss p.type conc=1.e18  x.min=10.50  junc=2.0  rat=0.1
53.  DOPING  gauss p.type conc=1.e20  x.min=10.50  x.max=11.00   junc=1.0  rat=0.1
54.  DOPING  gauss p.type conc=1.e20  x.min=12.00  x.max=12.75   junc=1.0  rat=0.1
55.  DOPING  gauss p.type conc=1.e20  x.min=13.75  x.max=14.50   junc=1.0  rat=0.1
56.  DOPING  gauss p.type conc=1.e20  x.min=15.50  x.max=16      junc=1.0  rat=0.1
57.
58.  ## N+ Substrate Region Doping
```

```
59. DOPING   uniform  n.type    conc=1.e20   y.min=30    y.max=180
60.
61. SAVE   outf=SCH_Structure.str  master.out
62.
63. ##### STEADY STATE SIMULATION CIRCUIT #####
64.
65. GO ATLAS SIMFLAGS ="-V 5.18.3.R -P 32 -160"
66.
67. .BEGIN
68.
69. VDC          1    0    0
70. RSW          1    2    1.e-12
71. R_CHARGE     2    3    500
72. C_BANK       3    0    6u
73. R_SERIES     3    4    0.80
74. L_SERIES     4    5    500n
75. RSWITCH      5    6    1.e18
76. ADIODE       6=anode   0=cathode     infile=SCH_Structure.str    width=3.e6
77.
78. .NODESET  v(1)=0  v(2)=0  v(3)=0  v(4)=0  v(5)=0  v(6)=0
79. .NUMERIC  imaxdc=100
80.
81. .DC    VDC    0.    10.    0.25
82. .DC    VDC    10.   100.   5.
83. .DC    VDC    100.  600.   20.
84.
85. .LOG  outfile=SCH_DC_log
86. .SAVE  outfile=SCH_RLC_Bias
87. .OPTIONS  m2ln print noshift relpot
88.
89. .END
90.
91. ##### PHYSICS USED #####
92.
93. CONTACT  DEVICE=ADIODE  NAME=ANODE   WORKFUNCTION=5.0  THERMION  PARABOLIC
    EXT.ALPHA=10
94. CONTACT  DEVICE=ADIODE  NAME=CATHODE    EXT.ALPHA=10
95.
96. THERMCONTACT  DEVICE=ADIODE   num=3   x.min=-6   x.max=16
    y.min=-1.0  y.max=182   alpha=10  ext.temp=300
97.
98. MATERIAL  material=4H-SiC  REGION=2  permittivity=9.76   eg300=3.26
    affinity=3.7   egalpha=3.3e-2   egbeta=1.e+5  nc300=1.7e+19  nv300=2.5e+19
    arichn=146  arichp=30  augn=3.e-29  augp=3.e-29  taun0=3.33e-6  taup0=6.7e-7
    nsrhn=3.e+17  nsrhp=3.e+17  edb=0.05  eab=0.20  tcon.polyn  tc.a=0.137534
    tc.b=0.00049662    tc.c=0.000000354  hc.a=2.35  hc.b=1.75e-3  hc.c=1.e-9
    hc.d=-6.6e4
99.
100. ## MODELS USED
101.
102. MODELS  DEVICE=ADIODE  REGION=2  MATERIAL=4H-SIC FERMIDIRAC ANALYTIC CONWELL
     SRH BGN AUGER INCOMPLETE LAT.TEMP  JOULE.HEAT GR.HEAT  PT.HEAT  PRINT
103.
104. ## MOBILITY
105.
106. MOBILITY  DEVICE=ADIODE  material=4H-SiC  REGION=2  vsatn=2.2e7  vsatp=2.2e7
     betan=1.2 betap=2  mu1n.caug=40  mu2n.caug=1136  ncritn.caug=2e17
     alphan.caug=-3 betan.caug=-3 gamman.caug=0.0 deltan.caug=0.76   mu1p.caug=20
     mu2p.caug=125 ncritp.caug=1.e19 alphap.caug=-3  betap.caug=-3
     gammap.caug=0.0  deltap.caug=0.5
```

```
107.
108. MOBILITY  DEVICE=ADIODE  material=4H-SiC  REGION=2  n.canali  n.angle=90
     p.angle=90 vsatn=2.2e7  vsatp=2.2e7  betan=1.2 betap=2  mu1n.caug=5
     mu2n.caug=947  ncritn.caug=2e17  alphan.caug=-3  betan.caug=-3  gamman.caug=0.0
     deltan.caug=0.76   mu1p.caug=2.5  mu2p.caug=20  ncritp.caug=1.e19
     alphap.caug=-3  betap.caug=-3  gammap.caug=0.0  deltap.caug=0.5
109.
110. ## Impact Ionization
111.
112. IMPACT  DEVICE=ADIODE  REGION=2  ANISO  E.SIDE  SELB  SIC4H0001  an1=3.44e6
     an2=3.44e6  bn1=2.58e7  bn2=2.58e7  ap1=3.5e6  ap2=3.5e6  bp1=1.7e7  bp2=1.7e7
     opphe=0.106
113.
114. METHOD  BLOCK climit=1.e-9 maxtraps=100  itlimit=100   max.temp=1000
     dvmax=1.e8  ir.tol=1.e-35  cr.tol=1.e-35  ix.tol=1.e-35  px.tol=1.e-30
     pr.tol=1.e-45  cx.tol=1.e-30
115.
116. GO ATLAS SIMFLAGS ="-V 5.18.3.R -P 32 -160"
117.
118. ##### TRANSIENT SIMULATION CIRCUIT #####
119.
120. .BEGIN
121.
122. VDC        1   0   600
123. RSW        1   2   1.e-12  PULSE  1.e-12  1.e18  5us  100ns  100ns  40us  80us
124. R_CHARGE   2   3   500
125. C_BANK     3   0   6u
126. R_SERIES   3   4   0.80
127. L_SERIES   4   5   500n
128. RSWITCH    5   6   1.e18   PULSE  1.e18  1.e-12  10us  100ns  100ns  40us  80us
129. ADIODE     6=anode   0=cathode    infile=SCH_Structure.str    width=3.e6
130.
131. .NUMERIC  imaxtr=100  dtmax=1.e-7
132. .OPTIONS  m2ln.tr  print  noshift  relpot  write=20
133. .LOAD     infile=SCH_RLC_Bias
134. .SAVE     master=SCH_Transient
135. .LOG      outfile=SCH_Ringdown_2000.log
136. .SAVE     outfile=SCH_Ringdown_2000.str
137.
138. .TRAN  0.01us 45us
139.
140. .END
141.
142. ##### PHYSICS USED #####
143.
144. CONTACT  DEVICE=ADIODE  NAME=ANODE   WORKFUNCTION=5.0  THERMION  PARABOLIC
     EXT.ALPHA=10
145. CONTACT  DEVICE=ADIODE  NAME=CATHODE   EXT.ALPHA=10
146.
147. THERMCONTACT DEVICE=ADIODE   num=3   x.min=-6   x.max=16  y.min=-1.0
     y.max=182   alpha=10   ext.temp=300
148.
149. MATERIAL  material=4H-SiC REGION=2  permittivity=9.76   eg300=3.26
     affinity=3.7 egalpha=3.3e-2  egbeta=1.e+5 nc300=1.7e+19 nv300=2.5e+19
     arichn=146 arichp=30 augn=3.e-29 augp=3.e-29 taun0=3.33e-6 taup0=6.7e-7
     nsrhn=3.e+17 nsrhp=3.e+17 edb=0.05 eab=0.20 tcon.polyn tc.a=0.137534
     tc.b=0.00049662   tc.c=0.000000354  hc.a=2.35  hc.b=1.75e-3  hc.c=1.e-9
     hc.d=-6.6e4
150.
151. ## MODELS USED
```

```
152.
153. MODELS  DEVICE=ADIODE  REGION=2 MATERIAL=4H-SIC FERMIDIRAC ANALYTIC CONWELL SRH
     BGN AUGER INCOMPLETE LAT.TEMP  JOULE.HEAT GR.HEAT  PT.HEAT  PRINT
154.
155. ## MOBILITY
156.
157. MOBILITY  DEVICE=ADIODE  material=4H-SiC REGION=2  vsatn=2.2e7  vsatp=2.2e7
     betan=1.2 betap=2  mu1n.caug=40  mu2n.caug=1136 ncritn.caug=2e17
     alphan.caug=-3 betan.caug=-3 gamman.caug=0.0 deltan.caug=0.76  mu1p.caug=20
     mu2p.caug=125 ncritp.caug=1.e19 alphap.caug=-3 betap.caug=-3
     gammap.caug=0.0 deltap.caug=0.5
158.
159. MOBILITY  DEVICE=ADIODE  material=4H-SiC  REGION=2  n.canali  n.angle=90
     p.angle=90 vsatn=2.2e7  vsatp=2.2e7  betan=1.2 betap=2  mu1n.caug=5
     mu2n.caug=947 ncritn.caug=2e17 alphan.caug=-3 betan.caug=-3 gamman.caug=0.0
     deltan.caug=0.76  mu1p.caug=2.5 mu2p.caug=20  ncritp.caug=1.e19
     alphap.caug=-3 betap.caug=-3 gammap.caug=0.0 deltap.caug=0.5
160.
161. ## Impact Ionization
162.
163. IMPACT  DEVICE=ADIODE  REGION=2 ANISO E.SIDE  SELB  SIC4H0001 an1=3.44e6
     an2=3.44e6  bn1=2.58e7  bn2=2.58e7  ap1=3.5e6  ap2=3.5e6  bp1=1.7e7
     bp2=1.7e7 opphe=0.106
164.
165. OUTPUT  FLOWLINES E.MOBILITY
166.
167. METHOD  BLOCK.TRAN  climit=1.e-9  maxtraps=100  itlimit=100   max.temp=1000
     dvmax=1.e8  ir.tol=1.e-25  cr.tol=1.e-25  ix.tol=1.e-30  px.tol=1.e-30
     pr.tol=1.e-36 cx.tol=1.e-30
168.
169. GO ATLAS SIMFLAGS ="-V 5.18.3.R -P 32 -128"
170.
171. QUIT
```

Table 6.   Code walkthrough: Planar junction Schottky diode complete-cell Mixed-Mode simulation.

Line No:	Functionality
1	Configure ATLAS simulator to use version 5.18.3.R, 160-bit extended precision and utilize 32 cores of the CPU if hardware resources are available.
5	Initialize device structure mesh information with width parameter.
7–28	X-axis and Y-axis mesh distribution.
32–33	Declare Oxide and 4H-SiC as the material for the area of the semiconductor specified by the x and y coordinates.
37–38	Electrode specifications for the Schottky diode (metal conductor anode and aluminum Cathode).
42–59	Specify doping profile, type, and concentration for different areas of the Schottky diode structure.
61	Save the device structure (**.str**) file on the local hard drive.

(*Continued*)

Table 6.   (*Continued*)

Line No:	Functionality
65	Initialize ATLAS simulator using GO ATLAS command (same as line 1).
67	Initialize the starting of SPICE-like code in Mixed-Mode steady-state simulation.
69–76	RLC ring-down circuit description in SPICE-like format.
78	Declare the initial node voltage for the RLC ring-down circuit nodes.
79	Set the maximum number of mixed circuit-device iterations to be performed during steady-state analysis (***imaxdc***) to 100.
81–83	Ramp up DC voltage to attain steady-state condition, i.e. VDC = 600 V. This can be split into multiple steps.
85	Save log file after steady-state simulation completion.
86	Save file with bias information which will be used for transient simulation.
87	Specify Mixed-Mode steady-state simulation conditions. Modified two-level Newton solution method (***m21n***), disable the shift of voltage for ATLAS devices (***noshift***), and enable the use of relative convergence criteria for potential especially when large voltage biases are involved (***relpot***).
89	Initialize the ending of SPICE-like code in Mixed-Mode steady-state simulation.
93–94	Specify heat transfer coefficient (***ext.alpha***) for the anode and cathode contacts.
96	Specify the thermal boundary for the Schottky diode. Parameters includes boundary dimensions, heat transfer coefficient (***alpha***), and temperature of the thermal boundary (***ext.temp***) which is typically at 300 K.
98	Specify material parameters for 4H-SiC.
102	Specify the various models to be included in the 4H-SiC Schottky diode simulation.
106	Specify parameters for mobility in 4H-SiC.
108	Specify parameters for anisotropic mobility in 4H-SiC.
112	Specify impact ionization parameters for 4H-SiC.
114	Specify the steady-state Block Newton solver type (***BLOCK***) and the tolerance values to be used during the simulation.
116	Initialize ATLAS simulator using GO ATLAS command (same as line 1) for steady-state bias point simulation.
120	Initialize the starting of SPICE-like code in Mixed-Mode transient simulation.
122–129	RLC ring-down circuit description in SPICE-like format. The magnitude of DC voltage source is initialized at 600 V, result of the steady-state simulation performed earlier. Transient parameters have been added to the Resistor which is acting like a switch.

(*Continued*)

Table 6. (*Continued*)

Line No:	Functionality
131	Set the maximum number of mixed circuit-device iterations to be performed during transient analysis (***imaxtr***) to 100 and the maximum transient simulation time step (***dtmax***) to 100 ns.
132	Specify Mixed-Mode transient simulation conditions. Modified two-level Newton solution method for transient simulation (***m2ln.tr***), disable the shift of voltage for ATLAS devices (***noshift***), enable the use of relative convergence criteria for potential especially when large voltage biases are involved (***relpot***), and write structure file after every 50 time-step iterations.
133	Load the steady-state simulations results saved in line 86.
134	Save the structure file after every 50 time-step iterations specified in line 132.
135	Save log file after the completion of transient simulation.
136	Save the structure file after the completion of transient simulation.
138	Specify the initial time interval of 10 ns and total simulation time of 45 μs.
140	Initialize the ending of SPICE-like code in Mixed-Mode transient simulation.
142–163	Same as line 91 to line 112.
165	Include current flowlines (***FLOWLINES***) and Electron Mobility (***E.MOBILITY***) in the output structure file.
167	Specify the transient Block Newton solver type (***BLOCK.TRAN***) and the tolerance values to be used during the simulation.
169	Initialize ATLAS simulator using GO ATLAS command (same as line 1) for transient simulation. A lower simulation precision of 128-bit has been used due to forward conduction mode of operation.
171	Terminate the simulation.

7.3.4.4. *Mixed-Mode transient simulation results*

The transient simulation for the planar junction Schottky diode complete-cell structure was carried out for varying magnitudes of peak current density ranging from $500\,\mathrm{A/cm^2}$ to $2000\,\mathrm{A/cm^2}$ in steps of 500. The reason behind limiting the peak pulse current density to $2000\,\mathrm{A/cm^2}$ will be discussed at the end of this chapter. The width parameter was used to change the peak current density through the diode without altering the waveform. In this section, the results pertaining to the maximum current density scenario of $2000\,\mathrm{A/cm^2}$ will be discussed followed by a summary of all the other cases. The anode voltage and current density waveforms are shown in Fig. 38, and the power and energy density waveforms are shown in Fig. 39.

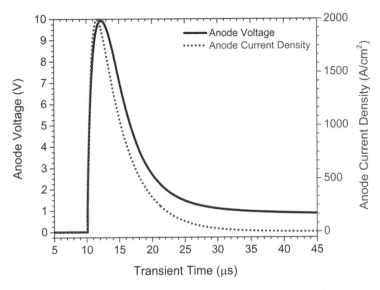

Fig. 38.   Anode voltage (solid) and current density (dotted) waveforms pertaining to 2000 A/cm^2 peak current density simulation.

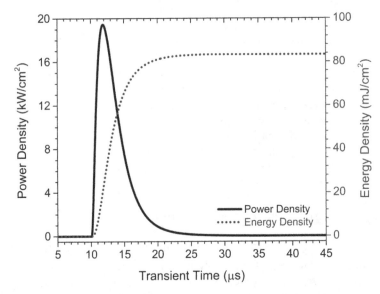

Fig. 39.   Power density (solid) and energy density (dotted) waveforms pertaining to 2000 A/cm^2 peak current density simulation.

   Peak voltage drop of 9.9 V was observed across the Schottky diode at peak current density of 2000 A/cm^2 which corresponds to a peak power dissipation density of 19.4 kW/cm^2. Integration of the power density waveform yielded an energy density of 83.4 mJ/cm^2. Peak lattice temperature of 303.3 K was

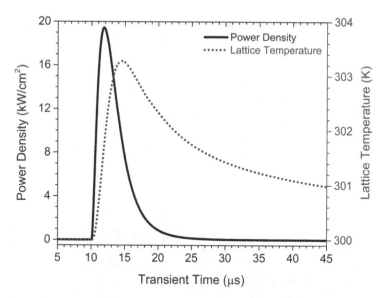

Fig. 40. Power density (solid) and lattice temperature (dotted) waveforms pertaining to 2000 A/cm^2 peak current density simulation.

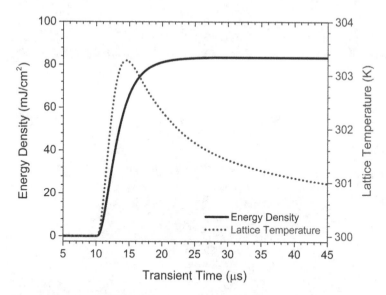

Fig. 41. Energy density (solid) and lattice temperature (dotted) waveforms pertaining to 2000 A/cm^2 peak current density simulation.

observed in the Schottky diode lattice during this pulsed operation. The variation of lattice temperature with power dissipation density and energy density during simulation is shown in Figs. 40 and 41, respectively. The simulation was run for only 45 μs, and hence does not show the complete decay of temperature waveform back to the ambient value. To identify the area of heat dissipation in the Schottky diode structure, intermediate structure files were generated during the simulation. These structure files were manually scanned for the transient time instant which corresponds to the maximum lattice temperature.

The lattice temperature profile of the planar junction Schottky diode structure recorded at the time instant corresponding to maximum temperature during high current density pulsed simulation are shown in Fig. 42(a)

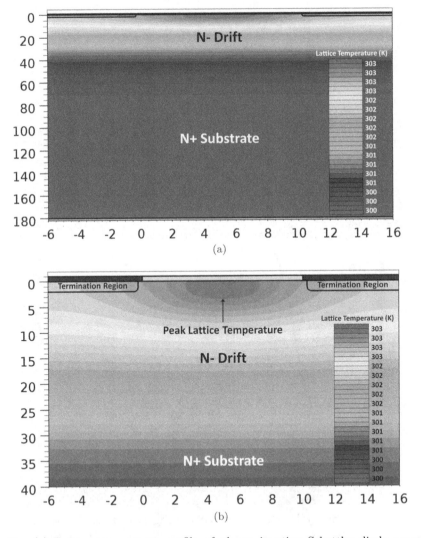

Fig. 42. (a) Lattice temperature profile of planar junction Schottky diode complete-cell structure during $2000\,\mathrm{A/cm^2}$ RLC ring-down. (b) Lattice temperature profile of planar junction Schottky diode complete-cell structure during $2000\,\mathrm{A/cm^2}$ RLC ring-down simulation (zoomed-in view).

and 42(b). Maximum temperature of 303.3 K was observed at the middle of active area closer to Schottky interface away. To investigate the heat dissipation source, joule heat power and current density profiles were extracted from same structure file and are shown in Fig. 43 and 44, respectively (p–n junction is shown in white). The heat power sources are expressed in W/cm^3 in **TonyPlot**, and the contour plots have been scaled to highlight the areas of interest.

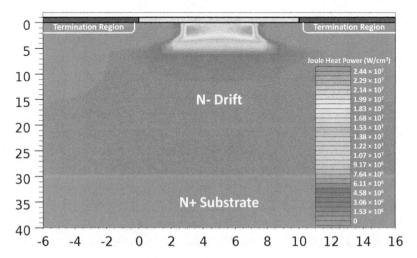

Fig. 43. Joule heat power profile of planar junction Schottky diode complete-cell structure during $2000\,A/cm^2$ RLC ring-down simulation (zoomed-in view).

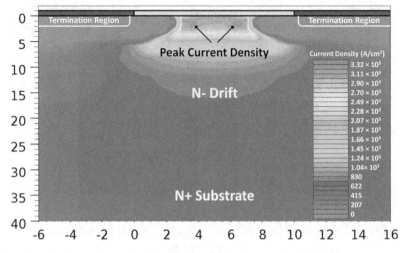

Fig. 44. Conduction current density profile of planar junction Schottky diode complete-cell structure during $2000\,A/cm^2$ RLC ring-down simulation (zoomed-in view).

It can be seen from the joule heat power profile that there is significant power dissipation due to resistive loss in the vicinity of the Schottky interface away from the junction termination. The reason behind the specific heat power profile can be attributed to the current flow path which is shown in the conduction current density profile extracted at the same time instant when the lattice temperature was at its maximum value. The current density distribution within the device at peak lattice temperature is shown in Fig. 44. The current density profile shows that the depletion region formed at the p–n junction of the JTE region and drift region is forcing the diode current into a narrower path thereby resulting in a peak current density of $3320 \, A/cm^2$.

The same effect can be seen in the current density contour plot (shown in Fig. 45) extracted at the time instant when the anode current density waveform is at its peak value of $2000 \, A/cm^2$. Even though the circuit was designed for $2000 \, A/cm^2$ peak current density, the actual current density in the device is close to $3180 \, A/cm^2$ due to the reduction in active area. The formation of depletion region can be validated through the electron concentration contour plot captured at the maximum anode current density time instant shown in Fig. 46. The electron concentration value in the space–charge region is of the order of $10^{-15} \, cm^{-3}$. As mentioned in the case of half-cell structure, it can be speculated that the resistive voltage drop across the Schottky diode is increasing the reverse-bias voltage across the p–n junction formed by the JTE region and drift region, thereby leading to the formation of a depletion/space–charge region.

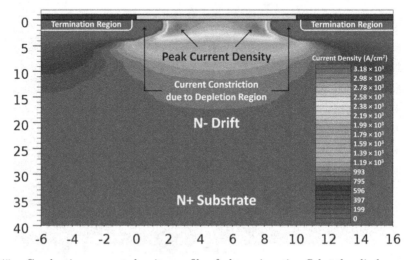

Fig. 45.   Conduction current density profile of planar junction Schottky diode complete-cell structure during $2000 \, A/cm^2$ RLC ring-down simulation at peak current density time instant (zoomed-in view).

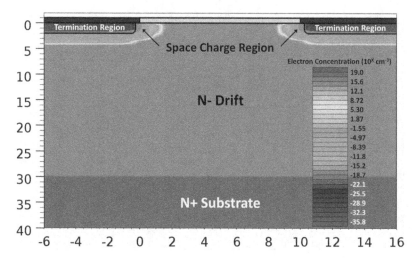

Fig. 46. Electron concentration profile of planar junction Schottky diode complete-cell structure during 2000 A/cm^2 RLC ring-down simulation at peak current density time instant (zoomed-in view).

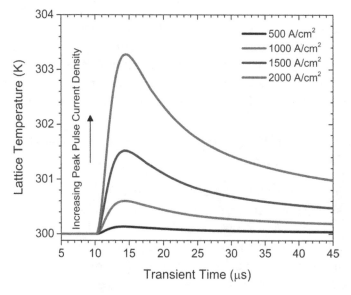

Fig. 47. Lattice temperature summary of planar junction SiC Schottky diode complete-cell structure during RLC ring-down simulation.

The summary of lattice temperature and anode voltage waveforms for the Schottky diode complete-cell structure with planar junction termination for all the values of peak pulsed current density are shown in Figs. 47 and 48, respectively. The summary of lattice temperature and anode voltage is

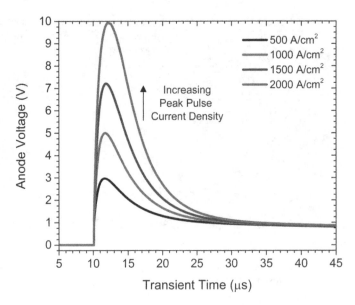

Fig. 48. Anode voltage summary of planar junction SiC Schottky diode complete-cell structure during RLC ring-down simulation.

similar to the results obtained for the half-cell design except for the difference induced due to the change in cell structure/pitch. The increase in cell pitch reduces the ON-state resistance and increases the area of the thermal boundary which reduces the ON-state power dissipation and increases the heat dissipation area, thereby resulting in lower lattice temperature rise.

7.4. Challenges during High Forward Current Density Pulsed Simulation

The RLC ring-down circuit was used to perform high current density Mixed-Mode transient simulation for the Schottky diode structures. The circuit was designed to generate current pulses with peak magnitude of current density ranging from $500 \, A/cm^2$ to $2000 \, A/cm^2$ in steps of 500 which was controlled using the scaling factor in the program. The intention of this circuit was to deliver current pulses to the device under test (in this case, Schottky diode) and understand the heat distribution within the device. The simulation was successful for all the values of peak current density for the parallel plane structure. However, when the same circuit was simulated using the Schottky diode half-cell and complete-cell structures with planar junction termination, program terminated for peak current density magnitudes above $2000 \, A/cm^2$ due to convergence error. To understand the reason behind this issue, half-cell and complete-cell Schottky diode structures with planar junction termination were simulated using the RLC ring-down circuit for a peak current density magnitude of $5000\,\mathrm{A/cm^2}$. The following sections will briefly discuss the results obtained for each structure.

7.4.1. Schottky diode half-cell structure

The anode voltage and current density waveforms during the transient simulation of half-cell Schottky diode are shown in Fig. 49. The time axis has been scaled to highlight the region of interest. The simulation terminated itself at the time instant $t = 11.58\,\mu s$ due to convergence error. Anode voltage of 83.5 V was observed across the diode at a circuit current density of $4720\,\mathrm{A/cm^2}$. This significantly high voltage drop across the device indicates high ON-state resistance in the Schottky diode structure. To investigate the cause for this abnormally high ON-state resistance, current density and lattice temperature profiles were extracted from the structure file generated during the simulation.

The current density and lattice temperature profiles for the Schottky diode half-cell structure are shown in Figs. 50 and 51, respectively (figures have been scaled to highlight the area of interest). It can be observed from the current density profile that the large depletion region formed due to the resistive drop across the diode is forcing the current flow towards the edge of the active area and away from the termination region. The

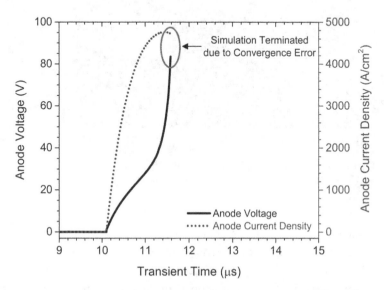

Fig. 49. Anode voltage (solid) and current density (dotted) waveforms pertaining to $5000\,\mathrm{A/cm^2}$ peak current density simulation of planar junction Schottky diode half-cell structure.

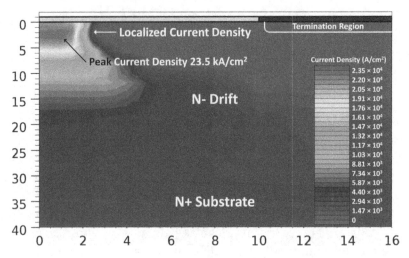

Fig. 50.   Conduction current density profile of planar junction Schottky diode half-cell structure during 5000 A/cm^2 RLC ring-down simulation (zoomed-in view).

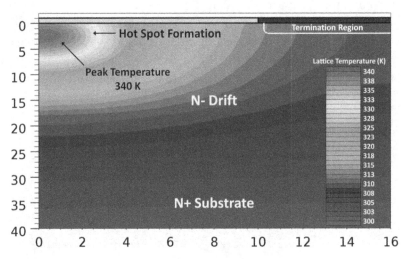

Fig. 51.   Lattice temperature profile of planar junction Schottky diode half-cell structure during 5000 A/cm^2 RLC ring-down simulation (zoomed-in view).

electron concentration profile (not shown) confirms the presence of a large depletion region extending outwards from the p-type termination region. This localization of current flow results in abnormally high current density of 23.5 kA/cm^2 within the device even though the circuit current density is 4720 A/cm^2. The concentration of high current density in a small area within the device causes the formation of thermal hot-spots which can be seen in lattice temperature profile. Peak lattice temperature of 340 K was observed in the thermal hot-spot.

7.4.2. Schottky diode complete-cell structure

The anode voltage and current density waveforms during the transient simulation of complete-cell Schottky diode are shown in Fig. 52. The time axis has been scaled to highlight the region of interest. The simulation terminated itself at the time instant $t = 11.37\,\mu s$ due to convergence error. Anode voltage of 164.3 V was observed across the diode at a circuit current density of 4680 A/cm^2. This significantly high voltage drop across the device indicates high ON-state resistance in the Schottky diode structure. To investigate the cause for this abnormally high ON-state resistance, the current density and lattice temperature profiles were extracted from the structure file generated during the simulation.

The current density and lattice temperature profiles for the Schottky diode complete-cell structure are shown in Figs. 53 and 54, respectively (figures have been scaled to highlight the area of interest). It can be observed from the current density profile that the large depletion region formed due to the resistive drop across the diode is forcing current flow towards the center of the active area and away from the termination regions. The electron concentration profile (not shown) confirms the presence of a large

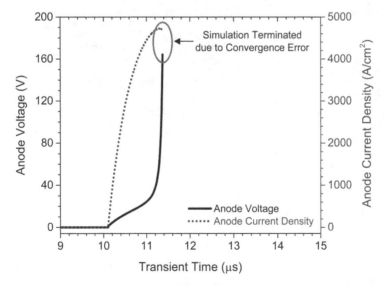

Fig. 52. Anode voltage (solid) and current density (dotted) waveforms pertaining to 5000 A/cm^2 peak current density simulation of planar junction Schottky diode complete-cell structure.

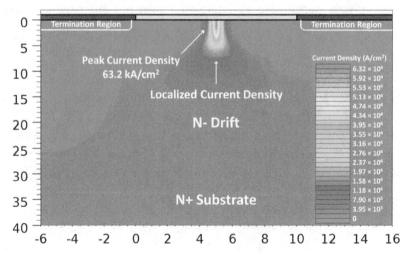

Fig. 53. Conduction current density profile of planar junction Schottky diode complete-cell structure during 5000 A/cm^2 RLC ring-down simulation (zoomed-in view).

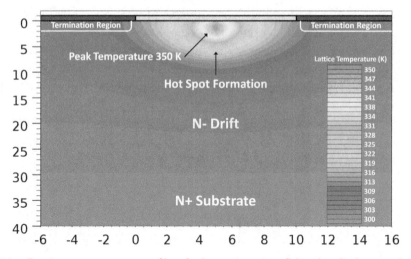

Fig. 54. Lattice temperature profile of planar junction Schottky diode complete-cell structure during 5000 A/cm^2 RLC ring-down simulation (zoomed-in view).

depletion region extending outwards from the p-type termination region. This localization of current flow results in abnormally high current density of 63.2 kA/cm^2 within the device even though the circuit current density is 4680 A/cm^2. The concentration of high current density in a small area within the device causes the formation of thermal hot-spots which can be seen in lattice temperature profile. Peak lattice temperature of 350 K was observed in the thermal hot-spot.

It is quite obvious from the complete-cell simulation data that the ON-state losses are much higher as compared to the half-cell data. This is due to the presence of termination regions on either side of the active area in a complete-cell structure which constricts current flow to a greater extent thereby resulting in extremely high current density. On the other hand, in a half-cell structure, current constriction occurs only from one side which provides a slightly better current path through the edge of the structure.

In general, the presence of extremely high current density within the device is an unfavorable condition which causes convergence issues during program simulation. Even though it is possible to have this simulation run for a longer duration by altering the tolerance parameters, it is highly unlikely that the simulation will complete the programmed duration. Moreover, the results obtained will be so unrealistic that it will hardly have any practical significance.

 It is highly recommended that the user checks the transient simulation log file at regular intervals to monitor the various circuit parameters. Any abnormal voltage/current value is generally an indicator of issues in either the circuit or the device model.

References

1. B. Baliga, *Fundamentals of Power Semiconductor Devices*, New York, NY: Springer Verlag, 2008.
2. J. Lutz, H. Schlangenotto, U. Scheuermann and R. D. Doncker, *Semiconductor Power Device — Physics Characteristic Reliability*, New York, NY: Springer-Verlag, 2011.
3. M. Philip and A. O'Neill, Calibration of 4H-SiC TCAD models and material parameters, *2006 Conference on Optoelectronic and Microelectronic Materials and Devices*, Perth, WA, 2006, pp. 137–140.
4. Z. Kamal and D. Lakhdar, Inhomogeneous barrier height effect on the current-voltage characteristics of a W/4H-SiC Schottky diode, *2017 5th International Conference on Electrical Engineering — Boumerdes (ICEE-B)*, Boumerdes, 2017, pp. 1–5.
5. *ATLAS User's Manual*, September 11, 2014, [online] Available at: www.silvaco.com.
6. B. N. Pushpakaran, S. B. Bayne and A. A. Ogunniyi, Electrothermal Simulation-Based Comparison of 4H-SiC p-i-n, Schottky, and JBS Diodes Under High Current Density Pulsed Operation, *IEEE Transactions on Plasma Science*, vol. 45, no. 1, January 2017, pp. 68–75.
7. W. Sung and B. J. Baliga, A near ideal edge termination technique for 4500V 4H-SiC Devices: The hybrid junction termination extension, *IEEE Electron Device Letters*, vol. 37, no. 12, December 2016, pp. 1609–1612.
8. W. Sung and B. J. Baliga, A comparative study 4500-V edge termination techniques for SiC devices, *IEEE Transactions on Electron Devices*, vol. 64, no. 4, April 2017, pp. 1647–1652.

Chapter 8

Junction Barrier Schottky (JBS) Diode

In the previous chapters on Silicon Carbide (SiC) p-i-n and Schottky rectifiers, device structures were simulated and analyzed for their electrical characteristics under steady-state and transient conditions. The superior electrothermal material properties of wide bandgap SiC enabled the development of high voltage power p-i-n and Schottky rectifiers. The electrical characteristics of SiC p-i-n diode revealed excellent high current capability, while providing high blocking voltage with low reverse-bias leakage current at high blocking voltage due to minority carrier conduction and conductivity modulation. However, the advantages of a p-i-n diode come at a price of higher built-in voltage (which directly affects the turn-ON voltage) due to larger material bandgap and limited switching frequency capability due to reverse recovery current. The electrical characteristics of SiC Schottky diode revealed lower ON-state voltage drop since it is independent of the material bandgap and higher switching frequency capability due to majority carrier conduction. However, the advantages of a Schottky diode come at a price of increased ON-state losses at high current density due to absence of conductivity modulation and elevated reverse-bias leakage current at high blocking voltage due to the interaction between the Schottky interface and blocking electric field. It can be concluded from this discussion that both p-i-n and Schottky diodes have their pros and cons which affect their suitability in power switching application. From a practical standpoint, the applications of SiC p-i-n and Schottky diode can be summarized as follows:

- P-i-N diode: Suitable for high-voltage and high-current switching operation if the turn-OFF di/dt and Pulse Repetition Frequency (PRF) is low enough to avoid device stress due to reverse recovery current.
- Schottky diode: Suitable for high-frequency and high-current switching operation if the blocking voltage results in acceptable reverse-bias leakage

current and the ON-state voltage drop is acceptable at the desired current density.

In order to utilize the advantages of p-i-n and Schottky diode while eliminating their respective limitations, Junction Barrier Schottky (JBS) diode structure was developed. JBS diode has the advantages of low turn-ON voltage, high blocking voltage with low leakage current, and high switching frequency with almost zero reverse recovery current, in other words ON-state and switching characteristics of a Schottky diode and OFF-state/blocking characteristics of a p-i-n diode.[1–3] The simplified cross-sectional structures of p-i-n, Schottky, and JBS diode are compared in Fig. 1.

The main aspect of a JBS diode which makes it unique and different with respect to a p-i-n and Schottky diode is the presence of interdigitated P+ regions at the metal–semiconductor/Schottky interface. The presence of P+ regions form an array of alternating p-i-n and Schottky diodes within the active area of the device. To obtain unipolar operation, it is necessary to suppress minority carrier injection by preventing the turn-ON of the p-i-n diode structures in the active area during normal device operation. This is achieved by controlling design parameters like spacing between the P+ regions and doping concentration of the P+ regions, which in turn would clamp the voltage drop across the P+/N− junction below the turn-ON voltage of SiC p-i-n diode under rated current density operation. Apart from the presence of interdigitated P+ regions, JBS diode structure consists of a

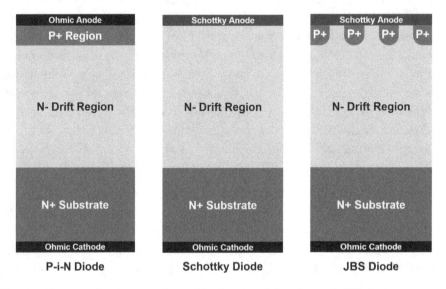

Fig. 1.　Cross-sectional comparison of basic p-i-n, Schottky, and JBS diode structure.

lightly doped n-type region, also known as the drift or intrinsic region, which is electrically connected to the metal anode to form the Schottky contact and a heavily doped n-type substrate which is electrically connected to the device cathode.

 In certain applications, it is required to have minority carrier injection into the drift region of a JBS diode to reduce ON-state resistance specifically during high current density operation. In such a scenario, the JBS diode is designed to enable bipolar turn-ON and is known as a Merged P-i-N Schottky (MPS) diode.

The working of a JBS diode is based on the forward characteristics of a Schottky diode and reverse-bias characteristics of a p-i-n diode. During forward operation, conduction occurs through the Schottky regions between the interdigitated P+ regions thereby providing lower turn-ON voltage which is dependent on the workfunction of the Schottky metal. In general, the reverse-bias leakage current in a Schottky diode is high due to Schottky barrier lowering. The increase in reverse-bias leakage current is more severe in SiC Schottky diode since the effect of barrier lowering is much stronger in silicon carbide as compared to silicon, a situation which gets worse with the addition of field emission or tunneling current component. Hence, it is necessary to shield the Schottky interface from high electric field during reverse-bias operation. This is accomplished using the interdigitated P+ regions spread across the active area of the diode. The spacing between the P+ regions is critical due to the tradeoff between forward ON-state resistance and reverse-bias leakage. When the P+ regions are spaced apart, there is a wider current path available during forward conduction even after subtracting the depletion regions at the P+/N− junctions. This is favorable for lower ON-state resistance; however, during reverse-bias operation, wider spacing between the P+ regions would expose the Schottky interface to high electric field which would increase the leakage current. Similarly, narrow P+ regions would provide excellent shielding of the Schottky interface during reverse-bias operation; however, this would form a constricted path for current conduction thereby increasing the forward ON-state resistance. This increase in ON-state resistance can be countered by implementing a larger die area which would impact the leakage current and also have financial implications considering the cost of SiC wafers.[4,5]

This tradeoff involved in the design of a JBS diode can be visualized using simplified cross-sectional images of a single-cell JBS diode shown in Figs. 2(a)

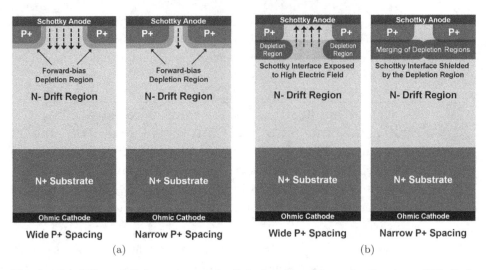

Fig. 2. (a) Effect of P+ spacing tradeoff during forward conduction in a JBS diode (current flow is marked using dashed arrows). (b) Effect of P+ spacing tradeoff during reverse-bias in a JBS diode (electric field is marked using dashed arrows).

and 2(b) highlighting the scenarios where the P+ spacing is wide and narrow. The effect of P+ region spacing during forward conduction is shown in Fig. 2(a) where current conduction through the diode is indicated by dashed arrows (more arrows represent less ON-state resistance). The impact of P+ region spacing during reverse-bias operation is shown in Fig. 2(b). As discussed before, when the P+ regions are spaced apart, depletion region formed at the P+/N− junction during reverse-bias does not completely merge, and this results in elevated leakage current through the device since the Schottky interface is now exposed to high electric field (indicated by dashed arrows), whereas closely spaced P+ regions enable complete merging of the depletion regions which shields the Schottky interface from the high electric field.[5]

Assuming the spacing between the P+ regions is optimized, there is another tradeoff which is related to the depth of the P+ implanted regions. The depth of the P+ region is also critical due to the tradeoff between forward ON-state resistance and reverse-bias leakage. Deeper P+ regions improve the reverse-bias leakage since they keep the pinch-off/depletion region away from the Schottky interface; however, deeper P+ regions introduce a longer narrow conduction path between the two P+ regions which increases the ON-state resistance, and hence power dissipation. Similarly, shallow P+ regions reduce the ON-state resistance by providing a shorter conduction path between the two P+ regions before current spreads

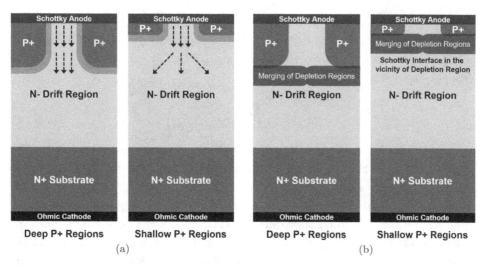

Fig. 3. (a) Effect of P+ depth tradeoff during forward conduction in a JBS diode (current flow is marked using dashed arrows). (b) Effect of P+ depth tradeoff during reverse-bias in a JBS diode focusing on the depletion regions.

into the drift region; however, shallow P+ regions cause the depletion region to be in close proximity to the Schottky interface, thereby increasing the leakage current due to the influence of electric field. This tradeoff involved in the design of a JBS diode can be visualized using simplified cross-sectional images of a single-cell JBS diode shown in Figs. 3(a) and 3(b) highlighting the scenarios where the P+ regions are deep and shallow.[5]

Since the primary mode of conduction in a JBS diode is through Schottky contact, forward-conduction and reverse-blocking characteristics are defined by the electronics properties of the Schottky contact metal, primarily the workfunction. In order to simplify the JBS diode design, the same metal can be used to form the Schottky contact to the N- epitaxial/drift region and ohmic contact to the P+ implanted region. The JBS diode structure can also be designed using different metals for the Schottky and ohmic contacts.

8.1. Forward-bias Characteristics

Under forward-bias operation, current flow across the diode is due to majority carriers via thermionic emission. This section will briefly discuss the forward conduction mechanism in a JBS diode. The basic equations used to define the current density at the Schottky contact and voltage drop across the JBS diode are same as those discussed in Chapter 7. The voltage drop across the JBS diode is given by Eq. (1) where Φ_B is the Schottky Barrier Height, k is Boltzmann constant, T is the absolute temperature, A is the effective Richardson's constant, and J_F is the current density at the Schottky contact.

$$V_F = \Phi_B + \frac{kT}{q} \ln \left(\frac{J_F}{AT^2} \right) \tag{1}$$

However, due to the difference in device structure, current density at the Schottky contact is much higher than the current density though the device cathode since Schottky contact area is a fraction of the cathode/substrate area. This difference in current density can be visualized in a single-cell JBS diode shown in Fig. 4 where x_{JP+} is the junction depth of P+ regions, x_{P+} is the width of P+ region, W_0 is the zero-bias depletion region width, d is the width of un-depleted portion between the P+ regions where current flow occurs, and t_{Drift} is the thickness of the epitaxial/drift region.[5]

Using the parameters indicated in Fig. 4, current density through the Schottky contact (J_F) is proportional to the cathode current density (J_{Cathode}) by a scaling factor which is expressed in Eq. (2). Since dimension

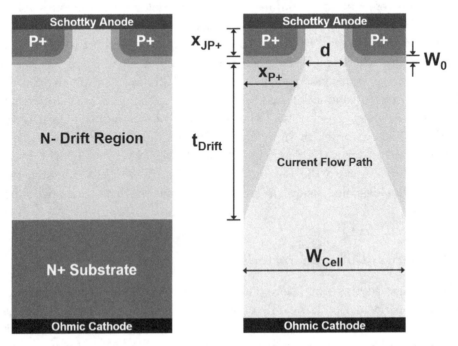

Fig. 4.   Single-cell JBS diode cross-sectional view showing current flow path during forward conduction.

"d" is much smaller than the cell pitch (W_{Cell}), J_F is much greater than J_{Cathode}

$$J_F = \left(\frac{W_{\text{Cell}}}{d}\right) J_{\text{Cathode}} \tag{2}$$

Calculation of dimension "d" requires values for the width of P+ region and zero-bias depletion region width. Due to the larger built-in potential for SiC (≈ 3 V) the zero-bias depletion region width is significant and should not be neglected. A detailed discussion and derivation of equations is out of scope of this textbook and can be found in the literature review.[5]

8.2. Reverse-bias Characteristics

This section will briefly discuss the behavior of a JBS diode under reverse-blocking phase. Under optimized design condition, magnitude of leakage current in a JBS diode is much smaller as compared to a Schottky diode due to the shielding of Schottky interface from high electric field. Since the Schottky interface is no longer exposed to high electric field, the impact of barrier lowering is significantly reduced. Another factor which contributes to reduced leakage current is the reduction in Schottky contact area/active area. The Schottky contact area in a JBS diode is a fraction of the cell area which decreases the reverse leakage current. The leakage current in a JBS diode can be calculated using Eq. (3), which is the same equation as for the Schottky diode with additional parameters to account for the JBS diode design

$$J_L = \left(\frac{d}{W_{\text{Cell}}}\right) AT^2 \cdot e^{-\left(\frac{q\Phi_B}{kT}\right)} \cdot e^{\left(\frac{q\Delta\Phi_{B\,\text{JBS}}}{kT}\right)} \cdot e^{\left(C_T \cdot E_{J\,\text{BS}}^2\right)} \tag{3}$$

The additional parameters in the JBS leakage current expression include the ratio of "d" to the cell pitch (which is also the current scaling term), tunneling coefficient C_T, impact of reduced barrier $\Delta\phi_{B\,\text{JBS}}$ and reduced electric field at the Schottky interface E_{JBS}. The decrease in Schottky barrier height in a JBS diode can be calculated using the following equation:

$$\Delta\Phi_{B\,\text{JBS}} = \sqrt{\frac{q\,E_{\text{JBS}}}{4\,\pi\,\varepsilon_S}} \tag{4}$$

The electric field at the Schottky interface can be expressed in terms of the applied reverse-bias/pinch-off voltage (V_P) using Eq. (5), where β is the factor used to account for the build-up of electric field after pinch-off, N_{Drift} is the doping concentration of the drift region, and V_{bi} is the built-in potential. The pinch-off voltage (V_P) is defined as the applied reverse-bias/pinch-off voltage at which the space between the P+ regions get fully depleted and can be expressed in terms of the device cell parameters (shown in Fig. 4) using Eq. (6). It may be noted that the expression for pinch-off voltage shown in Eq. (6) was derived for a half-cell JBS diode structure.[5]

$$E_{\text{JBS}} = \sqrt{\frac{2\,q\,N_{\text{Drift}}}{\varepsilon_S}\,(\beta V_P + V_{\text{bi}})} \tag{5}$$

$$V_P = \frac{q\,N_{\text{Drift}}}{2\,\varepsilon_S}\,(W_{\text{Cell}} - x_{P+})^2 - V_{\text{bi}} \tag{6}$$

8.3.   Silvaco© ATLAS Modeling and Simulation

Irrespective of the device being simulated, it is highly recommended that the user starts off the modeling process by developing TCAD model for the most basic device design. This would not only streamline the overall modeling process by reducing the initial simulation time, enabling faster troubleshooting, and better understanding of the device model, but also helps in optimizing the more complex device design approach. In case of p-i-n and Schottky diode simulation, user had the option to simulate the most basic diode design, which is the parallel plane structure. However, it is obvious that a parallel plane structure cannot be implemented for a JBS diode due to its design aspects. Hence, a different approach will be used in this chapter to explain the modeling and simulation of a JBS diode.

 It is highly recommended to design and simulate a single-cell JBS structure as a starting point. However, simulation of a single-cell structure fails to show current sharing, electric field distribution, and breakdown that occurs in a multi-cell structure.

The following sections will discuss the modeling and simulation of 3300 V SiC JBS diode structures with different active area implemented using multiple cells. A detailed discussion of the design equations used for the JBS diode is out of scope of this textbook. The simulations will consist of steady-state and transient characterization.

8.3.1.   Simulation models

The physics-based models used for JBS diode simulation are same as for the Schottky diode and accounted for Shockley–Read–Hall recombination

(**SRH**), auger recombination (**AUGER**), bandgap narrowing (**BGN**), low-field mobility (**ANALYTIC**), mobility due to carrier–carrier scattering (**CONWELL**), incomplete ionization of dopants (**INCOMPLETE**), and impact ionization (**SELB**). The **MODELS** statement was used to implement these models in the deckbuild code. The temperature parameter (**TEMP**) can be used to change the steady-state lattice temperature of the simulation. For non-isothermal Mixed-Mode or transient simulation, in addition to the aforementioned models, lattice temperature model (**LAT.TEMP**) was included to account for the change in device lattice temperature during the course of simulation. The lattice temperature model was used in conjunction with models to account for heat generation due to joule heating (**JOULE.HEAT**), Carrier Generation and Recombination heating (**GR.HEAT**), and Peltier–Thomson heating (**PT.HEAT**). Performing non-isothermal simulations also require models and parameters to define thermal conductivity and heat capacity and its variation as a function of lattice temperature. The Schottky diode simulations discussed in this chapter use the polynomial function (**TCON.POLYN**) for thermal conductivity and the standard model for heat capacity.

Since conduction in a JBS diode occurs through the Schottky contact, selection of Schottky metal is critical for the simulation since barrier height determines the forward and reverse characteristics. The parameters which define the behavior of the Schottky interface are specified using the **CONTACT** statement. The user can either specify the Schottky metal to be used or the workfunction of the conductor. If a Schottky metal is specified out of the default library of metals, ATLAS will use the workfunction which is internally associated with the particular metal. When the user explicitly specifies the workfunction (**WORKFUNCTION**), ATLAS will associate that particular value to the conductor. In addition to specifying the Schottky metal workfunction, parameters need to be added to account for thermionic emission (**THERMION**) and parabolic field emission (**PARABOLIC**).

As mentioned before, the user can define different metals to be used as Schottky and ohmic contact electrode. In that scenario, it is critical to short the Schottky and ohmic electrodes since the net anode current density is the sum of Schottky and ohmic contact current density components. Even though current density through the ohmic contact is several orders of magnitude lower than the Schottky contact current density, it is a good practice to short the electrodes together via **COMMON** and **SHORT** parameters in the **CONTACT** statement.[6] The usage of these parameters will be explained in the code walkthrough.

8.3.2.   JBS diode — Active area 5 μm^2

Since a parallel plane structure is impractical for a JBS diode, a multi-cell approach has been used in this simulation to implement a JBS diode structure for the given active area of 5 μm^2. The JBS diode structure was designed for a rated current density of 100 A/cm^2 and blocking voltage of 3300 V. Since the rated blocking voltage is typically considered as 80% of the actual breakdown voltage, the diode was designed for a breakdown voltage of 4200 V. The drift region was uniformly doped with a donor concentration (N_{Drift}) of 3.2 $\times$ 10^{15} cm^{-3} and the substrate was heavily doped with a uniform donor concentration of 1.0 $\times$ 10^{20} cm^{-3}. The interdigitated P+ regions were heavily doped with an acceptor concentration of 1.0 $\times$ 10^{20} cm^{-3} using a Gaussian doping profile. The P+ regions had a junction depth of 2 μm which was selected after several rounds of simulation and optimization. In order to reduce the ON-state resistance without affecting the breakdown voltage, the complete diode structure was uniformly doped with a donor concentration (N_{CSL}) of 1.0 $\times$ 10^{16} cm^{-3} up to a depth of 2.4 μm. In this diode model, n-type dopant is assumed to be nitrogen and p-type dopant is assumed to be Aluminum with corresponding ionization energies of 50 meV and 200 meV, respectively, which were used to account for incomplete ionization. The drift region thickness was calculated to be 30 μm based on the design equations. The anode Schottky metal was configured to be a conductor with a workfunction of 5.0 eV, anode ohmic contact was formed using titanium, and aluminum was used for the cathode ohmic contact. Since the JBS diode conducts only through the Schottky contact area, the active area of 5 μm^2 was realized using device width of 17.5 μm and the default Z-dimension is 1 μm.[7,8] Due to the large substrate thickness as compared to the drift layer, the complete device structure designed using Silvaco© ATLAS does not clearly show the device-specific details. Hence, device structure has been split into two Figs. 5(a) and 5(b), respectively. The interdigitated P+ regions along with the separate Schottky and ohmic contacts can be seen in Fig. 5(b).

8.3.2.1.   *Steady-state simulation*

Steady-state/DC simulation helps in verifying the basic operation of the device model. This section will discuss the forward conduction and reverse breakdown current density versus anode voltage (J–V) characteristics at 27°C, 75°C, 125°C, and 175°C device temperature. Steady-state simulations help the user to refine the device model which includes optimization of the

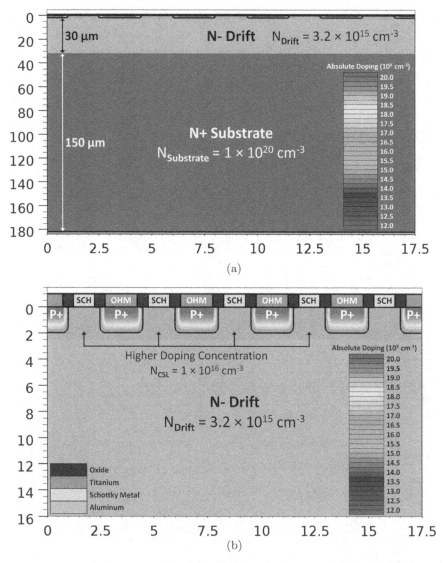

Fig. 5. (a) 3300 V SiC JBS diode (active area = 5 μm^2) multi-cell structure designed in Silvaco© ATLAS. (b) 3300 V SiC JBS diode (active area = 5 μm^2) multi-cell structure designed in Silvaco© ATLAS (zoomed-in view).

mesh profile, doping concentration adjustment to fine-tune the breakdown voltage. The following code was used to simulate the JBS diode J–V characteristics which includes forward conduction and reverse breakdown. A brief explanation of the steady-state simulation program is provided in the code walkthrough (Table 1).

```
Sample code: JBS diode (active area = 5 μm²) forward and breakdown J-V characteristics @ 27°C

1.  GO ATLAS SIMFLAGS ="-V 5.18.3.R -P 32 -160"
2.
3.  ##### 3300V JBS DIODE STEADY STATE @ 27C #####
4.
5.  MESH
6.
7.  ## X-MESH
8.
9.  X.MESH  loc=0.0     spac=0.25
10. X.MESH  loc=17.50   spac=0.25
11.
12. ## Y-MESH
13.
14. Y.MESH  loc=-1.0    spac=1.0
15. Y.MESH  loc=0.0     spac=0.5
16. Y.MESH  loc=0.2     spac=0.10
17. Y.MESH  loc=2.1     spac=0.02
18. Y.MESH  loc=30.0    spac=10.0
19. Y.MESH  loc=31.4    spac=0.25
20. Y.MESH  loc=32.4    spac=0.25
21. Y.MESH  loc=34.0    spac=20
22. Y.MESH  loc=180.0   spac=20
23. Y.MESH  loc=182.0   spac=1.0
24. Y.MESH  loc=184.0   spac=1.0
25.
26. ## Defining Regions
27.
28. REGION  num=1 material=Oxide    x.min=0  x.max=17.5   y.max=0
29. REGION  num=2 material=4H-SiC   x.min=0  x.max=17.5   y.min=0  y.max=182
30.
31. ## Electrode
32.
33. ELECTRODE  name=anode_ohm  material=titanium    x.min=0      x.max=0.75
    y.min=-1   y.max=0
34. ELECTRODE  name=anode      material=conductor   x.min=1.25   x.max=2.25
    y.min=-1   y.max=0
35. ELECTRODE  name=anode_ohm  material=titanium    x.min=2.75   x.max=4.25
    y.min=-1   y.max=0
36. ELECTRODE  name=anode      material=conductor   x.min=4.75   x.max=5.75
    y.min=-1   y.max=0
37. ELECTRODE  name=anode_ohm  material=titanium    x.min=6.25   x.max=7.75
    y.min=-1   y.max=0
38. ELECTRODE  name=anode      material=conductor   x.min=8.25   x.max=9.25
    y.min=-1   y.max=0
39. ELECTRODE  name=anode_ohm  material=titanium    x.min=9.75   x.max=11.25
    y.min=-1   y.max=0
40. ELECTRODE  name=anode      material=conductor   x.min=11.75  x.max=12.75
    y.min=-1   y.max=0
41. ELECTRODE  name=anode_ohm  material=titanium    x.min=13.25  x.max=14.75
    y.min=-1   y.max=0
42. ELECTRODE  name=anode      material=conductor   x.min=15.25  x.max=16.25
    y.min=-1   y.max=0
43. ELECTRODE  name=anode_ohm  material=titanium    x.min=16.75  x.max=17.50
    y.min=-1   y.max=0
44.
45. ELECTRODE  name=cathode    material=aluminum  y.min=182  y.max=184
46.
```

```
47. ## Doping Distribution
48.
49. ## Bulk Doping
50. DOPING  uniform  n.type conc=3.2e15   REGION=2
51. DOPING  uniform  n.type conc=1.e16     y.min=0  y.max=2.4
52.
53. ## P+ Doping
54. DOPING  gauss  p.type  conc=1.e20  x.min=0.0   x.max=0.80   junc=2.0  rat=0.1
55. DOPING  gauss  p.type  conc=1.e20  x.min=2.7   x.max=4.30   junc=2.0  rat=0.1
56. DOPING  gauss  p.type  conc=1.e20  x.min=6.2   x.max=7.80   junc=2.0   rat=0.1
57. DOPING  gauss  p.type  conc=1.e20  x.min=9.7   x.max=11.3   junc=2.0   rat=0.1
58. DOPING  gauss  p.type  conc=1.e20  x.min=13.2  x.max=14.80  junc=2.0  rat=0.1
59. DOPING  gauss  p.type  conc=1.e20  x.min=16.7  x.max=17.50  junc=2.0  rat=0.1
60.
61. ## N+ Substrate Region Doping
62. DOPING  uniform   n.type  conc=1.e20  y.min=32   y.max=182
63.
64. SAVE  outf=JBS_Structure.str  master.out
65.
66. MATERIAL  material=4H-SiC REGION=2  permittivity=9.76   eg300=3.26
     affinity=3.7  egalpha=3.3e-2   egbeta=1.e+5  nc300=1.7e+19  nv300=2.5e+19
     arichn=146  arichp=30  augn=3.e-29  augp=3.e-29   taun0=3.33e-6  taup0=6.7e-7
     nsrhn=3.e+17 nsrhp=3.e+17 edb=0.050  eab=0.200
67.
68. CONTACT  NAME=anode          WORKFUNCTION=5.0  THERMION  PARABOLIC
69. CONTACT  NAME=anode_ohm      COMMON=anode     SHORT
70.
71. ## MODELS USED
72.
73. MODELS  REGION=2  MATERIAL=4H-SIC FERMIDIRAC ANALYTIC CONWELL SRH BGN AUGER
     INCOMPLETE TEMP=300 PRINT
74.
75. ## MOBILITY
76.
77. MOBILITY  material=4H-SiC REGION=2  vsatn=2.2e7  vsatp=2.2e7  betan=1.2
     betap=2  mu1n.caug=40  mu2n.caug=1136  ncritn.caug=2e17  alphan.caug=-3
     betan.caug=-3  gamman.caug=0.0  deltan.caug=0.76  mu1p.caug=20  mu2p.caug=125
     ncritp.caug=1.e19  alphap.caug=-3  betap.caug=-3  gammap.caug=0.0
     deltap.caug=0.5
78.
79. MOBILITY  material=4H-SiC REGION=2  n.canali  n.angle=90  p.angle=90
     vsatn=2.2e7  vsatp=2.2e7  betan=1.2 betap=2  mu1n.caug=5  mu2n.caug=947
     ncritn.caug=2e17  alphan.caug=-3  betan.caug=-3  gamman.caug=0.0
     deltan.caug=0.76  mu1p.caug=2.5  mu2p.caug=20  ncritp.caug=1.e19
     alphap.caug=-3  betap.caug=-3  gammap.caug=0.0  deltap.caug=0.5
80.
81. IMPACT  REGION=2  ANISO  E.SIDE  SELB  SIC4H0001  an1=3.44e6  an2=3.44e6
     bn1=2.58e7  bn2=2.58e7  ap1=3.5e6  ap2=3.5e6  bp1=1.7e7 bp2=1.7e7 opphe=0.106
82.
83. METHOD NEWTON  AUTONR  TRAP  climit=1.e-9  maxtraps=40  itlimit=40
     dvmax=1.e8  ir.tol=1.e-40  cr.tol=1.e-40  ix.tol=1.e-40  px.tol=1.e-30
     pr.tol=1.e-45  cx.tol=1.e-30
84.
85. OUTPUT  FLOWLINES
86.
87. LOG  outf=JBS_Forward_27C.log
88.
89. SOLVE  init
90. SOLVE  vanode=0.02   vstep=0.02  vfinal=1.5  name=anode
91. SOLVE  vstep=0.05     vfinal=4.0  name=anode
```

```
92.
93. SAVE   outf=JBS_Forward_27C.str
94.
95. LOG   outf=JBS_Reverse_27C.log
96.
97.  SOLVE  init
98.  SOLVE  vanode=-0.2   vstep=-0.2    vfinal=-2.0   name=anode
99.  SOLVE  vstep=-2      vfinal=-20    name=anode
100. SOLVE  vstep=-5      vfinal=-100   name=anode
101. SOLVE  vstep=-10     vfinal=-1000  name=anode
102. SOLVE  vstep=-25     vfinal=-4000  name=anode
103. SOLVE  vstep=-10     vfinal=-4200  name=anode
104. SOLVE  vstep=-2      vfinal=-4500  name=anode   compl=1e-15  cname=anode
105.
106. SAVE   outf=JBS_Reverse_27C.str
107.
108. QUIT
```

Table 1. Code walkthrough: JBS diode (active area $= 5~\mu m^2$) forward and breakdown *J–V* characteristics.

Line No:	Functionality
1	Configure ATLAS simulator to use 160-bit extended precision and utilize 32 cores of the CPU if hardware resources are available. The version of ATLAS to be used by the simulator is set to 5.18.3.R using the -V option in the simflags command.
5	Initialize device structure mesh information.
7–24	*X*-axis and *Y*-axis mesh distribution.
28–29	Declare oxide and 4H-SiC as the material for the area specified by the *x* and *y* coordinates.
33–43	Separate electrode statements for the anode Schottky contact using metal conductor and anode ohmic contact using titanium.
45	Electrode statement to specify aluminum for cathode ohmic contact.
49–62	Specify doping profile, type, and concentration for different areas of the JBS diode structure.
64	Save the device structure (**.str**) file on the local hard drive. The device structure can be viewed by opening the file via **TonyPlot** to troubleshoot/optimize the structure.
66	Specify material parameters for 4H-SiC. Detailed description of these parameters is available in the Silvaco© ATLAS manual. The values for these parameters can either be obtained via material research or from literature.
68	Specify Schottky metal workfunction and model/parameters for thermionic emission and parabolic field emission using **Contact** statement.
69	Shorting the anode Schottky contact and anode ohmic contact using **Common** parameter.

(Continued)

Table 1.   (*Continued*)

Line No:	Functionality
73	Specify the various models to be included in the 4H-SiC JBS diode simulation.
77	Specify mobility parameters for 4H-SiC. Detailed description of these parameters is available in the Silvaco© ATLAS manual. The values for these parameters can either be obtained via material research or from literature.
79	Specify anisotropic mobility parameters for 4H-SiC. Detailed description of these parameters is available in the Silvaco© ATLAS manual. The values for these parameters can either be obtained via material research or from literature.
81	Specify impact ionization parameters for 4H-SiC. This statement is mandatory to obtain device breakdown characteristics.
83	Specify the solver type and the tolerance values to be used during the simulation. This is an extremely critical statement which can alter the simulation outcome.
85	Include current flowlines in the output structure file.
87	Save the simulation log (**.log**) file on the local hard drive. The simulation results can be viewed by opening the file via **TonyPlot**.
89–91	Solve for the initial bias conditions for the simulation followed by positive sweep of anode voltage for steady-state forward characteristics.
93	Save the post-forward-bias simulation device structure (**.str**) file on the local hard drive. Saving the file at this stage of the simulation will enable the user to visualize the variation in various electrothermal parameters within the device structure introduced due to the particular simulation.
95	Save the reverse-bias simulation log (**.log**) file on the local hard drive. The simulation results can be viewed by opening the file via **TonyPlot**.
97–104	Use solve statement to increment the negative anode voltage in discrete steps. The compliance parameter (**compl**) in line 104 forces the simulator to proceed to the next line once the anode current reaches the specified compliance value. This is important, especially in breakdown simulation because once the device enters the breakdown regime, it is not necessary to run the simulation for higher magnitude of current since the breakdown voltage would have already been determined.
106	Save the post-reverse-bias simulation device structure (**.str**) file on the local hard drive. Saving the file at this stage of the simulation will enable the user to visualize the variation in various electrothermal parameters within the device structure introduced due to the particular simulation.
108	Terminate the simulation.

8.3.2.2. *Steady-state simulation results*

The forward conduction J–V characteristics for the 3300 V SiC JBS diode on a linear and semi-log scale are shown in Figs. 6(a) and 6(b), respectively. It can be seen from Fig. 6(a) that there is a steady decrease in the diode turn-ON voltage as the lattice temperature increases from 27°C to 175°C, behavior already seen during Schottky diode simulation. This reduced ON-state voltage drop at low current density can be attributed to the reduction in Schottky barrier height with increase in lattice temperature. However, since JBS diode is a majority carrier device, degradation in the bulk mobility at elevated temperature increases the ON-state resistance, thereby leading to higher ON-state losses. At an ON-state current density of 100 A/cm^2, voltage drop of 1.18 V was observed across the JBS diode at 27°C device temperature.

One of the critical aspects in a multi-cell JBS diode structure is the current sharing between the interdigitated Schottky contacts during forward conduction since any imbalance between the cells may result in current crowding at a particular Schottky contact, which is not desirable for stable operation. The current density profile for the JBS diode during forward conduction is shown in Fig. 7. The structure file was generated when the current density through the device was 100 A/cm^2. The current density contour plot shows equal current sharing between the multiple Schottky contact regions within the diode structure. Uniform current sharing is also an indicator of mesh uniformity across the diode structure.

 The current density contour plot can also be used to verify the active area. The user can generate the structure file corresponding to the rated current density of the device and then use the current and current density data to calculate the active area obtained during device operation. This value can be compared to the designed value to validate the design phase calculations. The instantaneous bias point (voltage and current) corresponding to a structure file can be seen by pressing "B" on the keyboard once the structure file is loaded into TonyPlot. However, this technique is only valid for vertical current flow devices.

The reverse-bias breakdown J–V characteristics are shown in Fig. 8. Breakdown voltage of 4291 V was obtained for the JBS diode at 27°C

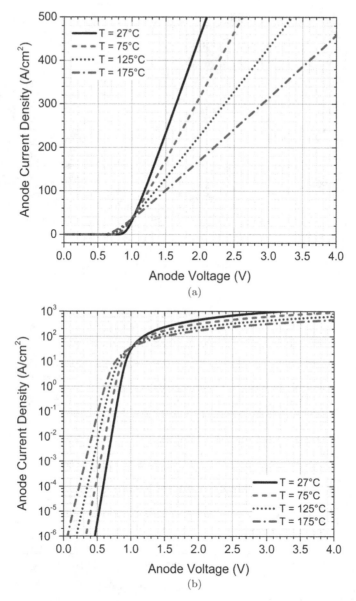

Fig. 6. (a) Forward *J–V* characteristics for the SiC JBS diode structure (active area = 5 μm^2) on a linear scale. (b) Forward *J–V* characteristics for the SiC JBS diode structure (active area = 5 μm^2) on a semi-log scale.

device temperature. There is a progressive increase in the leakage current with device temperature without any change in the breakdown voltage. The breakdown characteristics are dependent on the impact ionization coefficients, and it is up to the user to specify them based on experimental data or literature review.

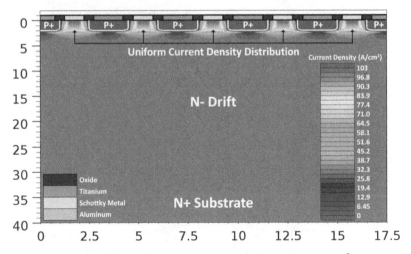

Fig. 7.   Contour plot of SiC JBS diode structure (active area = 5 μm^2) current density profile during forward conduction.

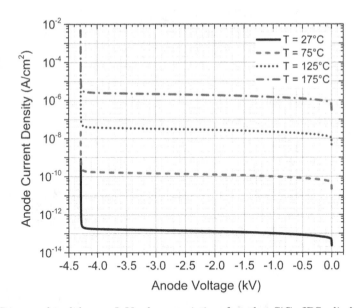

Fig. 8.   Reverse breakdown J–V characteristics for the SiC JBS diode structure (active area = 5 μm^2) on a semi-log scale.

The electric field distribution in the JBS diode structure during breakdown is shown in the contour plot in Figs. 9(a) and 9(b) (Images have been scaled to highlight the area of interest). Maximum electric field of 2.82 MV/cm was observed at the P+/N− junction shown in Fig. 9(a) which is also the point of breakdown. The salient aspect of a JBS diode structure

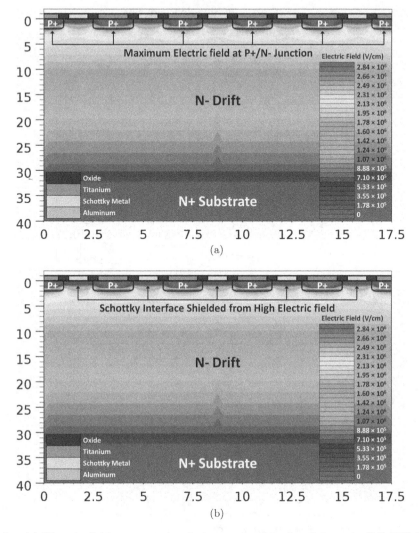

Fig. 9. (a) Electric field contour plot during reverse-bias breakdown in SiC JBS diode structure (active area = 5 μm^2) highlighting the distribution of electric field across the P+/N− junction. (b) Electric field contour plot during reverse-bias breakdown in SiC JBS diode structure (active area = 5 μm^2) highlighting the shielding of Schottky interface from high electric field.

is its ability to shield the Schottky interface from the high electric which tends to increase the reverse-bias leakage current due to barrier lowering. It can be seen from the electric field profile in Fig. 9(b) that the magnitude of electric field is significantly lower at the Schottky interface.

A quantitative analysis of the electric field distribution was performed by plotting the 1D electric field profiles as a function of device depth in

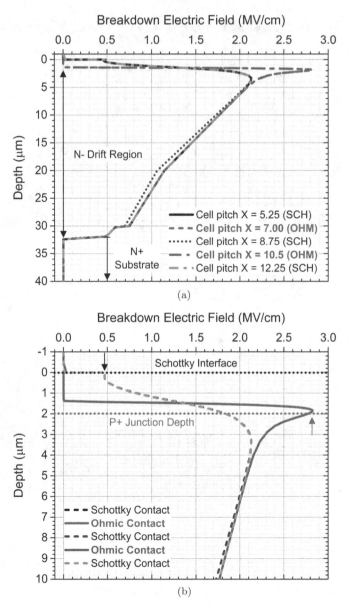

Fig. 10.   (a) 1D electric field profile as a function of device depth at varying points across the diode active area/cell pitch. (b) 1D electric field profile as a function of device depth at varying points across the diode active area/cell pitch zoomed in for details (breakdown electric field shown by solid lines).

Figs. 10(a) and 10(b). The plot has been scaled to highlight the region of interest. The electric field data was extracted for the following points: anode Schottky contact area ($x = 5.25$ μm, $x = 8.75$ μm, and $x = 12.25$ μm) and anode ohmic contact area which is also the point of breakdown ($x = 7$ μm

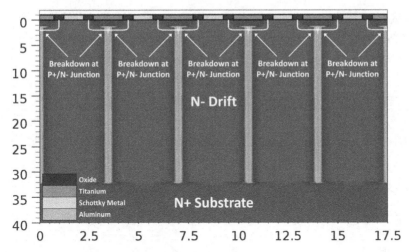

Fig. 11. Current density contour plot during reverse-bias breakdown highlighting the point of breakdown at P+/N− junction.

and $x = 10.5$ μm) using the **cutline** feature in **TonyPlot**. To have a closer look at the electric field distribution in the aforementioned points, individual electric field profiles are shown in Fig. 10(b), which is a zoomed-in version of Fig. 10(a). It can be seen from Figs. 10(a) and 10(b) that the P+ implanted regions shield the Schottky interface from high electric by pinching off the interdigitated Schottky contact area and distributing the electric field across P+ regions. The peak electric field observed at the P+/N− junction is 2.82 MV/cm, whereas the electric field at the Schottky interface is 0.48 MV/cm, which is almost 6 times less than the peak value.

The current density profile of the JBS diode during breakdown is shown in Fig. 11. The figure only highlights the point of breakdown in the device structure, and hence graph legend has not been included. Breakdown occurs at the P+/N− junction which is followed by the formation of current filaments through the P+ regions. Since diode breakdown is occurring at the p–n junction, sharp increase in the leakage current can be seen in the reverse-bias J–V characteristics shown in Fig. 8.

8.3.2.3. *Mixed-Mode transient simulation*

The Mixed-Mode transient simulation was performed using the RLC ring-down circuit. The simulation code was similar to that used for the p-i-n and Schottky diode simulation.[7,8] Changes were made to the program to include the JBS diode device mesh profile and dimensions of the thermal boundary based on the device structure. The scaling/width factor was altered to account for the 5 μm^2 active area. The following code was used to simulate the JBS diode for a peak forward current density of 5000 A/cm^2 under pulsed condition. A brief explanation of the Mixed-Mode simulation program is provided in the code walkthrough (Table 2).

```
Sample code: JBS diode (active area = 5 μm²) transient simulation

1.  GO ATLAS SIMFLAGS ="-V 5.18.3.R -P 32 -160"
2.
3.  ##### 3300V JBS DIODE RLC RINGDOWN PULSE 5000A/cm2 #####
4.
5.  MESH  WIDTH=2.4e6
6.
7.  ## X-MESH
8.
9.  X.MESH  loc=0.0    spac=0.25
10. X.MESH  loc=17.50  spac=0.25
11.
12. ## Y-MESH
13.
14. Y.MESH  loc=-1.0   spac=1.0
15. Y.MESH  loc=0.0    spac=0.5
16. Y.MESH  loc=0.2    spac=0.10
17. Y.MESH  loc=2.1    spac=0.02
18. Y.MESH  loc=30.0   spac=10.0
19. Y.MESH  loc=31.4   spac=0.25
20. Y.MESH  loc=32.4   spac=0.25
21. Y.MESH  loc=34.0   spac=20
22. Y.MESH  loc=180.0  spac=20
23. Y.MESH  loc=182.0  spac=1.0
24. Y.MESH  loc=184.0  spac=1.0
25.
26. ## Defining Regions
27.
28. REGION  num=1  material=Oxide   x.min=0  x.max=17.5  y.max=0
29. REGION  num=2  material=4H-SiC  x.min=0  x.max=17.5  y.min=0   y.max=182
30.
31. ## Electrode
32.
33. ELECTRODE  name=anode_ohm   material=titanium   x.min=0       x.max=0.75
        y.min=-1  y.max=0
34. ELECTRODE  name=anode       material=conductor  x.min=1.25    x.max=2.25
        y.min=-1  y.max=0
35. ELECTRODE  name=anode_ohm   material=titanium   x.min=2.75    x.max=4.25
        y.min=-1  y.max=0
36. ELECTRODE  name=anode       material=conductor  x.min=4.75    x.max=5.75
        y.min=-1  y.max=0
37. ELECTRODE  name=anode_ohm   material=titanium   x.min=6.25    x.max=7.75
        y.min=-1  y.max=0
38. ELECTRODE  name=anode       material=conductor  x.min=8.25    x.max=9.25
        y.min=-1  y.max=0
39. ELECTRODE  name=anode_ohm   material=titanium   x.min=9.75    x.max=11.25
        y.min=-1  y.max=0
40. ELECTRODE  name=anode       material=conductor  x.min=11.75   x.max=12.75
        y.min=-1  y.max=0
41. ELECTRODE  name=anode_ohm   material=titanium   x.min=13.25   x.max=14.75
        y.min=-1  y.max=0
42. ELECTRODE  name=anode       material=conductor  x.min=15.25   x.max=16.25
        y.min=-1  y.max=0
```

```
43. ELECTRODE   name=anode_ohm   material=titanium   x.min=16.75   x.max=17.50
    y.min=-1   y.max=0
44.
45. ELECTRODE   name=cathode     material=aluminum   y.min=182   y.max=184
46.
47. ## Doping Distribution
48.
49. ## Bulk Doping
50. DOPING   uniform   n.type conc=3.2e15   REGION=2
51. DOPING   uniform   n.type conc=1.e16    y.min=0 y.max=2.4
52.
53. ## P+ Doping
54. DOPING   gauss   p.type   conc=1.e20   x.min=0.0    x.max=0.80   junc=2.0  rat=0.1
55. DOPING   gauss   p.type   conc=1.e20   x.min=2.7    x.max=4.30   junc=2.0  rat=0.1
56. DOPING   gauss   p.type   conc=1.e20   x.min=6.2    x.max=7.80   junc=2.0  rat=0.1
57. DOPING   gauss   p.type   conc=1.e20   x.min=9.7    x.max=11.3   junc=2.0  rat=0.1
58. DOPING   gauss   p.type   conc=1.e20   x.min=13.2   x.max=14.80  junc=2.0  rat=0.1
59. DOPING   gauss   p.type   conc=1.e20   x.min=16.7   x.max=17.50  junc=2.0  rat=0.1
60.
61. ## N+ Substrate Region Doping
62. DOPING   uniform   n.type  conc=1.e20  y.min=32   y.max=182
63.
64. SAVE   outf=JBS_Structure.str   master.out
65.
66. ##### STEADY STATE SIMULATION CIRCUIT #####
67.
68. GO ATLAS SIMFLAGS ="-V 5.18.3.R -P 32 -160"
69.
70. .BEGIN
71.
72. VDC         1    0    0
73. RSW         1    2    1.e-12
74. R_CHARGE    2    3    500
75. C_BANK      3    0    6u
76. R_SERIES    3    4    0.80
77. L_SERIES    4    5    500n
78. RSWITCH     5    6    1.e18
79. ADIODE      6=anode_ohm  6=anode_sch  0=cathode   infile=JBS_Structure.str
    width=2.4e6
80.
81. .NODESET  v(1)=0  v(2)=0  v(3)=0  v(4)=0  v(5)=0  v(6)=0
82. .NUMERIC  imaxdc=100
83.
84. .DC   VDC   0.    10.   0.25
85. .DC   VDC   10.   100.  5.
86. .DC   VDC   100.  600.  25.
87.
88. .LOG  outfile=JBS_DC_log
89. .SAVE  outfile=JBS_RLC_Bias
90. .OPTIONS  m2ln print noshift relpot
91.
92. .END
93.
94. ##### PHYSICS USED #####
95.
96. CONTACT  DEVICE=ADIODE  NUMBER=1  NAME=anode_ohm   COMMON=anode_sch  SHORT
    EXT.ALPHA=10
97. CONTACT  DEVICE=ADIODE  NUMBER=3  NAME=anode_ohm   COMMON=anode_sch  SHORT
    EXT.ALPHA=10
```

```
98. CONTACT  DEVICE=ADIODE  NUMBER=5   NAME=anode_ohm   COMMON=anode_sch  SHORT
    EXT.ALPHA=10
99. CONTACT  DEVICE=ADIODE  NUMBER=7   NAME=anode_ohm   COMMON=anode_sch  SHORT
    EXT.ALPHA=10
100. CONTACT  DEVICE=ADIODE  NUMBER=9   NAME=anode_ohm   COMMON=anode_sch  SHORT
    EXT.ALPHA=10
101. CONTACT  DEVICE=ADIODE  NUMBER=11  NAME=anode_ohm   COMMON=anode_sch  SHORT
    EXT.ALPHA=10
102.
103. CONTACT  DEVICE=ADIODE  NUMBER=2  NAME=anode_sch   WORKFUNCTION=5.0  THERMION  PARABOLIC
    EXT.ALPHA=10
104. CONTACT  DEVICE=ADIODE  NUMBER=4  NAME=anode_sch   WORKFUNCTION=5.0  THERMION  PARABOLIC
    EXT.ALPHA=10
105. CONTACT  DEVICE=ADIODE  NUMBER=6  NAME=anode_sch   WORKFUNCTION=5.0  THERMION  PARABOLIC
    EXT.ALPHA=10
106. CONTACT  DEVICE=ADIODE  NUMBER=8  NAME=anode_sch   WORKFUNCTION=5.0  THERMION  PARABOLIC
    EXT.ALPHA=10
107. CONTACT  DEVICE=ADIODE  NUMBER=10 NAME=anode_sch   WORKFUNCTION=5.0  THERMION  PARABOLIC
    EXT.ALPHA=10
108.
109. CONTACT  DEVICE=ADIODE  NUMBER=12  NAME=cathode    EXT.ALPHA=10
110.
111. THERMCONTACT DEVICE=ADIODE   num=13   x.min=0   x.max=17.5  y.min=-1.0
    y.max=184   alpha=10   ext.temp=300
112.
113. MATERIAL  DEVICE=ADIODE   material=4H-SiC  REGION=2  permittivity=9.76
    eg300=3.26   affinity=3.7   egalpha=3.3e-2  egbeta=1.e+5  nc300=1.7e+19
    nv300=2.5e+19  arichn=146  arichp=30  augn=3.e-29  augp=3.e-29  taun0=3.33e-6
    taup0=6.7e-7  nsrhn=3.e+17  nsrhp=3.e+17  edb=0.050  eab=0.200  tcon.polyn
    tc.a=0.137534   tc.b=0.00049662   tc.c=0.000000354  hc.a=2.35  hc.b=1.75e-3
    hc.c=1.e-9  hc.d=-6.6e4
114.
115. ## MODELS USED
116.
117. MODELS  DEVICE=ADIODE  REGION=2 MATERIAL=4H-SiC FERMIDIRAC ANALYTIC CONWELL
    SRH BGN AUGER INCOMPLETE LAT.TEMP JOULE.HEAT  GR.HEAT  PT.HEAT PRINT
118.
119. ## MOBILITY
120.
121. MOBILITY  DEVICE=ADIODE material=4H-SiC REGION=2 vsatn=2.2e7  vsatp=2.2e7
    betan=1.2 betap=2 mu1n.caug=40 mu2n.caug=1136 ncritn.caug=2e17
    alphan.caug=-3 betan.caug=-3 gamman.caug=0.0 deltan.caug=0.76
    mu1p.caug=20 mu2p.caug=125 ncritp.caug=1.e19 alphap.caug=-3 betap.caug=-3
    gammap.caug=0.0 deltap.caug=0.5
122.
123. MOBILITY  DEVICE=ADIODE  material=4H-SiC  REGION=2 n.canali n.angle=90
    p.angle=90 vsatn=2.2e7 vsatp=2.2e7 betan=1.2 betap=2  mu1n.caug=5
    mu2n.caug=947 ncritn.caug=2e17 alphan.caug=-3  betan.caug=-3
    gamman.caug=0.0 deltan.caug=0.76  mu1p.caug=2.5 mu2p.caug=20
    ncritp.caug=1.e19 alphap.caug=-3 betap.caug=-3 gammap.caug=0.0
    deltap.caug=0.5
124.
125. ## Impact Ionization
126.
127. IMPACT  DEVICE=ADIODE   REGION=2 ANISO E.SIDE SELB SIC4H0001 an1=3.44e6
    an2=3.44e6 bn1=2.58e7 bn2=2.58e7 ap1=3.5e6 ap2=3.5e6 bp1=1.7e7 bp2=1.7e7
    opphe=0.106
128.
129. METHOD BLOCK  climit=1.e-9  maxtraps=100  itlimit=100   max.temp=1000
    dvmax=1.e8 ir.tol=1.e-35 cr.tol=1.e-35  ix.tol=1.e-35  px.tol=1.e-30
    pr.tol=1.e-45  cx.tol=1.e-30
```

```
130.
131. GO ATLAS SIMFLAGS ="-V 5.18.3.R -P 32 -160"
132.
133. ##### TRANSIENT SIMULATION CIRCUIT #####
134.
135. .BEGIN
136.
137. VDC        1    0    600
138. RSW        1    2    1.e-12  PULSE 1.e-12 1.e18  5us    50ns  50ns  40us  80us
139. R_CHARGE   2    3    500
140. C_BANK     3    0    6u
141. R_SERIES   3    4    0.80
142. L_SERIES   4    5    500n
143. RSWITCH    5    6    1.e18   PULSE 1.e18 1.e-12  10us   50ns  50ns  40us  80us
144. ADIODE     6=anode_ohm  6=anode_sch  0=cathode   infile=JBS_Structure.str
       width=2.4e6
145.
146. .NUMERIC  imaxtr=100  dtmax=5.e-8
147. .OPTIONS  m2ln.tr  print  noshift  relpot  write=10
148. .LOAD     infile=JBS_RLC_Bias
149. .SAVE     master=JBS_Transient
150. .LOG      outfile=JBS_RLC_Ringdown_5000.log
151. .SAVE     outfile=JBS_RLC_Ringdown_5000.str
152. .TRAN  0.01us 45us
153.
154. .END
155.
156. ##### PHYSICS USED #####
157.
158. CONTACT  DEVICE=ADIODE  NUMBER=1   NAME=anode_ohm  COMMON=anode_sch  SHORT
       EXT.ALPHA=10
159. CONTACT  DEVICE=ADIODE  NUMBER=3   NAME=anode_ohm  COMMON=anode_sch  SHORT
       EXT.ALPHA=10
160. CONTACT  DEVICE=ADIODE  NUMBER=5   NAME=anode_ohm  COMMON=anode_sch  SHORT
       EXT.ALPHA=10
161. CONTACT  DEVICE=ADIODE  NUMBER=7   NAME=anode_ohm  COMMON=anode_sch  SHORT
       EXT.ALPHA=10
162. CONTACT  DEVICE=ADIODE  NUMBER=9   NAME=anode_ohm  COMMON=anode_sch  SHORT
       EXT.ALPHA=10
163. CONTACT  DEVICE=ADIODE  NUMBER=11  NAME=anode_ohm  COMMON=anode_sch  SHORT
       EXT.ALPHA=10
164.
165. CONTACT  DEVICE=ADIODE  NUMBER=2  NAME=anode_sch  WORKFUNCTION=5.0  THERMION
       PARABOLIC  EXT.ALPHA=10
166. CONTACT  DEVICE=ADIODE  NUMBER=4  NAME=anode_sch  WORKFUNCTION=5.0  THERMION
       PARABOLIC  EXT.ALPHA=10
167. CONTACT  DEVICE=ADIODE  NUMBER=6  NAME=anode_sch  WORKFUNCTION=5.0  THERMION
       PARABOLIC  EXT.ALPHA=10
168. CONTACT  DEVICE=ADIODE  NUMBER=8  NAME=anode_sch  WORKFUNCTION=5.0  THERMION
       PARABOLIC  EXT.ALPHA=10
169. CONTACT  DEVICE=ADIODE  NUMBER=10 NAME=anode_sch  WORKFUNCTION=5.0  THERMION
       PARABOLIC  EXT.ALPHA=10
170.
171. CONTACT  DEVICE=ADIODE  NUMBER=12  NAME=cathode    EXT.ALPHA=10
172.
173. THERMCONTACT  DEVICE=ADIODE   num=13   x.min=0   x.max=17.5  y.min=-1.0
       y.max=184   alpha=10   EXT.TEMP=300
174.
175. MATERIAL  DEVICE=ADIODE   material=4H-SiC  REGION=2  permittivity=9.76
       eg300=3.26   affinity=3.7   egalpha=3.3e-2   egbeta=1.e+5  nc300=1.7e+19
```

```
         nv300=2.5e+19  arichn=146  arichp=30  augn=3.e-29  augp=3.e-29  taun0=3.33e-6
         taup0=6.7e-7  nsrhn=3.e+17 nsrhp=3.e+17 edb=0.050  eab=0.200  tcon.polyn
         tc.a=0.137534   tc.b=0.00049662   tc.c=0.000000354  hc.a=2.35  hc.b=1.75e-3
         hc.c=1.e-9  hc.d=-6.6e4
176.
177. ## MODELS USED
178.
179. MODELS  DEVICE=ADIODE  REGION=2  MATERIAL=4H-SIC FERMIDIRAC ANALYTIC  CONWELL
     SRH BGN AUGER INCOMPLETE LAT.TEMP  JOULE.HEAT  GR.HEAT  PT.HEAT  PRINT
180.
181. ## MOBILITY
182.
183. MOBILITY  DEVICE=ADIODE material=4H-SiC REGION=2  vsatn=2.2e7  vsatp=2.2e7
         betan=1.2 betap=2 mu1n.caug=40 mu2n.caug=1136 ncritn.caug=2e17
         alphan.caug=-3 betan.caug=-3 gamman.caug=0.0 deltan.caug=0.76
         mu1p.caug=20 mu2p.caug=125 ncritp.caug=1.e19 alphap.caug=-3 betap.caug=-3
         gammap.caug=0.0 deltap.caug=0.5
184.
185. MOBILITY  DEVICE=ADIODE material=4H-SiC REGION=2  n.canali n.angle=90
         p.angle=90 vsatn=2.2e7 vsatp=2.2e7 betan=1.2 betap=2 mu1n.caug=5
         mu2n.caug=947 ncritn.caug=2e17 alphan.caug=-3 betan.caug=-3
         gamman.caug=0.0 deltan.caug=0.76  mu1p.caug=2.5 mu2p.caug=20
         ncritp.caug=1.e19 alphap.caug=-3 betap.caug=-3 gammap.caug=0.0
         deltap.caug=0.5
186.
187. ## Impact Ionization
188.
189. IMPACT  DEVICE=ADIODE  REGION=2 ANISO E.SIDE  SELB  SIC4H0001  an1=3.44e6
         an2=3.44e6  bn1=2.58e7  bn2=2.58e7  ap1=3.5e6  ap2=3.5e6  bp1=1.7e7  bp2=1.7e7
         opphe=0.106
190.
191. OUTPUT  FLOWLINES  E.MOBILITY
192.
193. METHOD  BLOCK.TRAN climit=1.e-9  maxtraps=100  itlimit=100   max.temp=1000
         dvmax=1.e8 ir.tol=1.e-35  cr.tol=1.e-35  ix.tol=1.e-35  px.tol=1.e-30
         pr.tol=1.e-45  cx.tol=1.e-30
194.
195. GO ATLAS SIMFLAGS ="-V 5.18.3.R -P 32 -160"
196.
197. QUIT
```

Table 2.   Code walkthrough: JBS diode (active area $= 5~\mu\mathrm{m}^2$) Mixed-Mode simulation.

Line No:	Functionality
1	Configure ATLAS simulator to use version 5.18.3.R, 160-bit extended precision and utilize 32 cores of the CPU if hardware resources are available.
5	Initialize device structure mesh information with width parameter.
7–24	X-axis and Y-axis mesh distribution.
28–29	Declare oxide and 4H-SiC as the material for the area specified by the x and y coordinates.

(Continued)

Table 2.   (*Continued*)

Line No:	Functionality
33–43	Separate electrode statements for the anode Schottky contact using metal conductor and anode ohmic contact using titanium.
45	Electrode statement to specify aluminum for cathode ohmic contact.
49–62	Specify doping profile, type, and concentration for different areas of the JBS diode structure.
64	Save the device structure (*.str*) file on the local hard drive. The device structure can be viewed by opening the file via *TonyPlot* to troubleshoot/optimize the structure.
68	Initialize ATLAS simulator using GO ATLAS command (same as line 1).
70	Initialize the starting of SPICE-like code in Mixed-Mode steady-state simulation.
72–79	RLC ring-down circuit description in SPICE-like format.
81	Declare the initial node voltage for the RLC ring-down circuit nodes.
82	Set the maximum number of mixed circuit-device iterations to be performed during steady-state analysis (*imaxdc*) to 100.
84–86	Ramp up DC voltage to attain steady-state condition, i.e. VDC = 600 V. This can be split into multiple steps.
88	Save log file after steady-state simulation completion.
89	Save file with bias information which will be used for transient simulation.
90	Specify Mixed-Mode steady-state simulation conditions. Modified two-level Newton solution method (*m2ln*), disable the shift of voltage for ATLAS devices (*noshift*), and enable the use of relative convergence criteria for potential especially when large voltage biases are involved (*relpot*).
92	Initialize the ending of SPICE-like code in Mixed-Mode steady-state simulation.
96–101	Shorting the ohmic and Schottky anode contacts is different in MixedMode as compared to steady-state simulation. A separate statement is required for each ohmic contact and contact number must be specified for each contact using the parameter (*number*). The same statement is used to specify the heat transfer coefficient (*ext.alpha*).
103–107	Specify heat transfer coefficient (*ext.alpha*) and enable thermionic emission (*thermion*) and parabolic field emission (*parabolic*) for anode Schottky contact.
109	Specify heat transfer coefficient (*ext.alpha*) for cathode contact.
111	Specify the thermal boundary for the JBS diode. Parameters includes boundary dimensions, heat transfer coefficient (*alpha*), and temperature of the thermal boundary (*ext.temp*) which is typically at 300 K.

(*Continued*)

Table 2.   (*Continued*)

Line No:	Functionality
113	Specify material parameters for 4H-SiC.
117	Specify the various models to be included in the 4H-SiC JBS diode simulation.
121	Specify parameters for mobility in 4H-SiC.
123	Specify parameters for anisotropic mobility in 4H-SiC.
127	Specify impact ionization parameters for 4H-SiC.
129	Specify the steady-state Block Newton solver type (**BLOCK**) and the tolerance values to be used during the simulation.
131	Initialize ATLAS simulator using GO ATLAS command (same as line 1) for steady-state bias point simulation.
135	Initialize the starting of SPICE-like code in Mixed-Mode transient simulation.
137–144	RLC ring-down circuit description in SPICE-like format. The magnitude of DC voltage source is initialized at 600 V, result of the steady-state simulation performed earlier. Transient parameters have been added to the Resistor which is acting like a switch.
146	Set the maximum number of mixed circuit-device iterations to be performed during transient analysis (**imaxtr**) to 100 and the maximum transient simulation time step (**dtmax**) to 50 ns.
147	Specify Mixed-Mode transient simulation conditions. Modified two-level Newton solution method for transient simulation (**m2ln.tr**), disable the shift of voltage for ATLAS devices (**noshift**), enable the use of relative convergence criteria for potential especially when large voltage biases are involved (**relpot**), and write structure file after every 10 time-step iterations.
148	Load the steady-state simulations results saved in line 89.
149	Save the structure file after every 10 time-step iterations specified in line 147.
150	Save log file after the completion of transient simulation.
151	Save the structure file after the completion of transient simulation.
152	Specify the initial time interval of 10 ns and total simulation time of 45 μs.
154	Initialize the ending of SPICE-like code in Mixed-Mode transient simulation.
156–189	Same as line 94 to line 127.
191	Include current flowlines (**FLOWLINES**) and Electron Mobility (**E.MOBILITY**) in the output structure file.
193	Specify the transient Block Newton solver type (**BLOCK.TRAN**) and the tolerance values to be used during the simulation.
195	Initialize ATLAS simulator using GO ATLAS command (same as line 1) for transient simulation. A simulation precision of 160-bit has been used due to device complexity.
197	Terminate the simulation.

8.3.2.4. *Mixed-Mode transient simulation results*

The transient simulation for the SiC JBS diode structure was carried out for varying magnitudes of peak current density ranging from 500 A/cm^2 to 5000 A/cm^2 in steps of 500. The width parameter was used to change the peak current density through the diode without altering the waveform. In this section, the results pertaining to the maximum current density scenario of 5000 A/cm^2 will be discussed followed by a summary of all the other cases. The anode voltage and current density waveforms are shown in Fig. 12, and the power and energy density waveforms are shown in Fig. 13.

A peak voltage drop of 11.88 V was observed across the JBS diode at peak current density of 5000 A/cm^2 which corresponds to a peak power dissipation density of 59.1 kW/cm^2. Integration of the power density waveform yielded an energy density of 232.2 mJ/cm^2. Peak lattice temperature of 304.4 K was observed in the JBS diode lattice during this pulsed operation. The variation of lattice temperature with power dissipation density and energy density during simulation is shown in Figs. 14 and 15, respectively. The simulation was run for only 45 μs, and hence does not show the complete decay of temperature waveform back to the ambient value. To identify the area of heat dissipation in the JBS diode structure, intermediate structure files were generated during the simulation. These structure files were manually scanned

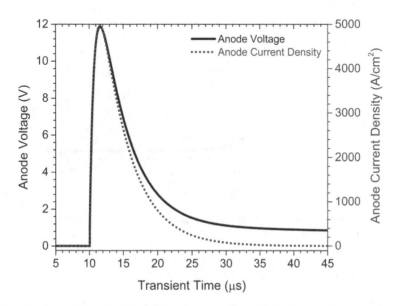

Fig. 12.   Anode voltage (solid) and current density (dotted) waveforms pertaining to 5000 A/cm^2 peak current density simulation.

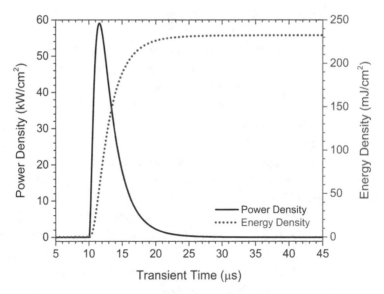

Fig. 13.   Power density (solid) and energy density (dotted) waveforms pertaining to 5000 A/cm^2 peak current density simulation.

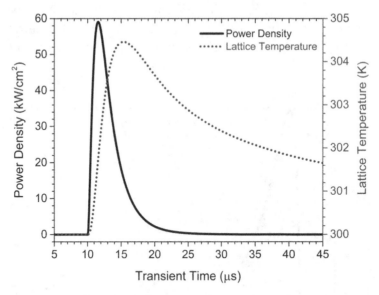

Fig. 14.   Power density (solid) and lattice temperature (dotted) waveforms pertaining to 5000 A/cm^2 peak current density simulation.

for the transient time instant which corresponds to the maximum lattice temperature.

The lattice temperature profiles of the JBS diode structure recorded at the time instant corresponding to maximum temperature during high current

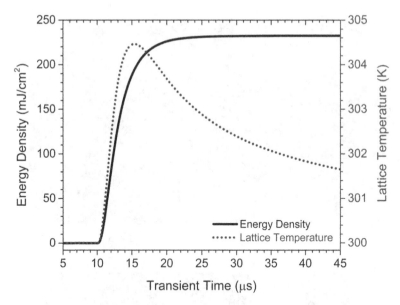

Fig. 15.   Energy density (solid) and lattice temperature (dotted) waveforms pertaining to 5000 A/cm^2 peak current density simulation.

density pulsed simulation are shown in Fig. 16(a) and 16(b). Maximum temperature of 304.4 K was observed in the drift region closer to the anode; however, the temperature distribution was uniform without any hot-spot formation. To investigate the heat dissipation source, joule heat power profile was extracted from same structure file and is shown in Fig. 17 (p–n junction is shown in white). The heat power sources are expressed in W/cm^3 in **TonyPlot**, and the contour plots have been scaled to highlight the areas of interest.

The joule heat power profile shows the resistive heat dissipation in the interdigitated Schottky regions and at the edges of the P+ regions where current constrictions begin due to the forward-bias depletion region. The larger device pitch assists in better heat dissipation to the ambient.

The uniform temperature distribution in the JBS diode structure indicates uniform density current distribution among the various Schottky contact regions. This can be validated through the current density profile extracted during the RLC ring-down simulation at the instant when circuit current density is at its peak value. It can be seen from Fig. 18 that during the peak current density instant, there is equal current sharing among the multiple Schottky diodes in the JBS diode structure, which is necessary to prevent localized heat generation.

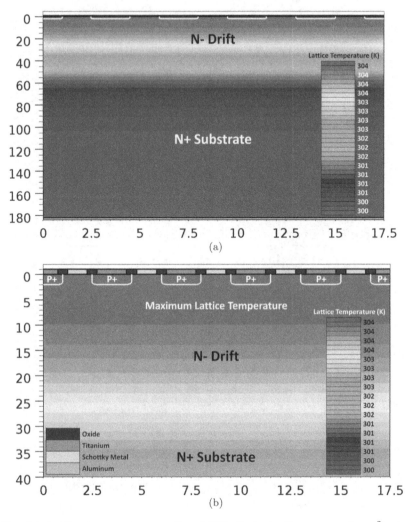

Fig. 16.   (a) Lattice temperature profile of JBS diode (active area $= 5\ \mu m^2$) structure during 2000 A/cm^2 RLC ring-down simulation. (b) Lattice temperature profile of JBS diode (active area $= 5\ \mu m^2$) structure during 5000 A/cm^2 RLC ring-down simulation (zoomed-in view).

 The user may notice that current density value in the contour plot may not always be same as the designed/circuit value during transient simulation. One of the reasons is the time instant at which the structure file is saved may not always coincide with the required time instant on the waveform. Another reason is the dynamic processes taking place within the device that may alter the current density, e.g. higher current constriction due to depletion region formation/extension.

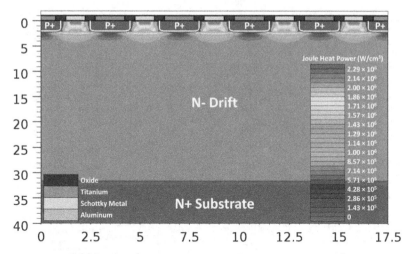

Fig. 17.   Joule heat power profile of JBS diode (active area = 5 μm^2) structure during 5000 A/cm^2 RLC ring-down simulation (zoomed-in view).

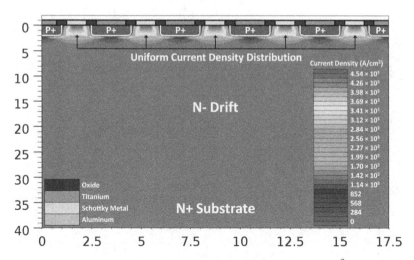

Fig. 18.   Current density profile of JBS diode (active area = 5 μm^2) structure during 5000 A/cm^2 RLC ring-down simulation at the maximum current density instant (zoomed-in view).

The summary of lattice temperature and anode voltage waveforms for the JBS diode structure for all the values of peak pulsed current density are shown in Figs. 19 and 20, respectively. The increase in device pitch for a given active area reduces the ON-state resistance and increases the area of the thermal boundary, which reduces the ON-state power dissipation and increases the heat dissipation area, thereby resulting in lower lattice temperature rise.

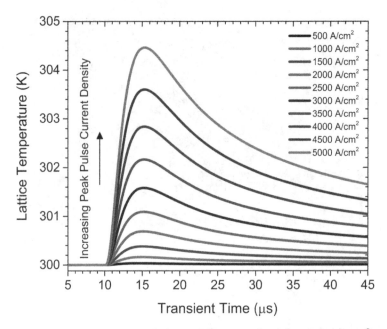

Fig. 19. Lattice temperature summary of JBS diode (active area = 5 μm^2) structure during RLC ring-down simulation.

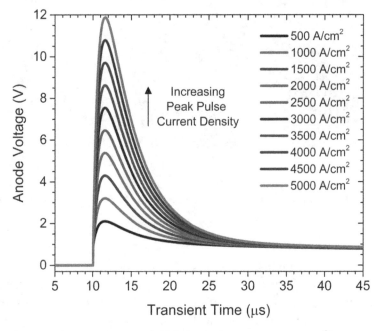

Fig. 20. Anode voltage summary of JBS diode (active area = 5 μm^2) structure during RLC ring-down simulation.

8.3.3. JBS diode — Active area $10\,\mu m^2$

In Section 8.3.2, a multi-cell JBS diode structure with an active area of 5 μm^2 was modeled and simulated under steady-state and transient conditions. In this section, the JBS diode structure is scaled for an active area of 10 μm^2. This increased the number of mesh points and the resulting simulation was much slower as compared to the 5 μm^2 structure. The larger active area JBS diode structure was designed for a rated current density of 100 A/cm^2 and blocking voltage of 3300 V. Since the rated blocking voltage is typically considered as 80% of the actual breakdown voltage, the diode was designed for a breakdown voltage of 4200 V. The drift region was uniformly doped with a donor concentration (N_{Drift}) of 1.6×10^{15} cm^{-3} and the substrate was heavily doped with a uniform donor concentration of 1.0×10^{20} cm^{-3}. The drift region doping concentration had to be reduced to obtain the required breakdown voltage. The interdigitated P+ regions were heavily doped with an acceptor concentration of 1.0×10^{20} cm^{-3} using a Gaussian doping profile. The P+ regions had a junction depth of 2 μm which was selected after several rounds of simulation and optimization. In order to reduce the ON-state resistance without affecting the breakdown voltage, the complete diode structure was uniformly doped with a donor concentration (N_{CSL}) of 1.0×10^{16} cm^{-3} up to a depth of 2.4 μm. In this diode model, n-type dopant is assumed to be nitrogen and p-type dopant is assumed to be Aluminum with corresponding ionization energies of 50 meV and 200 meV, respectively, which were used to account for incomplete ionization. The drift region thickness was calculated to be 30 μm based on the design equations. The anode Schottky metal was configured to be a conductor with a workfunction of 5.0 eV, anode ohmic contact was formed using titanium, and aluminum was used for the cathode ohmic contact. Since the JBS diode conducts only through the Schottky contact area, an active area of 10 μm^2 was realized using device width of 42 μm and a default Z-dimension of 1 μm.[7,8] Due to the large substrate thickness as compared to the drift layer, the complete device structure designed using Silvaco© ATLAS does not clearly show the device-specific details. Hence, the device structure has been split into Figs. 21(a) and 21(b) respectively. The interdigitated P+ regions along with the separate Schottky and ohmic contacts can be seen in Fig. 21(b).

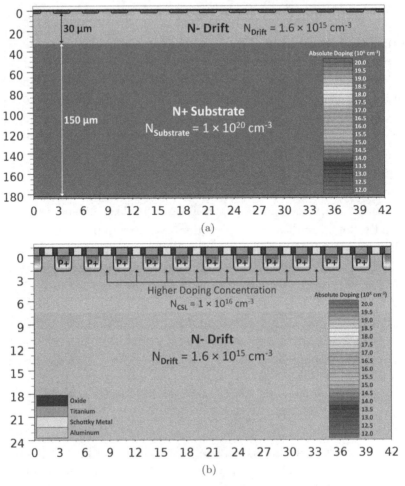

Fig. 21.   (a) 3300 V SiC JBS diode (active area $= 10\ \mu m^2$) multi-cell structure designed in Silvaco© ATLAS. (b) 3300 V SiC JBS diode (active area $= 10\ \mu m^2$) multi-cell structure designed in Silvaco© ATLAS (zoomed-in view).

8.3.3.1.   *Steady-state simulation*

Steady-state/DC simulation helps in verifying the basic operation of the device model. This section will discuss the forward conduction and reverse breakdown current density versus anode voltage (J–V) characteristics at 27°C, 75°C, 125°C, and 175°C device temperature. Steady-state simulations help the user to refine the device model, including optimization of the mesh profile and doping concentration adjustment to fine-tune the breakdown voltage. The following code was used to simulate the JBS diode J–V characteristics, including forward conduction and reverse breakdown. A brief explanation of the steady-state simulation program is provided in the code walkthrough (Table 3).

```
Sample code: JBS diode (active area = 10 μm²) forward and breakdown J-V characteristics @ 27°C
1.   GO ATLAS SIMFLAGS ="-V 5.18.3.R -P 32 -160"
2.
3.   ##### 3300V JBS DIODE STEADY STATE @ 27C #####
4.
5.   MESH
6.
7.   ## X-MESH
8.
9.   X.MESH  loc=0.0    spac=0.25
10.  X.MESH  loc=42.0   spac=0.25
11.
12.  ## Y-MESH
13.
14.  Y.MESH  loc=-1.0   spac=1.0
15.  Y.MESH  loc=0.0    spac=0.5
16.  Y.MESH  loc=0.2    spac=0.10
17.  Y.MESH  loc=2.1    spac=0.05
18.  Y.MESH  loc=2.2    spac=6.0
19.  Y.MESH  loc=30.0   spac=6.0
20.  Y.MESH  loc=31.5   spac=0.25
21.  Y.MESH  loc=32.5   spac=0.25
22.  Y.MESH  loc=33.0   spac=20
23.  Y.MESH  loc=180.0  spac=20
24.  Y.MESH  loc=182.0  spac=1.0
25.  Y.MESH  loc=184.0  spac=1.0
26.
27.  ## Defining Regions
28.
29.  REGION   num=1 material=Oxide    x.min=0  x.max=42   y.max=0
30.  REGION   num=2 material=4H-SiC   x.min=0  x.max=42   y.min=0   y.max=182
31.
32.  ## Electrode
33.
34.  ELECTRODE  name=anode_ohm   material=titanium   x.min=0      x.max=0.75
     y.min=-1   y.max=0
35.  ELECTRODE  name=anode       material=conductor  x.min=1.25   x.max=2.25
     y.min=-1   y.max=0
36.  ELECTRODE  name=anode_ohm   material=titanium   x.min=2.75   x.max=4.25
     y.min=-1   y.max=0
37.  ELECTRODE  name=anode       material=conductor  x.min=4.75   x.max=5.75
     y.min=-1   y.max=0
38.  ELECTRODE  name=anode_ohm   material=titanium   x.min=6.25   x.max=7.75
     y.min=-1   y.max=0
39.  ELECTRODE  name=anode       material=conductor  x.min=8.25   x.max=9.25
     y.min=-1   y.max=0
40.  ELECTRODE  name=anode_ohm   material=titanium   x.min=9.75   x.max=11.25
     y.min=-1   y.max=0
41.  ELECTRODE  name=anode       material=conductor  x.min=11.75  x.max=12.75
     y.min=-1   y.max=0
42.  ELECTRODE  name=anode_ohm   material=titanium   x.min=13.25  x.max=14.75
     y.min=-1   y.max=0
43.  ELECTRODE  name=anode       material=conductor  x.min=15.25  x.max=16.25
     y.min=-1   y.max=0
44.  ELECTRODE  name=anode_ohm   material=titanium   x.min=16.75  x.max=18.25
     y.min=-1   y.max=0
45.  ELECTRODE  name=anode       material=conductor  x.min=18.75  x.max=19.75
     y.min=-1   y.max=0
```

```
46. ELECTRODE  name=anode_ohm  material=titanium   x.min=20.25  x.max=21.75
    y.min=-1   y.max=0
47. ELECTRODE  name=anode      material=conductor  x.min=22.25  x.max=23.25
    y.min=-1   y.max=0
48. ELECTRODE  name=anode_ohm  material=titanium   x.min=23.75  x.max=25.25
    y.min=-1   y.max=0
49. ELECTRODE  name=anode      material=conductor  x.min=25.75  x.max=26.75
    y.min=-1   y.max=0
50. ELECTRODE  name=anode_ohm  material=titanium   x.min=27.25  x.max=28.75
    y.min=-1   y.max=0
51. ELECTRODE  name=anode      material=conductor  x.min=29.25  x.max=30.25
    y.min=-1   y.max=0
52. ELECTRODE  name=anode_ohm  material=titanium   x.min=30.75  x.max=32.25
    y.min=-1   y.max=0
53. ELECTRODE  name=anode      material=conductor  x.min=32.75  x.max=33.75
    y.min=-1   y.max=0
54. ELECTRODE  name=anode_ohm  material=titanium   x.min=34.25  x.max=35.75
    y.min=-1   y.max=0
55. ELECTRODE  name=anode      material=conductor  x.min=36.25  x.max=37.25
    y.min=-1   y.max=0
56. ELECTRODE  name=anode_ohm  material=titanium   x.min=37.75  x.max=39.25
    y.min=-1   y.max=0
57. ELECTRODE  name=anode      material=conductor  x.min=39.75  x.max=40.75
    y.min=-1   y.max=0
58. ELECTRODE  name=anode_ohm  material=titanium   x.min=41.25  x.max=42.00
    y.min=-1   y.max=0
59.
60. ELECTRODE  name=cathode    material=aluminum   y.min=182  y.max=184
61.
62. ## Doping Distribution
63.
64. ## Bulk Doping
65. DOPING  uniform  n.type conc=1.6e15   REGION=2
66. DOPING  uniform  n.type conc=1.e16    y.min=0 y.max=2.4
67.
68. ## P+ Doping
69. DOPING  gauss  p.type conc=1.e20  x.min=0.0   x.max=0.80   junc=2.0  rat=0.1
70. DOPING  gauss  p.type conc=1.e20  x.min=2.7   x.max=4.30   junc=2.0  rat=0.1
71. DOPING  gauss  p.type conc=1.e20  x.min=6.2   x.max=7.80   junc=2.0  rat=0.1
72. DOPING  gauss  p.type conc=1.e20  x.min=9.7   x.max=11.3   junc=2.0  rat=0.1
73. DOPING  gauss  p.type conc=1.e20  x.min=13.2  x.max=14.80  junc=2.0  rat=0.1
74. DOPING  gauss  p.type conc=1.e20  x.min=16.7  x.max=18.30  junc=2.0  rat=0.1
75. DOPING  gauss  p.type conc=1.e20  x.min=20.2  x.max=21.80  junc=2.0  rat=0.1
76. DOPING  gauss  p.type conc=1.e20  x.min=23.7  x.max=25.30  junc=2.0  rat=0.1
77. DOPING  gauss  p.type conc=1.e20  x.min=27.2  x.max=28.80  junc=2.0  rat=0.1
78. DOPING  gauss  p.type conc=1.e20  x.min=30.7  x.max=32.30  junc=2.0  rat=0.1
79. DOPING  gauss  p.type conc=1.e20  x.min=34.2  x.max=35.80  junc=2.0  rat=0.1
80. DOPING  gauss  p.type conc=1.e20  x.min=37.7  x.max=39.30  junc=2.0  rat=0.1
81. DOPING  gauss  p.type conc=1.e20  x.min=41.2  x.max=42.00  junc=2.0  rat=0.1
82.
83. ## N+ Substrate Region Doping
84. DOPING  uniform   n.type  conc=1.e20 y.min=32   y.max=182
85.
86. SAVE  outf=JBS_2D_Structure_27C.str  master.out
87.
88. MATERIAL  material=4H-SiC REGION=2  permittivity=9.76   eg300=3.26
    affinity=3.7  egalpha=3.3e-2  egbeta=1.e+5  nc300=1.7e+19  nv300=2.5e+19
    arichn=146  arichp=30  augn=3.e-29 augp=3.e-29 taun0=3.33e-6  taup0=6.7e-7
    nsrhn=3.e+17  nsrhp=3.e+17  edb=0.05  eab=0.20
```

```
89.
90. CONTACT  NAME=anode    WORKFUNCTION=5.0  THERMION  PARABOLIC
91. CONTACT  NAME=anode_ohm    COMMON=anode    SHORT
92.
93. ## MODELS USED
94.
95. MODELS  REGION=2 MATERIAL=4H-SIC FERMIDIRAC ANALYTIC CONWELL SRH BGN AUGER
    INCOMPLETE TEMP=300 PRINT
96.
97. ## MOBILITY
98.
99. MOBILITY  material=4H-SiC REGION=2  vsatn=2.2e7  vsatp=2.2e7  betan=1.2
    betap=2  mu1n.caug=40  mu2n.caug=1136  ncritn.caug=2e17  alphan.caug=-3
    betan.caug=-3  gamman.caug=0.0  deltan.caug=0.76  mu1p.caug=20  mu2p.caug=125
    ncritp.caug=1.e19  alphap.caug=-3  betap.caug=-3  gammap.caug=0.0
    deltap.caug=0.5
100.
101. MOBILITY  material=4H-SiC REGION=2  n.canali  n.angle=90 p.angle=90
     vsatn=2.2e7  vsatp=2.2e7  betan=1.2 betap=2  mu1n.caug=5  mu2n.caug=947
     ncritn.caug=2e17  alphan.caug=-3  betan.caug=-3  gamman.caug=0.0
     deltan.caug=0.76  mu1p.caug=2.5 mu2p.caug=20  ncritp.caug=1.e19
     alphap.caug=-3  betap.caug=-3  gammap.caug=0.0  deltap.caug=0.5
102.
103. IMPACT  REGION=2  ANISO  E.SIDE  SELB  SIC4H0001 an1=3.44e6  an2=3.44e6
     bn1=2.58e7  bn2=2.58e7  ap1=3.5e6  ap2=3.5e6  bp1=1.7e7  bp2=1.7e7 opphe=0.106
104.
105. METHOD  NEWTON    AUTONR  TRAP  climit=1.e-9  maxtraps=40  itlimit=40
     dvmax=1.e8  ir.tol=1.e-40  cr.tol=1.e-40  ix.tol=1.e-40  px.tol=1.e-30
     pr.tol=1.e-45  cx.tol=1.e-30
106.
107. OUTPUT  FLOWLINES
108.
109. LOG  outf=JBS_Forward_27C.log
110.
111. SOLVE  init
112. SOLVE  vanode=0.02    vstep=0.02  vfinal=1.5  name=anode
113. SOLVE  vstep=0.05    vfinal=5.0  name=anode
114.
115. SAVE  outf=JBS_Forward_27C.str
116.
117. LOG  outf=JBS_Reverse_27C.log
118.
119. SOLVE  init
120. SOLVE  vanode=-0.2    vstep=-0.2    vfinal=-2.0    name=anode
121. SOLVE  vstep=-2    vfinal=-20    name=anode
122. SOLVE  vstep=-5    vfinal=-100    name=anode
123. SOLVE  vstep=-10    vfinal=-1000    name=anode
124. SOLVE  vstep=-25    vfinal=-4000    name=anode
125. SOLVE  vstep=-10    vfinal=-4200    name=anode
126. SOLVE  vstep=-2    vfinal=-4500    name=anode    compl=5e-18  cname=anode
127.
128. SAVE  outf=JBS_Reverse_27C.str
129.
130. QUIT
```

Table 3. Code walkthrough: JBS diode (active area $= 10\,\mu m^2$) forward and breakdown J–V characteristics.

Line No:	Functionality
1	Configure ATLAS simulator to use 160-bit extended precision and utilize 32 cores of the CPU if hardware resources are available. The version of ATLAS to be used by the simulator is set to 5.18.3.R using the -V option in the simflags command.
5	Initialize device structure mesh information.
7–25	X-axis and Y-axis mesh distribution.
29–30	Declare oxide and 4H-SiC as the material for the area specified by the x and y coordinates.
34–58	Separate electrode statements for the anode Schottky contact using metal conductor and anode ohmic contact using titanium.
60	Electrode statement to specify aluminum for cathode ohmic contact.
64–84	Specify doping profile, type, and concentration for different areas of the JBS diode structure.
86	Save the device structure (**.str**) file on the local hard drive. The device structure can be viewed by opening the file via **TonyPlot** to troubleshoot/optimize the structure.
88	Specify material parameters for 4H-SiC. Detailed description of these parameters is available in the Silvaco© ATLAS manual. The values for these parameters can either be obtained via material research or from literature.
90	Specify Schottky metal workfunction and model/parameters for thermionic emission and parabolic field emission using **Contact** statement.
91	Shorting the anode Schottky contact and anode ohmic contact using **Common** parameter.
95	Specify the various models to be included in the 4H-SiC JBS diode simulation.
99	Specify mobility parameters for 4H-SiC. Detailed description of these parameters is available in the Silvaco© ATLAS manual. The values for these parameters can either be obtained via material research or from literature.
101	Specify anisotropic mobility parameters for 4H-SiC. Detailed description of these parameters is available in the Silvaco© ATLAS manual. The values for these parameters can either be obtained via material research or from literature.
103	Specify impact ionization parameters for 4H-SiC. This statement is mandatory to obtain device breakdown characteristics.
105	Specify the solver type and the tolerance values to be used during the simulation. This is an extremely critical statement which can alter the simulation outcome.

(Continued)

Table 3. (*Continued*)

Line No:	Functionality
107	Include current flowlines in the output structure file.
109	Save the simulation log (*.log*) file on the local hard drive. The simulation results can be viewed by opening the file via *TonyPlot*.
111–113	Solve for the initial bias conditions for the simulation followed by positive sweep of anode voltage for steady-state forward characteristics.
115	Save the post-forward-bias simulation device structure (*.str*) file on the local hard drive. Saving the file at this stage of the simulation will enable the user to visualize the variation in various electrothermal parameters within the device structure introduced due to the particular simulation.
117	Save the reverse-bias simulation log (*.log*) file on the local hard drive. The simulation results can be viewed by opening the file via *TonyPlot*.
119–126	Use solve statement to increment the negative anode voltage in discrete steps. The compliance parameter (*compl*) in line 126 forces the simulator to proceed to the next line once the anode current reaches the specified compliance value. This is important, especially in breakdown simulation because once the device enters the breakdown regime, it is not necessary to run the simulation for higher magnitude of current since the breakdown voltage would have already been determined.
128	Save the post-reverse-bias simulation device structure (*.str*) file on the local hard drive. Saving the file at this stage of the simulation will enable the user to visualize the variation in various electrothermal parameters within the device structure introduced due to the particular simulation.
130	Terminate the simulation.

8.3.3.2. *Steady-state simulation results*

The forward conduction J–V characteristics for the 3300 V SiC JBS diode on a linear and semi-log scale are shown in Figs. 22(a) and 22(b), respectively. It can be seen from Fig. 22(a) that there is a steady decrease in the diode turn-ON voltage as the lattice temperature increases from 27°C to 175°C. This reduced ON-state voltage drop at low current density can be attributed to the reduction in Schottky barrier height with increase in lattice temperature. However, since a JBS diode is a majority carrier device, the degradation in the bulk mobility at elevated temperature increases the ON-state resistance, thereby leading to higher ON-state losses. At an ON-state current density of 100 A/cm^2, voltage drop of 1.27 V was observed across the JBS diode at 27°C device temperature.

The current density profile for the JBS diode during forward conduction is shown in Fig. 23. The structure file was generated when the current density

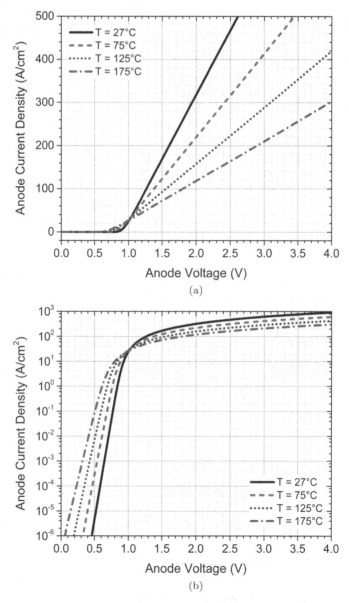

Fig. 22.   (a) Forward J–V characteristics for the SiC JBS diode structure (active area = $10\,\mu m^2$) on a linear scale. (b) Forward J–V characteristics for the SiC JBS diode structure (active area = $10\,\mu m^2$) on a semi-log scale.

through the device was $100\ A/cm^2$. The current density contour plot shows equal current sharing between the multiple Schottky contact regions within the diode structure. Uniform current sharing is also an indicator of mesh uniformity across the diode structure.

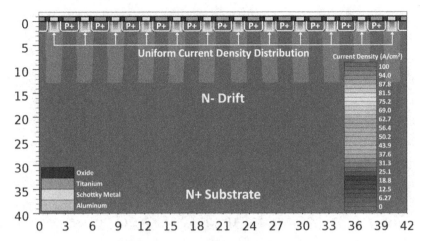

Fig. 23.   Contour plot of SiC JBS diode structure (active area = $10\,\mu\mathrm{m}^2$) current density profile during forward conduction.

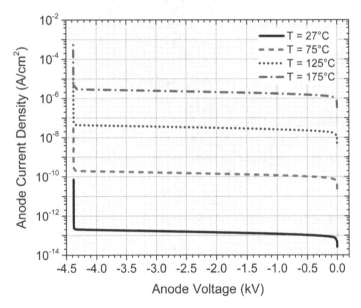

Fig. 24.   Reverse breakdown J–V characteristics for the SiC JBS diode structure (active area = $10\,\mu\mathrm{m}^2$) on a semi-log scale.

The reverse-bias breakdown J–V characteristics are shown in Fig. 24. A breakdown voltage of 4370 V was obtained for the JBS diode at 27°C device temperature. There is a progressive increase in the leakage current with device temperature without any change in the breakdown voltage.

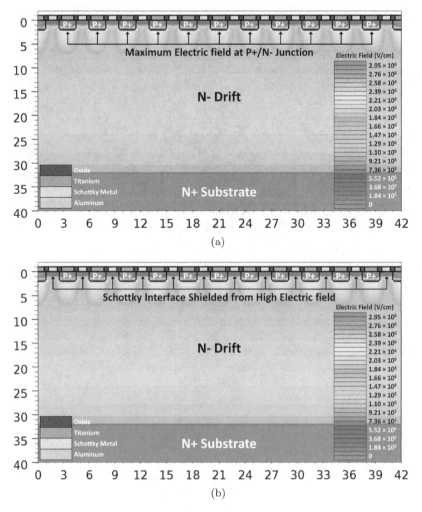

Fig. 25.   (a) Electric field contour plot during reverse-bias breakdown in SiC JBS diode structure (active area = $10 \, \mu m^2$) highlighting the distribution of electric field across the P+/N− junction. (b) Electric field contour plot during reverse-bias breakdown in SiC JBS diode structure (active area = $10 \, \mu m^2$) highlighting the shielding of Schottky interface from high electric field.

The electric field distribution in the JBS diode structure during break-down is shown in the contour plots in Figs. 25(a) and 25(b) (Images have been scaled to highlight the area of interest). A maximum electric field of 2.94 MV/cm was observed at the P+/N− junction shown in Fig. 25(a), which is also the point of breakdown. It can be seen from the electric field profile in Fig. 25(b) that the magnitude of electric field is significantly lower at the Schottky interface.

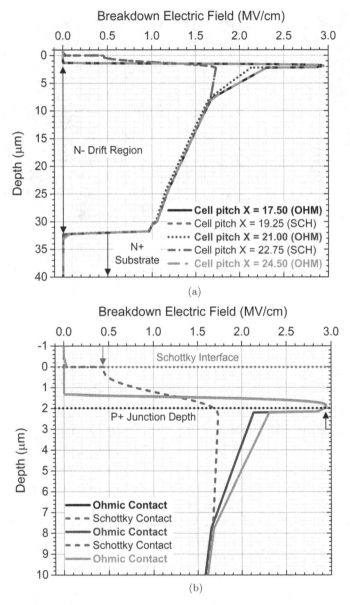

Fig. 26. (a) 1D electric field profile as a function of device depth at varying points across the diode active area/cell pitch. (b) 1D electric field profile as a function of device depth at varying points across the diode active area/cell pitch zoomed in for details (Breakdown electric field shown by solid lines).

A quantitative analysis of the electric field distribution was performed by plotting the 1D electric field profiles as a function of device depth in Figs. 26(a) and 26(b). The plot has been scaled to highlight the region of interest. The electric field data was extracted for the following points: anode

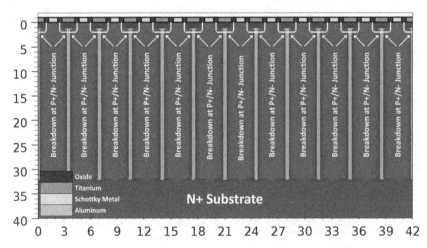

Fig. 27. Current density contour plot during reverse-bias breakdown highlighting the point of breakdown at P+/N− junction.

Schottky contact area ($x = 19.25$ μm and $x = 22.75$ μm) and anode ohmic contact area which is also the point of breakdown ($x = 17.7$ μm, $x = 21.0$ μm, and $x = 24.5$ μm) using the **cutline** feature in **TonyPlot**. To have a closer look at the electric field distribution in the aforementioned points, individual electric field profiles are shown in Fig. 26(b), which is a zoomed-in version of Fig. 26(a). The important electric field magnitudes have been indicated using arrows. It can be seen from Figs. 26(a) and 26(b) that the P+ implanted regions shield the Schottky interface from the high electric field by pinching off the interdigitated Schottky contact area and distributing the electric field across the P+ regions. The peak electric field observed at the P+/N− junction is 2.94 MV/cm, whereas the electric field at the Schottky interface is 0.45 MV/cm which is 6.5 times less than the peak value.

The current density profile of the JBS diode during breakdown is shown in Fig. 27. As in the case of smaller active area diode, the figure only highlights the point of breakdown in the device structure, and hence a graph legend has not been included. Breakdown occurs at the P+/N− junction, which is followed by the formation of current filaments through the P+ regions.

8.3.3.3. *Mixed-Mode transient simulation*

The Mixed-Mode transient simulation was performed using the RLC ring-down circuit. Changes were made to the program to include the JBS diode device mesh profile and dimensions of the thermal boundary based on the device structure.[7,8] The scaling/width factor was altered to account for the

10 μm^2 active area. The following code was used to simulate the JBS diode for a peak forward current density of 5000 A/cm^2 under pulsed condition. A brief explanation of the Mixed-Mode simulation program is provided in the code walkthrough (Table 4).

```
Sample code: JBS diode (active area = 10 μm²) transient simulation

1.  GO ATLAS SIMFLAGS ="-V 5.18.3.R -P 32 -160"
2.
3.  ##### 3300V JBS DIODE RLC RINGDOWN PULSE 5000A/cm2 #####
4.
5.  MESH WIDTH=1.2e6
6.
7.  ## X-MESH
8.
9.  X.MESH  loc=0.0    spac=0.25
10. X.MESH  loc=42.0   spac=0.25
11.
12. ## Y-MESH
13.
14. Y.MESH  loc=-1.0   spac=1.0
15. Y.MESH  loc=0.0    spac=0.5
16. Y.MESH  loc=0.2    spac=0.10
17. Y.MESH  loc=2.1    spac=0.05
18. Y.MESH  loc=2.2    spac=6.0
19. Y.MESH  loc=30.0   spac=6.0
20. Y.MESH  loc=31.5   spac=0.25
21. Y.MESH  loc=32.5   spac=0.25
22. Y.MESH  loc=33.0   spac=20
23. Y.MESH  loc=180.0  spac=20
24. Y.MESH  loc=182.0  spac=1.0
25. Y.MESH  loc=184.0  spac=1.0
26.
27. ## Defining Regions
28.
29. REGION  num=1 material=Oxide   x.min=0  x.max=42  y.max=0
30. REGION  num=2 material=4H-SiC  x.min=0  x.max=42  y.min=0   y.max=182
31.
32. ## Electrode
33.
34. ELECTRODE  name=anode_ohm  material=titanium   x.min=0     x.max=0.75
        y.min=-1  y.max=0
35. ELECTRODE  name=anode      material=conductor  x.min=1.25  x.max=2.25
        y.min=-1  y.max=0
36. ELECTRODE  name=anode_ohm  material=titanium   x.min=2.75  x.max=4.25
        y.min=-1  y.max=0
37. ELECTRODE  name=anode      material=conductor  x.min=4.75  x.max=5.75
        y.min=-1  y.max=0
38. ELECTRODE  name=anode_ohm  material=titanium   x.min=6.25  x.max=7.75
        y.min=-1  y.max=0
39. ELECTRODE  name=anode      material=conductor  x.min=8.25  x.max=9.25
        y.min=-1  y.max=0
40. ELECTRODE  name=anode_ohm  material=titanium   x.min=9.75  x.max=11.25
        y.min=-1  y.max=0
41. ELECTRODE  name=anode      material=conductor  x.min=11.75 x.max=12.75
        y.min=-1  y.max=0
42. ELECTRODE  name=anode_ohm  material=titanium   x.min=13.25 x.max=14.75
        y.min=-1  y.max=0
```

```
43. ELECTRODE  name=anode      material=conductor  x.min=15.25  x.max=16.25
    y.min=-1   y.max=0
44. ELECTRODE  name=anode_ohm  material=titanium   x.min=16.75  x.max=18.25
    y.min=-1   y.max=0
45. ELECTRODE  name=anode      material=conductor  x.min=18.75  x.max=19.75
    y.min=-1   y.max=0
46. ELECTRODE  name=anode_ohm  material=titanium   x.min=20.25  x.max=21.75
    y.min=-1   y.max=0
47. ELECTRODE  name=anode      material=conductor  x.min=22.25  x.max=23.25
    y.min=-1   y.max=0
48. ELECTRODE  name=anode_ohm  material=titanium   x.min=23.75  x.max=25.25
    y.min=-1   y.max=0
49. ELECTRODE  name=anode      material=conductor  x.min=25.75  x.max=26.75
    y.min=-1   y.max=0
50. ELECTRODE  name=anode_ohm  material=titanium   x.min=27.25  x.max=28.75
    y.min=-1   y.max=0
51. ELECTRODE  name=anode      material=conductor  x.min=29.25  x.max=30.25
    y.min=-1   y.max=0
52. ELECTRODE  name=anode_ohm  material=titanium   x.min=30.75  x.max=32.25
    y.min=-1   y.max=0
53. ELECTRODE  name=anode      material=conductor  x.min=32.75  x.max=33.75
    y.min=-1   y.max=0
54. ELECTRODE  name=anode_ohm  material=titanium   x.min=34.25  x.max=35.75
    y.min=-1   y.max=0
55. ELECTRODE  name=anode      material=conductor  x.min=36.25  x.max=37.25
    y.min=-1   y.max=0
56. ELECTRODE  name=anode_ohm  material=titanium   x.min=37.75  x.max=39.25
    y.min=-1   y.max=0
57. ELECTRODE  name=anode      material=conductor  x.min=39.75  x.max=40.75
    y.min=-1   y.max=0
58. ELECTRODE  name=anode_ohm  material=titanium   x.min=41.25  x.max=42.00
    y.min=-1   y.max=0
59.
60. ELECTRODE  name=cathode    material=aluminum   y.min=182    y.max=184
61.
62. ## Doping Distribution
63.
64. ## Bulk Doping
65. DOPING  uniform n.type conc=1.6e15   REGION=2
66. DOPING  uniform n.type conc=1.e16    y.min=0 y.max=2.4
67.
68. ## P+ Doping
69. DOPING  gauss  p.type  conc=1.e20  x.min=0.0   x.max=0.80   junc=2.0   rat=0.1
70. DOPING  gauss  p.type  conc=1.e20  x.min=2.7   x.max=4.30   junc=2.0   rat=0.1
71. DOPING  gauss  p.type  conc=1.e20  x.min=6.2   x.max=7.80   junc=2.0   rat=0.1
72. DOPING  gauss  p.type  conc=1.e20  x.min=9.7   x.max=11.3   junc=2.0   rat=0.1
73. DOPING  gauss  p.type  conc=1.e20  x.min=13.2  x.max=14.80  junc=2.0   rat=0.1
74. DOPING  gauss  p.type  conc=1.e20  x.min=16.7  x.max=18.30  junc=2.0   rat=0.1
75. DOPING  gauss  p.type  conc=1.e20  x.min=20.2  x.max=21.80  junc=2.0   rat=0.1
76. DOPING  gauss  p.type  conc=1.e20  x.min=23.7  x.max=25.30  junc=2.0   rat=0.1
77. DOPING  gauss  p.type  conc=1.e20  x.min=27.2  x.max=28.80  junc=2.0   rat=0.1
78. DOPING  gauss  p.type  conc=1.e20  x.min=30.7  x.max=32.30  junc=2.0   rat=0.1
79. DOPING  gauss  p.type  conc=1.e20  x.min=34.2  x.max=35.80  junc=2.0   rat=0.1
80. DOPING  gauss  p.type  conc=1.e20  x.min=37.7  x.max=39.30  junc=2.0   rat=0.1
81. DOPING  gauss  p.type  conc=1.e20  x.min=41.2  x.max=42.00  junc=2.0   rat=0.1
82.
83. ## N+ Substrate Region Doping
84. DOPING  uniform   n.type conc=1.e20  y.min=32   y.max=182
85.
86. SAVE  outf=JBS_Structure.str  master.out
```

```
 87.
 88. ##### STEADY STATE SIMULATION CIRCUIT #####
 89.
 90. GO ATLAS SIMFLAGS ="-V 5.18.3.R -P 32 -160"
 91.
 92. .BEGIN
 93.
 94. VDC         1    0    0
 95. RSW         1    2    1.e-12
 96. R_CHARGE    2    3    500
 97. C_BANK      3    0    6u
 98. R_SERIES    3    4    0.80
 99. L_SERIES    4    5    500n
100. RSWITCH     5    6    1.e18
101. ADIODE      6=anode_ohm  6=anode_sch   0=cathode    infile=JBS_Structure.str
     width=1.2e6
102.
103. .NODESET v(1)=0  v(2)=0  v(3)=0  v(4)=0  v(5)=0  v(6)=0
104. .NUMERIC imaxdc=100
105.
106. .DC    VDC   0.    10.   0.25
107. .DC    VDC   10.   100.  5.
108. .DC    VDC   100.  600.  25.
109.
110. .LOG  outfile=JBS_DC_log
111. .SAVE  outfile=JBS_RLC_Bias
112. .OPTIONS  m2ln print noshift relpot
113.
114. .END
115.
116. ##### PHYSICS USED #####
117.
118. CONTACT  DEVICE=ADIODE  NUMBER=1   NAME=anode_ohm   COMMON=anode_sch  SHORT
     EXT.ALPHA=10
119. CONTACT  DEVICE=ADIODE  NUMBER=2   NAME=anode_ohm   COMMON=anode_sch  SHORT
     EXT.ALPHA=10
120. CONTACT  DEVICE=ADIODE  NUMBER=3   NAME=anode_ohm   COMMON=anode_sch  SHORT
     EXT.ALPHA=10
121. CONTACT  DEVICE=ADIODE  NUMBER=4   NAME=anode_ohm   COMMON=anode_sch  SHORT
     EXT.ALPHA=10
122. CONTACT  DEVICE=ADIODE  NUMBER=5   NAME=anode_ohm   COMMON=anode_sch  SHORT
     EXT.ALPHA=10
123. CONTACT  DEVICE=ADIODE  NUMBER=6   NAME=anode_ohm   COMMON=anode_sch  SHORT
     EXT.ALPHA=10
124. CONTACT  DEVICE=ADIODE  NUMBER=7   NAME=anode_ohm   COMMON=anode_sch  SHORT
     EXT.ALPHA=10
125. CONTACT  DEVICE=ADIODE  NUMBER=8   NAME=anode_ohm   COMMON=anode_sch  SHORT
     EXT.ALPHA=10
126. CONTACT  DEVICE=ADIODE  NUMBER=9   NAME=anode_ohm   COMMON=anode_sch  SHORT
     EXT.ALPHA=10
127. CONTACT  DEVICE=ADIODE  NUMBER=10  NAME=anode_ohm   COMMON=anode_sch  SHORT
     EXT.ALPHA=10
128. CONTACT  DEVICE=ADIODE  NUMBER=11  NAME=anode_ohm   COMMON=anode_sch  SHORT
     EXT.ALPHA=10
129. CONTACT  DEVICE=ADIODE  NUMBER=12  NAME=anode_ohm   COMMON=anode_sch  SHORT
     EXT.ALPHA=10
130. CONTACT  DEVICE=ADIODE  NUMBER=13  NAME=anode_ohm   COMMON=anode_sch  SHORT
     EXT.ALPHA=10
131.
```

```
132. CONTACT  DEVICE=ADIODE  NUMBER=14 NAME=anode_sch   WORKFUNCTION=5.0  THERMION
     PARABOLIC  EXT.ALPHA=10
133. CONTACT  DEVICE=ADIODE  NUMBER=15 NAME=anode_sch   WORKFUNCTION=5.0  THERMION
     PARABOLIC  EXT.ALPHA=10
134. CONTACT  DEVICE=ADIODE  NUMBER=16 NAME=anode_sch   WORKFUNCTION=5.0  THERMION
     PARABOLIC  EXT.ALPHA=10
135. CONTACT  DEVICE=ADIODE  NUMBER=17 NAME=anode_sch   WORKFUNCTION=5.0  THERMION
     PARABOLIC  EXT.ALPHA=10
136. CONTACT  DEVICE=ADIODE  NUMBER=18 NAME=anode_sch   WORKFUNCTION=5.0  THERMION
     PARABOLIC  EXT.ALPHA=10
137. CONTACT  DEVICE=ADIODE  NUMBER=19 NAME=anode_sch   WORKFUNCTION=5.0  THERMION
     PARABOLIC  EXT.ALPHA=10
138. CONTACT  DEVICE=ADIODE  NUMBER=20 NAME=anode_sch   WORKFUNCTION=5.0  THERMION
     PARABOLIC  EXT.ALPHA=10
139. CONTACT  DEVICE=ADIODE  NUMBER=21 NAME=anode_sch   WORKFUNCTION=5.0  THERMION
     PARABOLIC  EXT.ALPHA=10
140. CONTACT  DEVICE=ADIODE  NUMBER=22 NAME=anode_sch   WORKFUNCTION=5.0  THERMION
     PARABOLIC  EXT.ALPHA=10
141. CONTACT  DEVICE=ADIODE  NUMBER=23 NAME=anode_sch   WORKFUNCTION=5.0  THERMION
     PARABOLIC  EXT.ALPHA=10
142. CONTACT  DEVICE=ADIODE  NUMBER=24 NAME=anode_sch   WORKFUNCTION=5.0  THERMION
     PARABOLIC  EXT.ALPHA=10
143. CONTACT  DEVICE=ADIODE  NUMBER=25 NAME=anode_sch   WORKFUNCTION=5.0  THERMION
     PARABOLIC  EXT.ALPHA=10
144.
145. CONTACT  DEVICE=ADIODE  NUMBER=26 NAME=cathode    EXT.ALPHA=10
146.
147. THERMCONTACT DEVICE=ADIODE   num=27   x.min=0    x.max=42  y.min=-1.0
     y.max=184   alpha=10   ext.temp=300
148.
149. MATERIAL DEVICE=ADIODE  MATERIAL=4H-SiC REGION=2  permittivity=9.76
     eg300=3.26   affinity=3.7   egalpha=3.3e-2  egbeta=1.e+5  nc300=1.7e+19
     nv300=2.5e+19  arichn=146  arichp=30  augn=3.e-29  augp=3.e-29  taun0=1e-9
     taup0=6.e-7  nsrhn=3.e+17 nsrhp=3.e+17 edb=0.050  eab=0.200  tcon.polyn
     tc.a=0.137534   tc.b=0.00049662   tc.c=0.000000354  hc.a=2.35  hc.b=1.75e-3
     hc.c=1.e-9  hc.d=-6.6e4
150.
151. ## MODELS USED
152.
153. MODELS  DEVICE=ADIODE   REGION=2 MATERIAL=4H-SIC FERMIDIRAC ANALYTIC CONWELL
     SRH BGN AUGER INCOMPLETE LAT.TEMP JOULE.HEAT  GR.HEAT  PT.HEAT PRINT
154.
155. ## MOBILITY
156.
157. MOBILITY  DEVICE=ADIODE material=4H-SiC REGION=2  vsatn=2.2e7  vsatp=2.2e7
     betan=1.2 betap=2  mu1n.caug=40  mu2n.caug=1136  ncritn.caug=2e17
     alphan.caug=-3  betan.caug=-3  gamman.caug=0.0  deltan.caug=0.76
     mu1p.caug=20  mu2p.caug=125  ncritp.caug=1.e19  alphap.caug=-3  betap.caug=-3
     gammap.caug=0.0  deltap.caug=0.5
158.
159. MOBILITY  DEVICE=ADIODE material=4H-SiC REGION=2  n.canali  n.angle=90
     p.angle=90 vsatn=2.2e7 vsatp=2.2e7  betan=1.2 betap=2  mu1n.caug=5
     mu2n.caug=947  ncritn.caug=2e17  alphan.caug=-3  betan.caug=-3
     gamman.caug=0.0  deltan.caug=0.76   mu1p.caug=2.5  mu2p.caug=20
     ncritp.caug=1.e19  alphap.caug=-3  betap.caug=-3  gammap.caug=0.0
     deltap.caug=0.5
160.
161. ## Impact Ionization
162.
```

```
163. IMPACT  DEVICE=ADIODE   REGION=2  ANISO  E.SIDE  SELB  SIC4H0001  an1=3.44e6
     an2=3.44e6  bn1=2.58e7  bn2=2.58e7  ap1=3.5e6  ap2=3.5e6  bp1=1.7e7  bp2=1.7e7
     opphe=0.106
164.
165. METHOD  BLOCK climit=1.e-9  maxtraps=100  itlimit=100   max.temp=1000
     dvmax=1.e8  ir.tol=1.e-35  cr.tol=1.e-35  ix.tol=1.e-35  px.tol=1.e-30
     pr.tol=1.e-45  cx.tol=1.e-30
166.
167. GO ATLAS SIMFLAGS ="-V 5.18.3.R -P 32 -160"
168.
169. ##### TRANSIENT SIMULATION CIRCUIT #####
170.
171. .BEGIN
172.
173. VDC        1   0    600
174. RSW        1   2    1.e-12 PULSE 1.e-12 1.e18  5us  50ns  50ns  40us  80us
175. R_CHARGE   2   3    500
176. C_BANK     3   0    6u
177. R_SERIES   3   4    0.80
178. L_SERIES   4   5    500n
179. RSWITCH    5   6    1.e18   PULSE 1.e18 1.e-12  10us  50ns  50ns  40us  80us
180. ADIODE      6=anode_ohm  6=anode_sch  0=cathode   infile=JBS_Structure.str
     width=1.2e6
181.
182. .NUMERIC  imaxtr=100  dtmax=5.e-8
183. .OPTIONS  m2ln.tr  print  noshift  relpot  write=10
184. .LOAD      infile=JBS_RLC_Bias
185. .SAVE      master=JBS_Transient
186. .LOG       outfile=JBS_RLC_Ringdown_5000.log
187. .SAVE      outfile=JBS_RLC_Ringdown_5000.str
188. .TRAN   0.01us 45us
189.
190. .END
191.
192. ##### PHYSICS USED #####
193.
194. CONTACT  DEVICE=ADIODE  NUMBER=1    NAME=anode_ohm    COMMON=anode_sch  SHORT
     EXT.ALPHA=10
195. CONTACT  DEVICE=ADIODE  NUMBER=2    NAME=anode_ohm    COMMON=anode_sch  SHORT
     EXT.ALPHA=10
196. CONTACT  DEVICE=ADIODE  NUMBER=3    NAME=anode_ohm    COMMON=anode_sch  SHORT
     EXT.ALPHA=10
197. CONTACT  DEVICE=ADIODE  NUMBER=4    NAME=anode_ohm    COMMON=anode_sch  SHORT
     EXT.ALPHA=10
198. CONTACT  DEVICE=ADIODE  NUMBER=5    NAME=anode_ohm    COMMON=anode_sch  SHORT
     EXT.ALPHA=10
199. CONTACT  DEVICE=ADIODE  NUMBER=6    NAME=anode_ohm    COMMON=anode_sch  SHORT
     EXT.ALPHA=10
200. CONTACT  DEVICE=ADIODE  NUMBER=7    NAME=anode_ohm    COMMON=anode_sch  SHORT
     EXT.ALPHA=10
201. CONTACT  DEVICE=ADIODE  NUMBER=8    NAME=anode_ohm    COMMON=anode_sch  SHORT
     EXT.ALPHA=10
202. CONTACT  DEVICE=ADIODE  NUMBER=9    NAME=anode_ohm    COMMON=anode_sch  SHORT
     EXT.ALPHA=10
203. CONTACT  DEVICE=ADIODE  NUMBER=10   NAME=anode_ohm    COMMON=anode_sch  SHORT
     EXT.ALPHA=10
204. CONTACT  DEVICE=ADIODE  NUMBER=11   NAME=anode_ohm    COMMON=anode_sch  SHORT
     EXT.ALPHA=10
205. CONTACT  DEVICE=ADIODE  NUMBER=12   NAME=anode_ohm    COMMON=anode_sch  SHORT
     EXT.ALPHA=10
```

```
206. CONTACT  DEVICE=ADIODE  NUMBER=13  NAME=anode_ohm    COMMON=anode_sch SHORT
     EXT.ALPHA=10
207.
208. CONTACT  DEVICE=ADIODE  NUMBER=14  NAME=anode_sch    WORKFUNCTION=5.0 THERMION
     PARABOLIC  EXT.ALPHA=10
209. CONTACT  DEVICE=ADIODE  NUMBER=15  NAME=anode_sch    WORKFUNCTION=5.0 THERMION
     PARABOLIC  EXT.ALPHA=10
210. CONTACT  DEVICE=ADIODE  NUMBER=16  NAME=anode_sch    WORKFUNCTION=5.0 THERMION
     PARABOLIC  EXT.ALPHA=10
211. CONTACT  DEVICE=ADIODE  NUMBER=17  NAME=anode_sch    WORKFUNCTION=5.0 THERMION
     PARABOLIC  EXT.ALPHA=10
212. CONTACT  DEVICE=ADIODE  NUMBER=18  NAME=anode_sch    WORKFUNCTION=5.0 THERMION
     PARABOLIC  EXT.ALPHA=10
213. CONTACT  DEVICE=ADIODE  NUMBER=19  NAME=anode_sch    WORKFUNCTION=5.0 THERMION
     PARABOLIC  EXT.ALPHA=10
214. CONTACT  DEVICE=ADIODE  NUMBER=20  NAME=anode_sch    WORKFUNCTION=5.0 THERMION
     PARABOLIC  EXT.ALPHA=10
215. CONTACT  DEVICE=ADIODE  NUMBER=21  NAME=anode_sch    WORKFUNCTION=5.0 THERMION
     PARABOLIC  EXT.ALPHA=10
216. CONTACT  DEVICE=ADIODE  NUMBER=22  NAME=anode_sch    WORKFUNCTION=5.0 THERMION
     PARABOLIC  EXT.ALPHA=10
217. CONTACT  DEVICE=ADIODE  NUMBER=23  NAME=anode_sch    WORKFUNCTION=5.0 THERMION
     PARABOLIC  EXT.ALPHA=10
218. CONTACT  DEVICE=ADIODE  NUMBER=24  NAME=anode_sch    WORKFUNCTION=5.0 THERMION
     PARABOLIC  EXT.ALPHA=10
219. CONTACT  DEVICE=ADIODE  NUMBER=25  NAME=anode_sch    WORKFUNCTION=5.0 THERMION
     PARABOLIC  EXT.ALPHA=10
220.
221. CONTACT  DEVICE=ADIODE  NUMBER=26  NAME=cathode       EXT.ALPHA=10
222.
223. THERMCONTACT DEVICE=ADIODE    num=27    x.min=0    x.max=42  y.min=-1.0
     y.max=184    alpha=10    ext.temp=300
224.
225. MATERIAL   DEVICE=ADIODE   MATERIAL=4H-SiC REGION=2  permittivity=9.76
     eg300=3.26    affinity=3.7    egalpha=3.3e-2    egbeta=1.e+5  nc300=1.7e+19
     nv300=2.5e+19 arichn=146  arichp=30  augn=3.e-29  augp=3.e-29  taun0=1e-9
     taup0=6.e-7  nsrhn=3.e+17 nsrhp=3.e+17 edb=0.050  eab=0.200  tcon.polyn
     tc.a=0.137534   tc.b=0.00049662    tc.c=0.000000354  hc.a=2.35  hc.b=1.75e-3
     hc.c=1.e-9  hc.d=-6.6e4
226.
227. ## MODELS USED
228.
229. MODELS  DEVICE=ADIODE  REGION=2 MATERIAL=4H-SIC FERMIDIRAC ANALYTIC CONWELL
     SRH BGN AUGER INCOMPLETE LAT.TEMP JOULE.HEAT  GR.HEAT  PT.HEAT PRINT
230.
231. ## MOBILITY
232.
233. MOBILITY  DEVICE=ADIODE  material=4H-SiC REGION=2  vsatn=2.2e7  vsatp=2.2e7
     betan=1.2 betap=2  mu1n.caug=40  mu2n.caug=1136  ncritn.caug=2e17
     alphan.caug=-3  betan.caug=-3  gamman.caug=0.0  deltan.caug=0.76
     mu1p.caug=20  mu2p.caug=125  ncritp.caug=1.e19  alphap.caug=-3  betap.caug=-3
     gammap.caug=0.0  deltap.caug=0.5
234.
235. MOBILITY  DEVICE=ADIODE  material=4H-SiC REGION=2  n.canali  n.angle=90
     p.angle=90 vsatn=2.2e7  vsatp=2.2e7  betan=1.2 betap=2  mu1n.caug=5
     mu2n.caug=947  ncritn.caug=2e17  alphan.caug=-3  betan.caug=-3
     gamman.caug=0.0  deltan.caug=0.76  mu1p.caug=2.5  mu2p.caug=20
     ncritp.caug=1.e19  alphap.caug=-3  betap.caug=-3  gammap.caug=0.0
     deltap.caug=0.5
236.
```

```
237. ## Impact Ionization
238.
239. IMPACT  DEVICE=ADIODE   REGION=2  ANISO  E.SIDE  SELB  SIC4H0001  an1=3.44e6
     an2=3.44e6  bn1=2.58e7  bn2=2.58e7  ap1=3.5e6  ap2=3.5e6  bp1=1.7e7  bp2=1.7e7
     opphe=0.106
240.
241. OUTPUT  FLOWLINES E.MOBILITY
242.
243. METHOD  BLOCK.TRAN climit=1.e-9 maxtraps=100  itlimit=100   max.temp=1000
     dvmax=1.e8  ir.tol=1.e-35  cr.tol=1.e-35  ix.tol=1.e-35  px.tol=1.e-30
     pr.tol=1.e-45  cx.tol=1.e-30
244.
245. GO ATLAS SIMFLAGS ="-V 5.18.3.R -P 32 -160"
246.
247. QUIT
```

Table 4.   Code walkthrough: JBS diode (active area $= 10\,\mu m^2$) Mixed-Mode simulation.

Line No:	Functionality
1	Configure ATLAS simulator to use version 5.18.3.R, 160-bit extended precision and utilize 32 cores of the CPU if hardware resources are available.
5	Initialize device structure mesh information with width parameter.
7–25	X-axis and Y-axis mesh distribution.
29–30	Declare oxide and 4H-SiC as the material for the area specified by the x and y coordinates.
34–58	Separate electrode statements for the anode Schottky contact using metal conductor and anode ohmic contact using titanium.
60	Electrode statement to specify aluminum for cathode ohmic contact.
64–84	Specify doping profile, type, and concentration for different areas of the JBS diode structure.
86	Save the device structure (**.str**) file on the local hard drive. The device structure can be viewed by opening the file via **TonyPlot** to troubleshoot/optimize the structure.
90	Initialize ATLAS simulator using GO ATLAS command (same as line 1).
92	Initialize the starting of SPICE-like code in Mixed-Mode steady-state simulation.
94–101	RLC ring-down circuit description in SPICE-like format.
103	Declare the initial node voltage for the RLC ring-down circuit nodes.
104	Set the maximum number of mixed circuit-device iterations to be performed during steady-state analysis (**imaxdc**) to 100.
106–108	Ramp up DC voltage to attain steady-state condition, i.e. VDC = 600 V. This can be split into multiple steps.
110	Save log file after steady-state simulation completion.

(Continued)

Table 4.   (*Continued*)

Line No:	Functionality
111	Save file with bias information which will be used for transient simulation.
112	Specify Mixed-Mode steady-state simulation conditions. Modified two-level Newton solution method (**m2ln**), disable the shift of voltage for ATLAS devices (**noshift**), and enable the use of relative convergence criteria for potential especially when large voltage biases are involved (**relpot**).
114	Initialize the ending of SPICE-like code in Mixed-Mode steady-state simulation.
118–130	Shorting the ohmic and Schottky anode contacts is different in Mixed-Mode as compared to steady-state simulation. A separate statement is required for each ohmic contact and contact number must be specified for each contact using the parameter (**number**). The same statement is used to specify the heat transfer coefficient (**ext.alpha**).
132–143	Specify heat transfer coefficient (**ext.alpha**) and enable thermionic emission (**thermion**) and parabolic field emission (**parabolic**) for anode Schottky contact.
145	Specify heat transfer coefficient (**ext.alpha**) for cathode contact.
147	Specify the thermal boundary for the JBS diode. Parameters includes boundary dimensions, heat transfer coefficient (**alpha**), and temperature of the thermal boundary (**ext.temp**) which is typically at 300 K.
149	Specify material parameters for 4H-SiC.
153	Specify the various models to be included in the 4H-SiC JBS diode simulation.
157	Specify parameters for mobility in 4H-SiC.
159	Specify parameters for anisotropic mobility in 4H-SiC.
163	Specify impact ionization parameters for 4H-SiC.
165	Specify the steady-state Block Newton solver type (**BLOCK**) and the tolerance values to be used during the simulation.
167	Initialize ATLAS simulator using GO ATLAS command (same as line 1) for steady-state bias point simulation.
171	Initialize the starting of SPICE-like code in Mixed-Mode transient simulation.
173–180	RLC ring-down circuit description in SPICE-like format. The magnitude of DC voltage source is initialized at 600 V, result of the steady-state simulation performed earlier. Transient parameters have been added to the Resistor which is acting like a switch.
182	Set the maximum number of mixed circuit-device iterations to be performed during transient analysis (**imaxtr**) to 100 and the maximum transient simulation time step (**dtmax**) to 50 ns.

(*Continued*)

Table 4.   (*Continued*)

Line No:	Functionality
183	Specify Mixed-Mode transient simulation conditions. Modified two-level Newton solution method for transient simulation (**m2ln.tr**), disable the shift of voltage for ATLAS devices (**noshift**), enable the use of relative convergence criteria for potential especially when large voltage biases are involved (**relpot**), and write structure file after every 10 time-step iterations.
184	Load the steady-state simulations results saved in line 111.
185	Save the structure file after every 10 time-step iterations specified in line 183.
186	Save log file after the completion of transient simulation.
187	Save the structure file after the completion of transient simulation.
188	Specify the initial time interval of 10 ns and total simulation time of 45 μs.
190	Initialize the ending of SPICE-like code in Mixed-Mode transient simulation.
192–239	Same as line 116 to line 163.
241	Include current flowlines (**FLOWLINES**) and Electron Mobility (**E.MOBILITY**) in the output structure file.
243	Specify the transient Block Newton solver type (**BLOCK.TRAN**) and the tolerance values to be used during the simulation.
245	Initialize ATLAS simulator using GO ATLAS command (same as line 1) for transient simulation. A simulation precision of 160-bit has been used due to device complexity.
247	Terminate the simulation.

8.3.3.4.   *Mixed-Mode transient simulation results*

The transient simulation for the SiC JBS diode structure was carried out for varying magnitudes of peak current density ranging from 500 A/cm^2 to 5000 A/cm^2 in steps of 500. The **width** parameter was used to change the peak current density through the diode without altering the waveform. In this section, the results pertaining to the maximum current density scenario of 5000 A/cm^2 will be discussed followed by a summary of all the other cases. The anode voltage and current density waveforms are shown in Fig. 28, and the power and energy density waveforms are shown in Fig. 29.

Peak voltage drop of 17.13 V was observed across the JBS diode at peak current density of 5000 A/cm^2 which corresponds to a peak power dissipation density of 84.3 kW/cm^2. Integration of the power density waveform yielded an energy density of 339 mJ/cm^2. Peak lattice temperature of 307.3 K

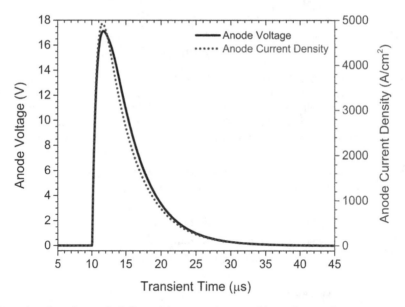

Fig. 28.   Anode voltage (solid) and current density (dotted) waveforms pertaining to 5000 A/cm^2 peak current density simulation.

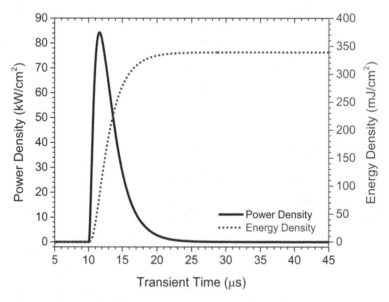

Fig. 29.   Power density (solid) and energy density (dotted) waveforms pertaining to 5000 A/cm^2 peak current density simulation.

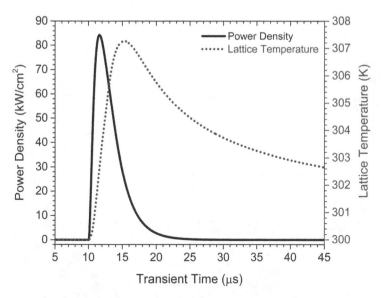

Fig. 30. Power density (solid) and lattice temperature (dotted) waveforms pertaining to 5000 A/cm^2 peak current density simulation.

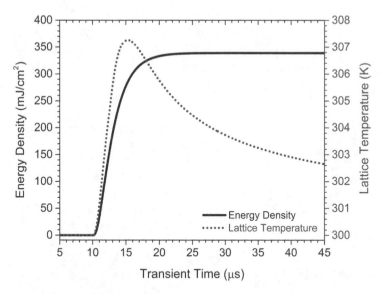

Fig. 31. Energy density (solid) and lattice temperature (dotted) waveforms pertaining to 5000 A/cm^2 peak current density simulation.

was observed in the JBS diode lattice during this pulsed operation. The variation of lattice temperature with power dissipation density and energy density during simulation is shown in Figs. 30 and 31, respectively. To identify the area of heat dissipation in the JBS diode structure, intermediate structure files were generated during the simulation. These structure files were manually scanned for the transient time instant which corresponds to the maximum lattice temperature.

The lattice temperature profile of the JBS diode structure recorded at the time instant corresponding to maximum temperature during high current density pulsed simulation is shown in Figs. 32(a) and 32(b). A maximum temperature of 307.3 K was observed in the drift region closer to the anode; however, the temperature distribution was not uniform and localized heating was observed to the left side of the device structure. The lattice temperature

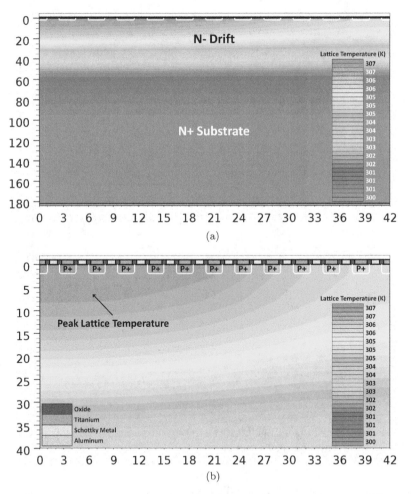

Fig. 32. (a) Lattice temperature profile of JBS diode (active area = 10 μm^2) structure during 5000 A/cm^2 RLC ring-down simulation. (b) Lattice temperature profile of JBS diode (active area = 10 μm^2) structure during 5000 A/cm^2 RLC ring-down simulation (zoomed-in view).

profile and data from the waveforms lead to the speculation that there may not be equal current sharing happening between the multiple cells in the larger JBS diode structure. Since the larger device has a larger thermal boundary, the power dissipation and lattice temperature should not be greater than the smaller device simulation results, which is not the case.

To further investigate this issue, joule heat power and current density profiles were extracted from the same structure file and are shown in Figs. 33 and 34, respectively (*p–n* junction is shown in white). The joule heat power

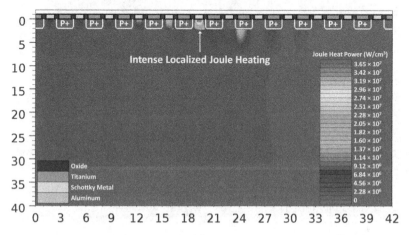

Fig. 33.   Joule heat power profile of JBS diode (active area = 10 μm^2) structure during 5000 A/cm^2 RLC ring-down simulation highlighting localized power dissipation due to non-uniform current density sharing (zoomed-in view).

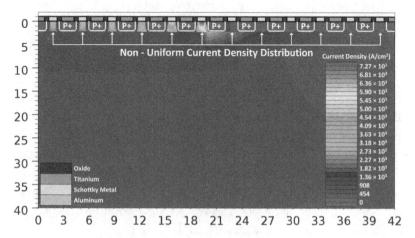

Fig. 34.   Conduction current density profile of JBS diode (active area = 10 μm^2) structure during 5000 A/cm^2 RLC ring-down simulation highlighting extremely high current density in a single cell (zoomed-in view).

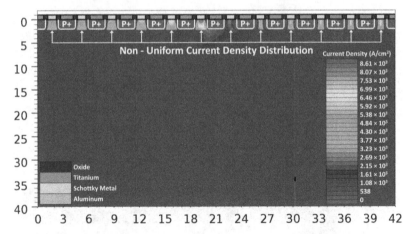

Fig. 35.   Conduction current density profile of JBS diode (active area = $10~\mu m^2$) structure during 5000 A/cm^2 RLC ring-down simulation at peak current density time instant (zoomed-in view).

and current density profiles clearly indicate non-uniform current conduction through the JBS diode, thereby leading to localized power dissipation in the particular cell which conducts majority of the circuit current. From an applications perspective, this is not a favorable scenario since the device will undergo severe electrothermal stress which will eventually lead to device failure.

The current density profile was also extracted for the time instant when the circuit current was at its peak magnitude and is shown in Fig. 35. During the maximum current density time instant, the Schottky cell closer to the middle of the device structure is experiencing extremely high current density while the other cells in the device are conducting much lower magnitude of current density. From these results, it can be confirmed that the high power dissipation and elevated lattice temperature was a result of non-uniform current sharing within the device.

The summary of lattice temperature and anode voltage waveforms for the JBS diode structure for all the values of peak pulsed current density are shown in Figs. 36 and 37, respectively. In general, the ON-state voltage drop and lattice temperature values for the larger JBS diode is higher than that for the smaller device, and this is due to the current sharing issue observed in the larger active area device. The intention of this particular device simulation is to introduce the reader to a potential issue they could face during the simulation of a multi-cell JBS diode.

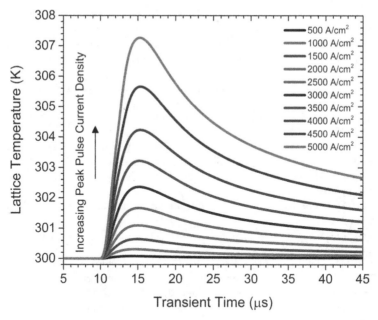

Fig. 36.   Lattice temperature summary of JBS diode (active area $= 10~\mu m^2$) structure during RLC ring-down simulation.

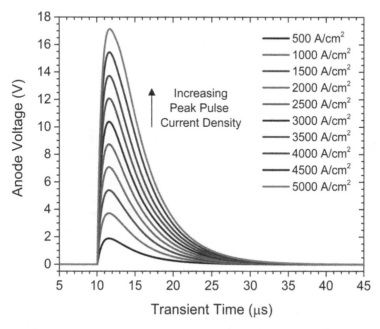

Fig. 37.   Anode voltage summary of JBS diode (active area $= 10~\mu m^2$) structure during RLC ring-down simulation.

References

1. R. Singh, D. C. Capell, A. R. Hefner, J. Lai and J. W. Palmour, High-power 4H-SiC JBS rectifiers, *IEEE Transactions on Electron Devices*, vol. 49, no. 11, November 2002, pp. 2054–2063.
2. H. Yuan, Q. W. Song, X. Y. Tang, Y. M. Zhang, Y. M. Zhang and Y. M. Zhang, Design and experiment of 4H-SiC JBS diodes achieving a near-theoretical breakdown voltage with non-uniform floating limiting rings terminal, *Solid-State Electronics*, vol. 123, September 2016, pp. 28–62.
3. R. J. Callanan, A. Agarwal, A. Burk, M. Das, B. Hull, F. Husna, A. Powell, J. Richmond, S. H. Ryu and Q. Zhang, Recent progress in SiC DMOSFETs and JBS diodes at Cree, *2008 34th Annual Conference of IEEE Industrial Electronics*, Orlando, FL, 2008, pp. 2885–2890.
4. B. Baliga, *Fundamentals of Power Semiconductor Devices*, New York, NY: Springer Verlag, 2008.
5. B. Baliga, *Silicon Carbide Power Devices*, Singapore: World Scientific Publishing Company, 2006.
6. ATLAS User's Manual, September 11, 2014, [online] Available at: www.silvaco.com.
7. B. N. Pushpakaran, S. B. Bayne and A. A. Ogunniyi, Electrothermal Simulation-Based Comparison of 4H-SiC p-i-n, Schottky, and JBS Diodes Under High Current Density Pulsed Operation, *IEEE Transactions on Plasma Science*, vol. 45, no. 1, January 2017, pp. 68–75.
8. B. N. Pushpakaran, S. B. Bayne and A. A. Ogunniyi, Physics based electro-thermal transient simulation of 4H-SiC JBS diode using Silvaco© ATLAS, *2015 IEEE Pulsed Power Conference (PPC)*, Austin, TX, 2015, pp. 1–5.

Chapter 9

Power MOSFET

The power Metal Oxide Semiconductor Field Effect Transistor (MOSFET) is a popular choice for power electronics designers because of the high input impedance and high operating frequency. Unlike small signal MOSFETs which utilize a lateral structure, power MOSFETs generally have a vertical device structure to enable large blocking voltage across the epitaxial/drift region. Besides having greater blocking voltage capability, the vertical structure also enables higher cell density which is necessary to reduce the ON-state resistance for high current applications. It has been discussed in the previous chapters that the blocking voltage capability of a power device is directly proportional to the thickness and inversely proportional to the doping concentration of the epitaxial/drift region. Since a power MOSFET is a majority carrier device, the ON-state resistance is not reduced by conductivity modulation which places an upper limit on the rated blocking voltage. The impact of high blocking voltage on a silicon power MOSFET ON-state resistance can be realized by the following example: *N-channel enhancement power MOSFET IXTU01N100* from IXYS is rated for a blocking of 1000 V; however, the ON-state resistance of the device is 80 Ω which limits the ON-state current to 100 mA.[1] The high ON-state resistance of high-voltage silicon MOSFET can be reduced by increasing the active area which results in a larger chip size. This can be seen for an *N-channel enhancement power MOSFET IXFN32N120P* from IXYS which is rated for a blocking voltage of 1200 V and ON-state drain current of 32 A. The device has an ON-state resistance of 310 mΩ; however, the larger die area resulted in an input capacitance of 21,000 pF and output capacitance of 1100 pF which are extremely high values for a discrete device and would result in elevated switching loss.[2] Due to this reason, silicon-based power MOSFET is the switching device of choice for power electronic applications where the operating voltage is typically below 100 V.

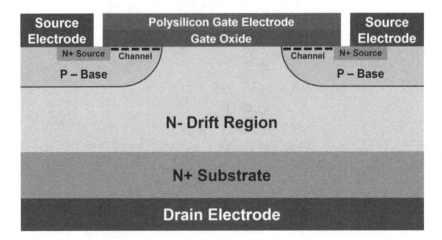

Fig. 1.   Simplified cross-sectional structure of a vertical D-MOSFET.

The advent of wide bandgap SiC semiconductor technology has enabled the development of high-voltage SiC power MOSFETs with low ON-state resistance making them suitable for high-voltage, high-current, and high-speed switching power applications. As a comparable example second-generation 1200 V SiC *N-channel enhancement power MOSFET C2M0080120D* from Wolfspeed (A Cree company) is rated for a blocking voltage of 1200 V and ON-state drain current of 36 A with an ON-state resistance of only 80 mΩ. The device has input and output capacitance values of 950 pF and 80 pF, respectively, which is much lower as compared to the silicon MOSFET example discussed earlier and would result in lower switching losses.[3] Power MOSFET structure can be classified into two major types: Vertical D-MOSFET (also known as VD-MOSFET) and the Trench or U-MOSFET. This textbook will focus on the modeling and simulation of vertical D-MOSFET structure using Silvaco© ATLAS TCAD software. The critical electrical parameters for a power MOSFET include threshold voltage (V_{th}), ON-state resistance (R_{DSON}), and input and output capacitance (C_{ISS}, C_{OSS}, and C_{RSS}). Figure 1 shows a simplified cross-sectional structure of a vertical D-MOSFET.

9.1.   Forward Conduction

An enhancement-mode power MOSFET can be designed either for an N-channel (electrons) or P-channel (holes). Power MOSFETs are generally designed for N-channel due to the higher electron mobility and process-specific reasons (in case of silicon carbide); hence, N-channel power

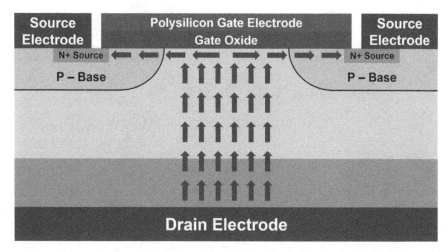

Fig. 2. Cross-sectional structure of a D-MOSFET showing current conduction (arrows) from drain to source.

MOSFETs will be discussed in this textbook. MOSFET turn-ON is associated with the formation of an electron channel between N+ source and N− drift region which provides a conductive path for the flow of electrons from source to drain or current flow from drain to source as shown in Fig. 2.

The channel is formed when a positive voltage is applied to the gate terminal with respect to the source terminal which attracts minority carriers (electrons) from the P-base region towards the oxide–semiconductor interface thereby forming an inversion layer in the P-base region closer to the surface. The gate–source voltage required to form the inversion channel is dependent on the device design parameters and will be discussed in the following section on threshold voltage.[4]

9.1.1. Threshold voltage

Threshold voltage (V_{th}) is one of the most important electrical parameters for a power MOSFET and is defined as the gate to source voltage at which an inversion layer forms in the P-base region at the oxide–semiconductor interface. The selection of threshold voltage is critical since a lower threshold voltage would make the MOSFET susceptible to noise/transient voltage turn-ON while a higher threshold voltage would require large gate to source voltage to form the inversion layer necessary for device turn-ON. In an actual circuit, a much larger gate to source voltage $(V_{Gate} > V_{th})$ is applied to the power MOSFET to form a strong inversion layer which lowers the channel resistance. The channel resistance will be discussed in the section on ON-state resistance. The brief derivation of the equation for MOSFET threshold voltage is shown by the following set of equations where the MOSFET gate electrode voltage (V_{Gate}) is expressed as the sum of voltage across the gate oxide (V_{Oxide}) and semiconductor surface potential (ψ_S):[4]

$$V_{\text{Gate}} = V_{\text{Oxide}} + \psi_S \tag{1}$$

$$V_{\text{Oxide}} = \frac{Q_S}{\varepsilon_{\text{ox}}} t_{\text{ox}} = \frac{Q_S}{C_{\text{ox}}} \tag{2}$$

where ε_{OX} is the permittivity, t_{ox} is the thickness of gate oxide, and C_{OX} is the specific capacitance of gate oxide. In a SiC power MOSFET, gate oxide thickness is typically between 400 Å and 500 Å. Under strong inversion condition, the surface potential becomes equal to twice the bulk potential (ψ_B) and V_{Gate} can be defined as the threshold voltage (V_{th}). The threshold voltage and bulk potential can be expressed in terms of the P-base doping concentration (N_A) in the following equations:

$$V_{\text{th}} = \frac{Q_S}{C_{\text{ox}}} + 2\psi_B \tag{3}$$

$$V_{\text{th}} = \frac{\sqrt{4\,\varepsilon_{\text{SiC}}\,k\,T N_A \ln\left(\frac{N_A}{n_i}\right)}}{C_{\text{ox}}} + \frac{2kT}{q} \ln\left(\frac{N_A}{n_i}\right) \tag{4}$$

Since the first term in Eq. (4) is dominant, the threshold voltage can be expressed by the following equation which relates threshold voltage to the P-base doping concentration and gate oxide thickness. The threshold voltage increases linearly with gate oxide thickness and as a square root of P-base region doping.

$$V_{\text{th}} = \frac{\sqrt{4\,\varepsilon_{\text{SiC}}\,k\,T N_A \ln\left(\frac{N_A}{n_i}\right)}}{C_{\text{ox}}} \tag{5}$$

In SiC MOSFET, the thermal oxidation process for gate oxide growth results in oxide charge which comprises of mobile ion charge, trapped oxide charge, fixed oxide charge, and interface state charge. The total charge (Q_{Oxide}) present in the gate oxide reduces the threshold voltage which can be calculated using the following equation:[4,5]

$$V_{\text{th}} = \frac{\sqrt{4\,\varepsilon_{\text{SiC}}\,k\,T N_A \ln\left(\frac{N_A}{n_i}\right)}}{C_{\text{ox}}} - \frac{Q_{\text{Oxide}}}{C_{\text{ox}}} \tag{6}$$

9.1.2. ON-state resistance

The total ON-state resistance (R_{DSON}) of a D-MOSFET is an important
parameter in determining the performance of the power MOSFET and
is provided in the device datasheet. During ON-state operation, power
dissipation (P_D) in the device is given by the following equation:

$$P_D = I_{\text{Drain}}^2 \cdot R_{\text{DSON}} \tag{7}$$

where I_{Drain} is the drain current. The maximum current that can be
conducted by the MOSFET is limited by the thermal impedance of the
package and cooling system. The total ON-state resistance is the sum of
different resistances present in a Power D-MOSFET structure.[4] The various
components of the MOSFET ON-state resistance is shown in the following
equation:

$$R_{\text{DSON}} = R_{\text{Source}} + R_{N+} + R_{\text{CH}} + R_{\text{ACC}} + R_{\text{JFET}} + R_{\text{Drift}}$$
$$+ R_{\text{Sub}} + R_{\text{Drain}} \tag{8}$$

where R_{Source} is the source contact resistance, R_{N+} is the resistance of source
N+ region, R_{CH} is the channel resistance, R_{ACC} is the accumulation region
resistance, R_{JFET} is the JFET region resistance, R_{Drift} is the resistance of
the drift region, R_{Sub} is the N+ substrate resistance, and R_{Drain} is the drain
contact resistance. The various components that contribute to the total ON-
state resistance are shown in Fig. 3.

Since the source contact, drain contact, and N+ source region resistances
can be minimized by device design and processing techniques, the ON-state

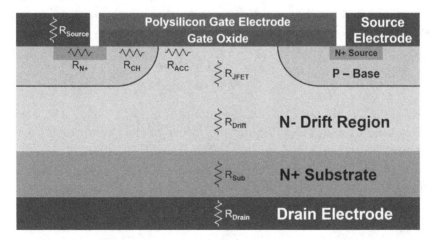

Fig. 3.   Vertical D-MOSFET structure showing the various components contributing to
the ON-state resistance.

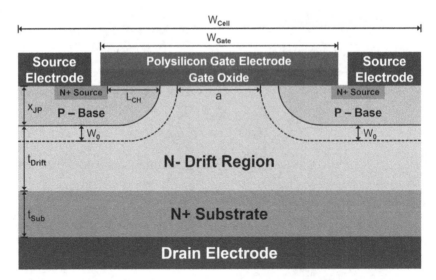

Fig. 4.   Cross-sectional structure of a vertical D-MOSFET highlighting critical dimensions.

resistance can be approximated to the following equation:

$$R_{\text{DSON}} \cong R_{\text{CH}} + R_{\text{ACC}} + R_{\text{JFET}} + R_{\text{Drift}} + R_{\text{Sub}} \qquad (9)$$

The discussion of major components contributing to the ON-state resistance of a D-MOSFET will be based on the dimensions marked in the cross-sectional image shown in Fig. 4.

In a SiC MOSFET, channel resistance has a great impact on the overall ON-state resistance because of the reduced mobility of the carriers due to high interface state density and surface scattering effect. The specific channel resistance is given by the following equation:

$$R_{\text{CH, SP}} = \frac{L_{\text{CH}} \cdot W_{\text{Cell}}}{2\mu_{\text{ni}} C_{\text{ox}(V_{\text{Gate}} - V_{\text{th}})}} \qquad (10)$$

where L_{CH} is the channel length, W_{Cell} is the cell pitch, μ_{ni} is the inversion layer/channel mobility, C_{OX} is the capacitance of the gate oxide layer, V_{Gate} is the applied gate voltage, and V_{th} is the threshold voltage. The difference between the applied gate voltage and the threshold voltage ($V_{\text{Gate}} - V_{\text{th}}$) is known as the gate overdrive voltage. A large gate overdrive voltage helps in reducing the channel resistance during ON-state conduction as long as the applied gate voltage does not exceed the absolute maximum rating for the device. When the carriers transition from the channel, they spread into the accumulation region.[4] The specific resistance for the accumulation region is given by

$$R_{\text{ACC,SP}} = K_A \frac{(W_{\text{Gate}} - 2x_{\text{JP}}) \cdot W_{\text{Cell}}}{4\mu_{\text{nA}} C_{\text{ox}}(V_{\text{Gate}} - V_{\text{th}})} \tag{11}$$

where K_A is the coefficient (which has a typical value of 0.6) to account for current spreading from accumulation region to the JFET region, W_{Gate} is the width of the gate polysilicon electrode, x_{JP} is the depth of the P-base region, and μ_{nA} is the mobility within the accumulation region. Once the carriers transition through the accumulation region, they then go into the JFET region of the MOSFET.[4] The specific resistance contributed by the JFET resistance is given by the following equations:

$$R_{\text{JFET,SP}} = \frac{\rho_{\text{JFET}} \cdot x_{\text{JP}} \cdot W_{\text{Cell}}}{a} \tag{12}$$

$$a = W_{\text{Gate}} - 2x_{\text{JP}} - 2W_0 \tag{13}$$

where ρ_{JFET} is the resistivity of the JFET region, and W_0 is the zero-bias depletion width at the p–n junction in the JFET region. Due to unipolar conduction in a MOSFET, drift region resistance is very important due to its direct impact on breakdown voltage. A higher blocking voltage would require thicker drift region which would increase its contribution to the total ON-state resistance.[4] The specific resistance of the drift region is given by the following equation which assumes that current spreads into the entire cell width once it reaches the N−Drift/N+ substrate interface

$$R_{\text{Drift,SP}} = \frac{\rho_{\text{Drift}} \cdot t_{\text{Drift}} \cdot W_{\text{Cell}}}{W_{\text{Cell}} - a} \ln\left(\frac{W_{\text{Cell}}}{a}\right) \tag{14}$$

where ρ_{Drift} is the resistivity and t_{Drift} is the thickness of the drift region. Even though the substrate is heavily doped, the typical resistivity of an N+ 4H-SiC substrate is $20\,\text{m}\Omega \cdot \text{cm}$. For a SiC power device with very high blocking voltage (typically 6500 V or above), the substrate resistance can be neglected since the drift region thickness will be significant as compared to the substrate thickness. However, in case of a relatively lower voltage device (650 V–3300 V), the substrate resistance is significant and must be accounted for. The specific resistance of the substrate region is given by the following equation:

$$R_{\text{Sub,SP}} = \rho_{\text{Sub}} \cdot t_{\text{Sub}} \tag{15}$$

where ρ_{Sub} is the resistivity and t_{Sub} is the thickness of the substrate region. The substrate resistance is the primary reason behind wafer back-grinding process to thin the substrate and optimize the ON-state resistance.

9.2.   Forward Blocking

When a positive voltage bias is applied across the drain to source of the device, p–n junction formed at the P-base/N− drift interface is reverse biased and the drain to source voltage is supported by the depletion region which extends into the lightly doped N− drift region. The forward blocking scenario can also be visualized as a reverse-biased p-i-n diode formed at the P-base/N− drift interface. This p-i-n diode is known as the intrinsic body diode which enables reverse conduction in a D-MOSFET. The width of the depletion region that extends into the P-base region can be calculated using the following equation:

$$W_{P-\text{Depletion}} = \frac{\varepsilon_{\text{SiC}} \cdot E_{\text{max}}}{qN_A} \tag{16}$$

where E_{max} is the maximum electric field and N_A is the acceptor doping concentration of the P-base region. Since the maximum blocking electric field is present at the P-base/N− drift junction, minimum thickness of the P-base region required to support the blocking voltage while preventing reach-through breakdown can be estimated using the following equation

$$t_{P-\text{base}} = \frac{\varepsilon_{\text{SiC}} \cdot E_C}{qN_A} \tag{17}$$

where E_C is the critical electric field. The D-MOSFET structure also has an NPN parasitic Bipolar Junction Transistor (BJT) formed between the N+ Source (emitter), P-base (base), and N− drift (collector) regions. The parasitic p-i-n and BJT formation can be seen in Fig. 5 which is

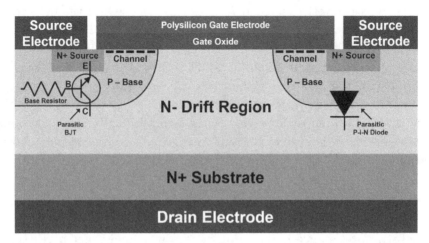

Fig. 5.   Cross-sectional structure of a D-MOSFET cell highlighting the parasitic BJT and intrinsic body p-i-n diode.

the cross-sectional view of a D-MOSFET complete-cell structure. Turn-ON of the parasitic BJT would result in uncontrolled current flow between drain and source terminal thereby leading to thermal runaway which would eventually cause catastrophic device failure; hence it is critical to ensure that the parasitic BJT never turns ON. This is achieved by shorting the N+ source and P-base regions using the source electrode which would short the emitter-base junction of the BJT, thereby suppressing bipolar turn-ON. Since the p–n junction formed at the P-base/N+ source interface is shorted, it does not support any voltage when a positive drain to source voltage is applied.[4]

9.3. Trade-OFF Study

Multiple tradeoffs exist in the design of a vertical D-MOSFET structure which has critical impact on the electrical parameters of the device. These tradeoffs exist due to the presence of P-base regions in the device structure and can be classified into

---

- **Blocking characteristics, gate oxide reliability, and ON-state resistance**

The tradeoff study discussed in this section will be based on the complete-cell structure shown in Fig. 1. The spacing between the P-base regions is a critical design parameter and must be carefully designed to obtain an optimum balance between the blocking voltage capability, gate oxide integrity and ON-state resistance. These tradeoffs will be explained using two scenarios which highlight the impact of wider and narrow P-base region spacing/separation on the electric field distribution during blocking phase and ON-state resistance during forward conduction.

Figures 6 and 7 show a D-MOSFET complete-cell structure, where the P-base regions are separated by a wider spacing, under forward blocking and conduction mode, respectively. Increasing the P-base region spacing results in the lowering of the ON-state resistance due to reduction in the JFET region resistance component since current constriction due to the P-base/N− drift depletion region is reduced. However, wider P-base spacing has a detrimental effect on the blocking characteristics of the device. Firstly, in a D-MOSFET structure, the blocking electric field is supported across the P-base/N− drift p–n junction. Since the N− drift region is lightly doped as compared to the P-base region, space–charge region extends into the drift region and the magnitude of electric field is highest at the P-base/N−drift

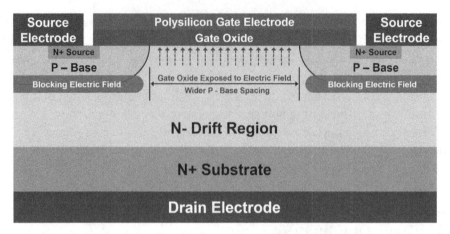

Fig. 6. Cross-sectional structure of a D-MOSFET cell with wider P-base spacing under forward blocking mode.

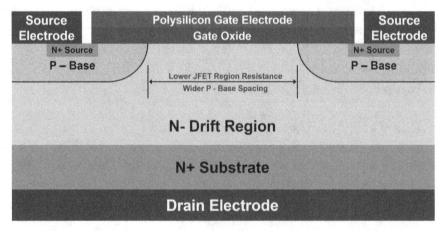

Fig. 7. Cross-sectional structure of a D-MOSFET cell with wider P-base spacing under forward conduction mode.

interface. A widely spaced P-base regions prevents the distribution of electric field across the two P-base regions (like floating field rings) thereby increasing the drain to source leakage current and lowering the forward breakdown voltage. Secondly, now that the P-base regions are spaced apart, the gate oxide/semiconductor interface is exposed to the high electric field which not only increases the gate leakage but also affects the long-term reliability of the MOSFET. This is due to electric field enhancement at the interface between two materials with different values of permittivity. Electric field developed in the oxide (E_{Oxide}) due to electric field in the underlying SiC semiconductor (E_{SiC}) can be calculated using Gauss's law given by the equation

$$E_{\text{Oxide}} = \left(\frac{\varepsilon_{\text{SiC}}}{\varepsilon_{\text{Oxide}}} \right) \cdot E_{\text{SiC}} \qquad (18)$$

where ε_{SiC} and $\varepsilon_{\text{Oxide}}$ are the relative permittivities of SiC and oxide, respectively.[4,5] The relative permittivity of 4H-SiC is 9.7 which is almost 2.5 times greater than that of oxide which is 3.9. Hence, a typical breakdown electric field of 3 MV/cm in SiC would result in 7.5 MV/cm in the oxide, which is not favorable for gate oxide integrity. The details regarding the mechanisms responsible for affecting the gate oxide reliability can be found in the references and will not be discussed in this chapter.

Figures 8 and 9 show a D-MOSFET complete-cell structure, where the P-base regions are closer to each other, under forward blocking and conduction mode, respectively. This results in a uniform distribution of electric field across the P-base regions which not only optimizes the blocking voltage but also shields the gate oxide region from high electric field. However, the optimization of blocking characteristics is at the expense of increased ON-state resistance since the closer P-base regions constrict the flow of drain current resulting in localized power dissipation in the JFET region. The optimization of spacing between the P-base regions is an iterative process and requires multiple simulations.[5,6]

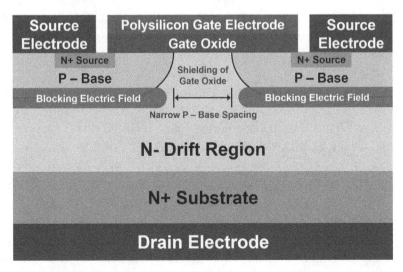

Fig. 8.   Cross-sectional structure of a D-MOSFET cell with narrow P-base spacing under forward blocking mode.

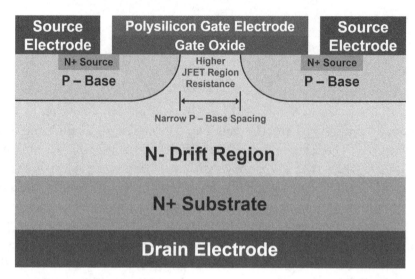

Fig. 9.   Cross-sectional structure of a D-MOSFET cell with narrow P-base spacing under forward conduction mode.

• Blocking characteristics and gate threshold voltage

The tradeoff between blocking characteristics and gate threshold voltage exists due to the doping concentration in the P-base region. As discussed before, threshold voltage of a MOSFET is directly proportional to the square root of acceptor concentration in the P-base regions. A lightly doped P-base region helps in reducing the threshold voltage which is favorable for a power MOSFET; however, reducing the P-base doping concentration causes the space–charge region to extend into the P-base region thereby making the MOSFET susceptible to reach-through breakdown. Similarly, higher doping concentration in the P-base region restricts the extension of space–charge region thereby preventing reach-through breakdown; however, this increases the gate threshold voltage, which is not desirable for a power MOSFET.

Unlike the tradeoff due to spacing between the P-base regions, the impact of P-base doping concentration on the threshold voltage and device breakdown is not critical since retrograde doping profile can be implemented for the P-base region where the area closer to the P-base/N− drift interface will have higher doping concentration which is beneficial to preventing reach-through breakdown while a lower doping concentration close to the surface reduces the threshold voltage.[4,5]

9.4. MOS Capacitance

The switching performance of a power MOSFET is dominated by the charging and discharging of various capacitances present in the device structure. The equivalent D-MOSFET circuit with the various parasitic capacitances is shown in Fig. 10. The capacitances in a power MOSFET are of three types: Gate to Source capacitance (C_{GS}), Drain to Source capacitance (C_{DS}), and Gate to Drain capacitance (C_{GD}), which is also known as the reverse transfer or *Miller* capacitance. Understanding of these parasitic capacitors and its behavior is extremely important for switching applications.[4]

In a power MOSFET datasheet, parasitic capacitance is mentioned as Input capacitance (C_{ISS}), Output Capacitance (C_{OSS}), and Reverse transfer capacitance (C_{RSS}) whose relationship with respect to the device terminals are expressed by Eqs. (19)–(21). Using these equations, individual device capacitances at the given bias voltage can be calculated.

$$C_{ISS} = C_{GS} + C_{GD} \tag{19}$$
$$C_{OSS} = C_{DS} + C_{GD} \tag{20}$$
$$C_{RSS} = C_{GD} \tag{21}$$

The discussion on MOSFET capacitance will be based on the cross-sectional device structure shown in Fig. 11 and some of the dimensions mentioned in Section 9.1.2 on ON-state resistance. The gate to source capacitance is defined as the sum of individual capacitances due to source metal overlap to gate (C_{SM}), gate overlap to N+ source (C_{N+}), and gate overlap to P-base

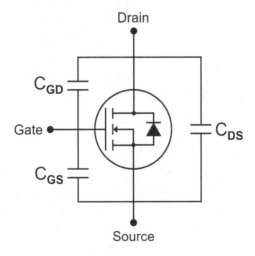

Fig. 10.   Vertical D-MOSFET equivalent circuit focusing on the parasitic capacitance.

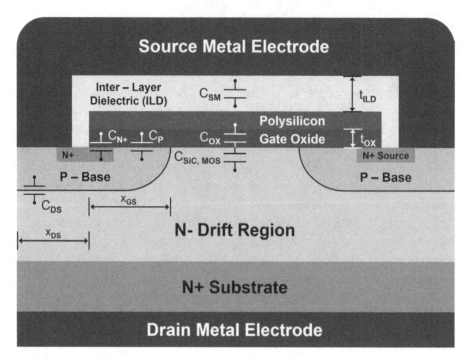

Fig. 11.   Cross-sectional image of D-MOSFET structure highlighting the various device capacitance.

region (C_P). However, since the doping concentrations of N+ source and P-base regions are relatively higher, their capacitance is determined by the oxide capacitance. The contribution of source metal overlap capacitance can be minimized by using a thick Inter-Layer Dielectric (ILD) layer (typically oxide) between the source metal and gate polysilicon.[4]

The specific gate–source capacitance $(C_{\mathrm{GS,SP}})$ is given by Eqs. (22) and (23) where x_{GS} is the overlap between gate electrode and N+ source and P-base region, W_{Cell} is the width of MOSFET cell, W_{Gate} is the width of polysilicon gate electrode, $\varepsilon_{\mathrm{OX}}$ is the permittivity of oxide, and t_{OX} and t_{ILD} are the gate oxide and ILD oxide thickness, respectively.[4]

$$C_{\mathrm{GS,SP}} = C_{N+} + C_P + C_{\mathrm{SM}} \tag{22}$$

$$C_{\mathrm{GS,SP}} = \frac{2x_{GS}}{W_{\mathrm{Cell}}}\left(\frac{\varepsilon_{\mathrm{ox}}}{t_{\mathrm{ox}}}\right) + \frac{W_{\mathrm{Gate}}}{W_{\mathrm{Cell}}}\left(\frac{\varepsilon_{\mathrm{ox}}}{t_{\mathrm{ILD}}}\right) \tag{23}$$

The next capacitance in the vertical D-MOSFET structure is the gate to drain *Miller* capacitance (C_{GD}). The C_{GD} capacitor is formed due to the overlapping of gate electrode and the N-drift/substrate/drain region and is dependent on the width of the JFET region. The net capacitance of C_{GD} is equal to the series combination of gate oxide capacitor (C_{OX}) and SiC semiconductor capacitance under the gate oxide ($C_{\text{SiC, MOS}}$) which decreases with increasing drain voltage. The specific gate–drain Miller capacitance is given by the following equation:

$$C_{\text{GD, SP}} = \frac{W_{\text{Gate}} - 2x_{\text{GS}}}{W_{\text{Cell}}} \left(\frac{C_{\text{ox}} \cdot C_{\text{SiC, MOS}}}{C_{\text{ox}} + C_{\text{SiC, MOS}}} \right) \qquad (24)$$

The specific semiconductor capacitance can be obtained by calculating the depletion layer width that extends into the semiconductor under deep depletion mode operation where the application of drain voltage is followed by the removal of minority carriers by the reverse-biased p–n junctions formed at the P-base/N- drift interface.[4] The 1D electric field profile of the MOS capacitor under deep depletion mode is shown in Fig. 12.

The applied drain voltage is shared between the gate oxide layer and the semiconductor and is given by Eq. (25) where voltage drop across the semiconductor region is supported by the depletion region width ($W_{\text{D.MOS}}$) due to the electric field at the oxide–semiconductor interface ($E_{\text{Ox/SiC}}$) and is equal to the area of the shaded triangle in Fig. 12.

$$V_{\text{Drain}} = V_{\text{Oxide}} + V_{\text{SiC}} = E_{\text{Oxide}} \cdot t_{\text{OX}} + \frac{1}{2} \cdot W_{\text{D.MOS}} \cdot E_{\text{Ox/SiC}} \qquad (25)$$

The electric field in the gate oxide can be expressed in terms of the electric field at the oxide–semiconductor interface using Gauss's law and the electric field at the oxide–semiconductor interface can be expressed as a function of

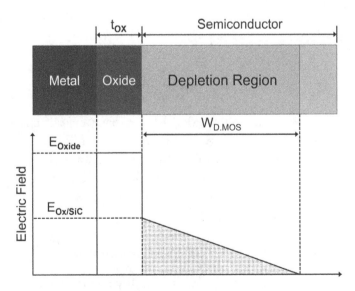

Fig. 12.   MOS structure 1D electric field profile under deep depletion mode operation.

the depletion layer width in Eqs. (26) and (27), respectively.[4]

$$E_{\text{Oxide}} = \left(\frac{\varepsilon_{\text{SiC}}}{\varepsilon_{\text{Oxide}}} \right) \cdot E_{\text{Ox/SiC}} \tag{26}$$

$$E_{\text{Ox/SiC}} = \left(\frac{q N_{\text{Drift}}}{\varepsilon_{\text{SiC}}} \right) \cdot W_{\text{D.MOS}} \tag{27}$$

By substituting the expressions for E_{Oxide} and $E_{\text{Ox/SiC}}$ in Eq. (25), the value of depletion region width ($W_{\text{D.MOS}}$) can be obtained by solving the quadratic equation. The specific semiconductor capacitance ($C_{\text{SiC,MOS}}$) is obtained using the following equation which can then be used to calculate the specific gate–drain *Miller* capacitance:

$$C_{\text{SiC, MOS}} = \frac{\varepsilon_{\text{SiC}}}{W_{\text{D.MOS}}} \tag{28}$$

The output capacitance (C_{DS}) is driven by the formation of depletion layer at the p–n junction formed at the interface of P-base/N−drift region. The specific output capacitance can be expressed using the following equation:

$$C_{\text{DS, SP}} = \left(\frac{x_{\text{DS}} + x_{\text{GS}}}{W_{\text{Cell}}} \right) \cdot C_{\text{SiC, J}} \tag{29}$$

where $(x_{\text{DS}} + x_{\text{GS}})$ is the lateral junction width and $C_{\text{SiC, J}}$ is the semiconductor junction capacitance which is defined by Eq. (30). The depletion layer width ($W_{\text{D.J}}$) can be calculated using Eq. (31) which is a function of drain voltage (V_{Drain}), built-in potential (V_{bi}) and the doping concentration of drift region (N_{Drift}).

$$C_{\text{SiC, J}} = \frac{\varepsilon_{\text{SiC}}}{W_{\text{D.J}}} \tag{30}$$

$$W_{\text{D.J}} = \sqrt{\frac{2\varepsilon_{\text{SiC}}(V_{\text{Drain}} + V_{\text{bi}})}{q N_{\text{Drift}}}} \tag{31}$$

Based on the above discussion on MOSFET capacitance, it can be inferred that the gate–source capacitance of a Power MOSFET has more or less a constant value. However, gate–drain *Miller* capacitance (C_{GD}) and drain–source capacitance (C_{DS}) are dependent on semiconductor capacitance and depletion layer width making them highly nonlinear and dependent on the applied drain bias voltage.[4]

9.5. Silvaco© ATLAS Modeling and Simulation

As discussed in the previous chapters, it is highly recommended that the user starts off the modeling process by developing TCAD model for the most basic device design. This would not only streamline the overall modeling process by reducing the initial simulation time, enabling faster troubleshooting, and better understanding of the device model, but also helps in optimizing the more complex device design approach. The scenario involving a vertical D-MOSFET is similar to that of a JBS diode since it is not possible to design a parallel plane structure for either of these devices. In order to understand the basic working of D-MOSFET, a half-cell structure is the suggested design to begin with.

The following sections will discuss the modeling and simulation of a 3300 V SiC vertical D-MOSFET using half-cell and complete-cell structure designs. Since a complete-cell D-MOSFET structure is the ultimate goal, only forward conduction and forward breakdown J–V simulations will be discussed for the half-cell structure. The complete-cell D-MOSFET structure will be explained using a variety of steady-state and transient simulations. Detailed discussion of the design equations used for the MOSFET is out of scope of this textbook. The simulations will consist of steady-state and transient characterization.

9.5.1.   Simulation models

The physics-based models used for MOSFET simulation accounted for Shockley–Read–Hall recombination (***SRH***), auger recombination (***AUGER***), bandgap narrowing (***BGN***), low-field mobility (***ANALYTIC***), high-field mobility (***FLDMOB***) mobility due to carrier–carrier scattering (***CONWELL***), incomplete ionization of dopants (***INCOMPLETE***), and impact ionization (***SELB***). The ***MODELS*** statement was used to implement these models in the deckbuild code. The high-field mobility model was added for MOSFET to account for the effects of velocity saturation in the channel. Since current conduction in a D-MOSEFT structure occurs vertically in the drift and JFET regions and horizontally in the accumulation region and channel, it is necessary to model both low-field and high-field mobility effects, respectively. The temperature parameter (***TEMP***) can be used to change the steady-state lattice temperature of the simulation. For non-isothermal Mixed-Mode or transient simulation, in addition to the aforementioned models, lattice temperature model (***LAT.TEMP***) was included to account for the change in device lattice temperature during the course of simulation. The lattice temperature model was used in conjunction with models to account for heat generation due to joule heating (***JOULE.HEAT***), Carrier Generation and Recombination heating (***GR.HEAT***) and Peltier–Thomson heating (***PT.HEAT***). Performing non-isothermal simulations also require models and parameters to define thermal conductivity and heat capacity and its variation as a function of lattice temperature. The MOSFET simulations discussed in this chapter use the polynomial function (**TCON.POLYN**) for thermal conductivity and the standard model for heat capacity.[6]

The presence of trapped charges at the SiC/SiO$_2$ interface is a well-known phenomenon, and it is critical to model the effect of trapped interface charge on the device behavior, especially threshold voltage. Interface charge density is implemented in Silvaco© ATLAS using the **INTERFACE** statement. The value of interface charge density has been based on ballpark value found in the literature.[7,8]

 The inclusion of interface charge density tends to reduce the MOSFET threshold voltage and must be taken into account during the design phase.

Since n-type polysilicon is typically used to form gate contact, it is specified using the **CONTACT** statement. This will associate the built-in properties of n-type polysilicon to the gate electrode. The **CONTACT** statement can also be used to declare source and drain electrodes as ohmic contact during transient simulation. The MOSFET structure consists of multiple regions and electrodes in the simulation code and the user must be careful while specifying the material properties for the respective regions, mainly silicon carbide.[6]

 The MOSFET simulations discussed in this chapter does not include interface traps.

9.5.2. Vertical D-MOSFET half-cell structure

The MOSFET half-cell structure was designed for a rated current density of 100 A/cm^2 and blocking voltage of 3300 V. Since the rated blocking voltage is typically considered as 80% of the actual breakdown voltage, the MOSFET was designed for a breakdown voltage of 4200 V. The design equations used for the MOSFET structure can be found in the references. The drift region had a thickness of 30 μm based on the design equations and was uniformly doped with a donor concentration of 3.3×10^{15} cm^{-3}. The N+ source region was 0.5 μm deep and was heavily doped with a uniform donor concentration of 1.0×10^{20} cm^{-3}. The N+ substrate was 150 μm thick and was heavily doped with a uniform donor concentration of 1.0×10^{20} cm^{-3}. The P-base region was doped with an acceptor concentration of 4.5×10^{17} cm^{-3} using a Gaussian

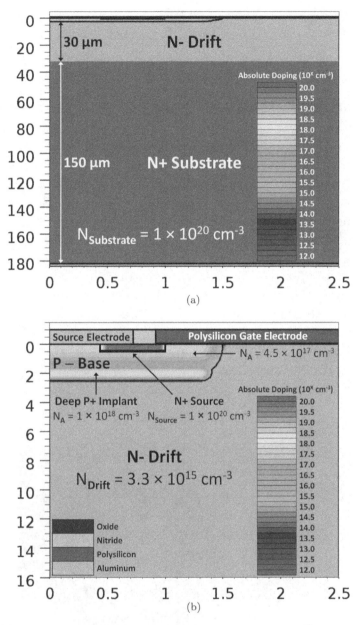

Fig. 13. (a) 3300 V SiC vertical D-MOSFET (active area $= 2.5\,\mu\text{m}^2$) half-cell structure designed in Silvaco© ATLAS. (b) 3300 V SiC vertical D-MOSFET (active area $= 2.5\,\mu\text{m}^2$) half-cell structure designed in Silvaco© ATLAS (zoomed-in view).

doping profile and had a width of $1.5\,\mu$m and maximum junction depth of
$2\,\mu$m. The P-base region dimensions were selected for a D-MOSFET channel
length of $0.5\,\mu$m. Due to the high blocking voltage, a deep P+ region with
an acceptor concentration of $1.0 \times 10^{18}\,\mathrm{cm}^{-3}$ was formed using a Gaussian
doping profile at a depth of $2.5\,\mu$m beneath the P-base region to restrict the
electric field and prevent reach-through breakdown. In this MOSFET model,
n-type dopant is assumed to be nitrogen and p-type dopant is assumed to be
Aluminum with corresponding ionization energies of $50\,$meV and $200\,$meV,
respectively, which were used to account for incomplete ionization. Gate
oxide thickness of $500\,$Å was used along with an interface charge density of
$2.5 \times 10^{12}\,\mathrm{cm}^{-2}$ at the SiO_2/SiC interface.[7,8] The gate contact was made
using n-type polysilicon and aluminum was used for source and drain ohmic
contacts. The 2D MOSFET half-cell structure was designed for an approxi-
mate active area of $2.5\,\mu\mathrm{m}^2$ where the X-dimension is $2.5\,\mu$m and the default
Z-dimension is $1\,\mu$m. Due to the large substrate thickness as compared to
the drift layer, the half-cell D-MOSFET device structure designed using
Silvaco© ATLAS has been split into Figs. 13(a) and 13(b), respectively.

The zoomed-in image of the gate–source region in the MOSFET half-cell
structure is shown in Fig. 14. Silicon nitride insulator is used between the
gate and source electrode. Gate oxide thickness of $500\,$Å has been used in
all the simulation models discussed in this chapter.

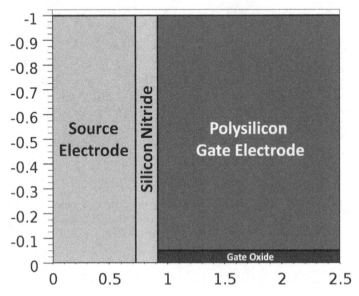

Fig. 14.   Enlarged view of the gate–source regions in the $3300\,$V SiC vertical D-MOSFET
half-cell structure.

9.5.2.1. *Steady-state simulation*

Steady-state/DC simulation helps in verifying the basic operation of the device model. This section will discuss the drain current density versus drain to source voltage (J–V) characteristics at 27°C, 75°C, 125°C, and 175°C device temperature under forward conduction and breakdown condition. Steady-state simulations help the user to refine the device model and includes optimization of the mesh profile and doping concentration adjustment to fine-tune the breakdown voltage. Due to significant difference between the forward conduction and breakdown simulation code, it is recommended to perform the simulations using separate deckbuild programs. Only forward conduction and breakdown simulation examples will be discussed for the half-cell structure. Detailed steady-state and transient simulations will be discussed using the complete-cell structure.

9.5.2.1.1. Forward conduction J–V characteristics

The following code was used to simulate the D-MOSFET forward J–V characteristics at a gate to source voltage (V_{GS}) of +20 V and lattice temperature of 27°C. A brief explanation of the steady-state simulation program is provided in the code walkthrough (Table 1).

```
Sample code: Vertical D-MOSFET half-cell structure forward conduction J-V characteristics
@ 27°C

1.   GO ATLAS SIMFLAGS ="-V 5.18.3.R -P 32 -160"
2.
3.   ##### 3300V D-MOSFET HALF CELL FORWARD J-V @ 27C #####
4.
5.   MESH  WIDTH=1
6.
7.   ## X-MESH
8.
9.   X.MESH  loc=0.00    spac=0.08
10. X.MESH  loc=1.00    spac=0.04
11. X.MESH  loc=1.30    spac=0.025
12. X.MESH  loc=1.50    spac=0.025
13. X.MESH  loc=1.70    spac=0.15
14. X.MESH  loc=2.50    spac=0.15
15.
16. ## Y-MESH
17.
18. Y.MESH  loc=-1.00   spac=0.94
19. Y.MESH  loc=-0.06   spac=0.94
20. Y.MESH  loc=-0.05   spac=0.025
21. Y.MESH  loc=0.00    spac=0.025
22. Y.MESH  loc=0.02    spac=0.098
23. Y.MESH  loc=1.00    spac=0.098
24. Y.MESH  loc=1.20    spac=0.1
25. Y.MESH  loc=1.80    spac=0.1
26. Y.MESH  loc=2.20    spac=0.1
```

```
27. Y.MESH   loc=3.50     spac=2.50
28. Y.MESH   loc=30.0     spac=5.0
29. Y.MESH   loc=31.5     spac=0.25
30. Y.MESH   loc=32.5     spac=0.25
31. Y.MESH   loc=33.0     spac=20
32. Y.MESH   loc=180.0    spac=20
33. Y.MESH   loc=182.0    spac=1.0
34. Y.MESH   loc=184.0    spac=1.0
35.
36. ##### DEFINING REGIONS
37.
38. REGION  num=1   y.max=0      material=Si3N4
39. REGION  num=2   x.min=0.91  x.max=2.50  y.min=-0.05  y.max=0  material=Oxide
40. REGION  num=3   y.min=0      material=4H-SiC
41.
42. ##### DEFINING ELECTRODES
43.
44. ELECTRODE  name=source x.min=0.0   x.max=0.75  y.max=0    material=aluminum
45. ELECTRODE  name=gate  x.min=0.90  x.max=2.50  y.max=-0.05  material=polysilicon
46. ELECTRODE  name=drain  y.min=182  y.max=184   material=aluminum
47.
48. ##### DOPING DISTRIBUTION
49.
50. ## BULK DOPING
51. DOPING  uniform  n.type  conc=3.3e15   REGION=3
52.
53. ## N+ SOURCE DOPING
54. DOPING  uniform  n.type  conc=1.e20  x.min=0.44  x.max=0.99  y.min=0  y.max=0.5
55.
56. ## P-BASE DOPING
57. DOPING  gauss  p.type  conc=4.5e17  x.min=0.0  x.max=1.3   junc=2.0  rat=0.1
58. DOPING  gauss  p.type  conc=1.0e18  x.min=0.0  x.max=1.3   junc=2.5  rat=0.2
    start=2.0
59.
60. ## N+ SUBSTRATE DOPING
61. DOPING  uniform  n.type   conc=1.e20   y.min=32    y.max=182
62.
63. SAVE  outf=MOSFET_3300V.str  master.out
64.
65. MATERIAL  material=4H-SiC REGION=3  permittivity=9.76    eg300=3.26    affinity=3.7
    egalpha=3.3e-2  egbeta=1.e+5  nc300=1.7e+19  nv300=2.5e+19  arichn=146  arichp=30
    augn=3.e-29  augp=3.e-29    taun0=3.33e-6  taup0=6.7e-7  nsrhn=3.e+17  nsrhp=3.e+17
    edb=0.050  eab=0.200
66.
67. ## MODELS USED
68.
69. MODELS  REGION=3 MATERIAL=4H-SIC FERMIDIRAC ANALYTIC CONWELL FLDMOB SRH BGN AUGER
    INCOMPLETE TEMP=300  PRINT
70.
71. INTERFACE  REGION=2  charge=2.5e12  s.n=1.e4  s.p=1.e4  s.i
72.
73. CONTACT  NAME=GATE  n.polysilicon
74.
75. ## MOBILITY
76.
77. MOBILITY  material=4H-SiC  REGION=3  vsatn=2.2e7  vsatp=2.2e7  betan=1.2 betap=2
    mu1n.caug=40  mu2n.caug=1136  ncritn.caug=2e17  alphan.caug=-3  betan.caug=-3
    gamman.caug=0.0  deltan.caug=0.76   mu1p.caug=20  mu2p.caug=125  ncritp.caug=1.e19
    alphap.caug=-3  betap.caug=-3  gammap.caug=0.0  deltap.caug=0.5
78.
```

```
79. ######################### Anisotropic Mobility #########################
80.
81. MOBILITY  material=4H-SiC  REGION=3  n.angle=90 p.angle=90 vsatn=2.2e7
    vsatp=2.2e7  betan=1.2 betap=2  mu1n.caug=5  mu2n.caug=947  ncritn.caug=2e17
    alphan.caug=-3  betan.caug=-3  gamman.caug=0.0  deltan.caug=0.76  mu1p.caug=2.5
    mu2p.caug=20  ncritp.caug=1.e19  alphap.caug=-3  betap.caug=-3  gammap.caug=0.0
    deltap.caug=0.5
82.
83. #########################################################################
84.
85. IMPACT  REGION=3  ANISO  E.SIDE  SELB  SIC4H0001  an1=3.44e6  an2=3.44e6
    bn1=2.58e7  bn2=2.58e7  ap1=3.5e6  ap2=3.5e6  bp1=1.7e7  bp2=1.7e7  opphe=0.106
86.
87. METHOD  NEWTON  AUTONR  dvmax=1e8  climit=1e-9  maxtraps=40  itlimit=40  ir.tol=1.e-
    40  cr.tol=1.e-40  ix.tol=1.e-40  px.tol=1.e-30  pr.tol=1.e-45  cx.tol=1.e-30
88.
89. OUTPUT  FLOWLINES
90.
91. ## SOLVING INITIAL VALUE
92.
93.  SOLVE   initial
94.  SOLVE   vgate=4
95.  SOLVE   vgate=6
96.  SOLVE   vgate=8
97.  SOLVE   vgate=10
98.  SOLVE   vgate=12
99.  SOLVE   vgate=14
100. SOLVE   vgate=16
101. SOLVE   vgate=18
102. SOLVE   vgate=20    outf=Vgs20
103.
104. LOAD  infile=Vgs20
105.
106. LOG  outf=MOSFET_Vgs20_27C.log
107.
108. SOLVE  vdrain=0.05    vstep=0.05     vfinal=1.00    name=drain
109. SOLVE  vstep=0.25     vfinal=10.0    name=drain
110.
111. SAVE  outf=MOSFET_Vgs20_27C.str
112.
113. QUIT
```

Table 1.   Code walkthrough: Vertical D-MOSFET half-cell structure forward conduction J–V characteristics.

Line No:	Functionality
1	Configure ATLAS simulator to use 160-bit extended precision and utilize 32 cores of the CPU if hardware resources are available. The version of ATLAS to be used by the simulator is set to 5.18.3.R using the $-V$ option in the simflags command.
5	Initialize device structure mesh information.
7–34	X-axis and Y-axis mesh distribution.
38–40	Declare nitride, oxide and 4H-SiC as the material for the areas specified by the x and y coordinates.

(Continued)

Table 1. (*Continued*)

Line No:	Functionality
44–46	Electrode specifications for the MOSFET (Aluminum source and drain electrode and polysilicon gate electrode).
50–61	Specify doping profile, type, and concentration for different areas of the MOSFET half-cell structure.
63	Save the device structure (`.str`) file on the local hard drive. The device structure can be viewed by opening the file via **TonyPlot** to troubleshoot/optimize the structure.
65	Specify material parameters for 4H-SiC. Detailed description of these parameters is available in the Silvaco© ATLAS manual. The values for these parameters can either be obtained via material research or from literature.
69	Specify the various models to be included in the 4H-SiC MOSFET simulation.
71	Specify trapped charge density at the oxide–semiconductor interface.
73	Use contact statement to configure n-type polysilicon gate contact.
77	Specify mobility parameters for 4H-SiC. Detailed description of these parameters is available in the Silvaco© ATLAS manual. The values for these parameters can either be obtained via material research or from literature.
81	Specify anisotropic mobility parameters for 4H-SiC. Detailed description of these parameters is available in the Silvaco© ATLAS manual. The values for these parameters can either be obtained via material research or from literature.
85	Specify impact ionization parameters for 4H-SiC. This statement is mandatory to obtain device breakdown characteristics.
87	Specify the solver type and the tolerance values to be used during the simulation. This is an extremely critical statement which can alter the simulation outcome.
89	Include current flowlines in the output structure file.
93–102	Solve for the initial bias conditions followed by solving for increasing discrete gate voltages. The results are saved in a binary file after solving for the final required gate bias voltage.
104	Load the binary file saved in step 102.
106	Save the simulation log (`.log`) file on the local hard drive. The simulation results can be viewed by opening the file via **TonyPlot**.
108–109	Positive sweep of drain voltage for steady-state forward J–V characteristics.
111	Save the post-forward-bias simulation device structure (`.str`) file on the local hard drive. Saving the file at this stage of the simulation will enable the user to visualize the variation in various electrothermal parameters within the device structure introduced due to the particular simulation. For example in this simulation, the user can view the electron concentration profile in the MOSFET during forward conduction.
113	Terminate the simulation.

9.5.2.1.2.   Forward conduction simulation results

The forward conduction J–V characteristics for the 3300 V SiC MOSFET is shown in Fig. 15. The data was obtained for lattice temperature values of 27°C, 75°C, 125°C, and 175°C at a gate to source voltage of +20 V/0 V. It can be seen from Fig. 15 that, unlike silicon power MOSFET, there is no well-defined/sharp transition between linear and saturation region of operation in a SiC MOSFET. In fact, there is no defined "saturation region" for a SiC MOSFET and the device behaves more or less like a variable resistor. As the lattice temperature increases from 27°C to 175°C, the ON-state resistance (R_{DSON}) of the MOSFET increases which is evident from the forward J–V graph.

The increase in ON-state resistance is due to the Positive Temperature Coefficient (PTC) of JFET and drift region resistance at high gate to source voltage (typically $V_{\text{GS}} > 18\,\text{V}$). At an ON-state drain current density of 100 A/cm², drain to source voltage drop of 1.5 V was observed across the MOSFET at 27°C device temperature which corresponds to a specific ON-state resistance ($R_{\text{DSON,SP}}$) of $15\,\text{m}\Omega \cdot \text{cm}^2$, whereas at 175°C lattice temperature, drain to source voltage drop increases to 6 V which corresponds to an $R_{\text{DSON,SP}}$ of $60\,\text{m}\Omega \cdot \text{cm}^2$.

The current conduction in a vertical D-MOSFET structure can be visualized using the electron concentration contour plots extracted from the forward J–V simulation shown in Figs. 16(a) and 16(b) (images have been

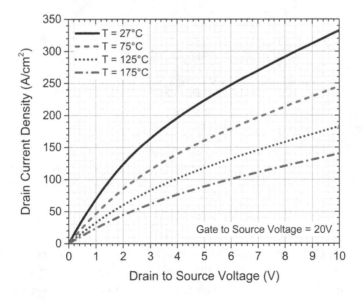

Fig. 15.   Forward J–V characteristics for the SiC D-MOSFET half-cell structure.

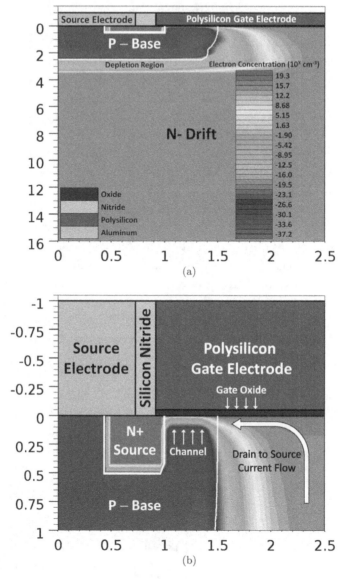

Fig. 16.   (a) Contour plot of SiC D-MOSFET half-cell structure electron concentration profile during forward conduction. (b) Contour plot of SiC D-MOSFET half-cell structure electron concentration profile during forward conduction highlighting current conduction through the channel formed in the P-base region.

scaled to highlight the area of interest). The current conduction path from drain to source can be seen Fig. 16(a), which also shows the depletion region formed at the P-base/N−drift region p–n junction. The zoomed-in version of electron concentration contour plot in Fig. 16(b) shows high electron

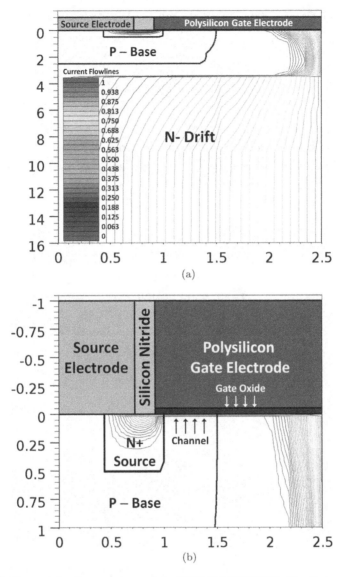

Fig. 17. (a) Current flowlines contour plot of SiC D-MOSFET half-cell structure during forward conduction. (b) Current flowlines contour plot of SiC D-MOSFET half-cell structure during forward conduction (zoomed-in view).

concentration in the P-base region underneath the gate oxide which is the result of channel/inversion layer formation.

The current flow path during forward conduction can also be visualized by extracting the **Current Flowlines** profile from the structure file saved after the completion of simulation. The current flowlines profile shown in Figs. 17(a) and 17(b) is a normalized contour plot which depicts the magnitude of current flow through the device structure. Since the plot is normalized, maximum current has a magnitude of one and is color coded to red. The current flowlines contour plot shows the current path during forward conduction. Current flow occurs from drain to source via N− Drift region, JFET region, accumulation region, and the inversion layer/channel.

 Current flowlines are useful in a vertical D-MOSFET structure because of vertical and horizontal current flow through the device which makes it difficult to be visualized in a current density profile.

9.5.2.1.3.   Forward breakdown *J–V* characteristics

The following code was used to simulate the D-MOSFET forward breakdown *J–V* characteristics at a gate to source voltage (V_{GS}) of 0 V and lattice temperature of 27°C. A brief explanation of the steady-state simulation program is provided in the code walkthrough (Table 2).

```
Sample code: Vertical D-MOSFET half-cell structure forward breakdown J-V characteristics
@ 27°C

1.   GO ATLAS SIMFLAGS ="-V 5.18.3.R -P 32 -160"
2.
3.   ##### 3300V D-MOSFET HALF CELL FORWARD BREAKDOWN J-V @ 27C #####
4.
5.   MESH   WIDTH=1
6.
7.   ## X-MESH
8.
9.   X.MESH  loc=0.00      spac=0.08
10.  X.MESH  loc=1.00      spac=0.04
11.  X.MESH  loc=1.30      spac=0.025
12.  X.MESH  loc=1.50      spac=0.025
13.  X.MESH  loc=1.70      spac=0.15
14.  X.MESH  loc=2.50      spac=0.15
15.
16.  ## Y-MESH
17.
18.  Y.MESH  loc=-1.00     spac=0.94
19.  Y.MESH  loc=-0.06     spac=0.94
20.  Y.MESH  loc=-0.05     spac=0.025
21.  Y.MESH  loc=0.00      spac=0.025
22.  Y.MESH  loc=0.02      spac=0.098
23.  Y.MESH  loc=1.00      spac=0.098
24.  Y.MESH  loc=1.20      spac=0.1
25.  Y.MESH  loc=1.80      spac=0.1
26.  Y.MESH  loc=2.20      spac=0.1
27.  Y.MESH  loc=3.50      spac=2.50
28.  Y.MESH  loc=30.0      spac=5.0
29.  Y.MESH  loc=31.5      spac=0.25
30.  Y.MESH  loc=32.5      spac=0.25
31.  Y.MESH  loc=33.0      spac=20
```

```
32. Y.MESH   loc=180.0    spac=20
33. Y.MESH   loc=182.0    spac=1.0
34. Y.MESH   loc=184.0    spac=1.0
35.
36. ##### DEFINING REGIONS
37.
38. REGION   num=1  y.max=0      material=Si3N4
39. REGION   num=2  x.min=0.91  x.max=2.50   y.min=-0.05   y.max=0   material=Oxide
40. REGION   num=3  y.min=0      material=4H-SiC
41.
42. ##### DEFINING ELECTRODES
43.
44. ELECTRODE  name=source  x.min=0.0   x.max=0.75  y.max=0  material=aluminum
45. ELECTRODE  name=gate  x.min=0.90  x.max=2.50  y.max=-0.05  material=polysilicon
46. ELECTRODE  name=drain    y.min=182  y.max=184   material=aluminum
47.
48. ##### DOPING DISTRIBUTION
49.
50. ## BULK DOPING
51. DOPING  uniform  n.type conc=3.3e15   REGION=3
52.
53. ## N+ SOURCE DOPING
54. DOPING  uniform  n.type conc=1.e20  x.min=0.44  x.max=0.99  y.min=0  y.max=0.5
55.
56. ## P-BASE DOPING
57. DOPING  gauss  p.type  conc=4.5e17   x.min=0.0   x.max=1.3   junc=2.0  rat=0.1
58. DOPING  gauss  p.type  conc=1.0e18   x.min=0.0   x.max=1.3   junc=2.5  rat=0.2
    start=2.0
59.
60. ## N+ SUBSTRATE DOPING
61. DOPING  uniform  n.type   conc=1.e20   y.min=32    y.max=182
62.
63. SAVE  outf=MOSFET_3300V.str  master.out
64.
65. MATERIAL  material=4H-SiC  REGION=3  permittivity=9.76   eg300=3.26   affinity=3.7
    egalpha=3.3e-2   egbeta=1.e+5  nc300=1.7e+19  nv300=2.5e+19  arichn=146  arichp=30
    augn=3.e-29  augp=3.e-29  taun0=3.33e-6  taup0=6.7e-7  nsrhn=3.e+17  nsrhp=3.e+17
    edb=0.050  eab=0.200
66.
67. ## MODELS USED
68.
69. MODELS  REGION=3 MATERIAL=4H-SiC FERMIDIRAC ANALYTIC CONWELL FLDMOB SRH BGN AUGER
    INCOMPLETE TEMP=300  PRINT
70.
71. INTERFACE  REGION=2 charge=2.5e12  s.n=1.e4  s.p=1.e4  s.i
72.
73. CONTACT   NAME=GATE n.polysilicon
74.
75. ## MOBILITY
76.
77. MOBILITY  material=4H-SiC REGION=3  vsatn=2.2e7  vsatp=2.2e7  betan=1.2 betap=2
    mu1n.caug=40  mu2n.caug=1136  ncritn.caug=2e17  alphan.caug=-3  betan.caug=-3
    gamman.caug=0.0  deltan.caug=0.76   mu1p.caug=20  mu2p.caug=125  ncritp.caug=1.e19
    alphap.caug=-3  betap.caug=-3  gammap.caug=0.0  deltap.caug=0.5
78.
79. ######################## Anisotropic Mobility ########################
80.
81. MOBILITY  material=4H-SiC REGION=3  n.angle=90  p.angle=90  vsatn=2.2e7  vsatp=2.2e7
    betan=1.2 betap=2  mu1n.caug=5  mu2n.caug=947  ncritn.caug=2e17  alphan.caug=-3
    betan.caug=-3  gamman.caug=0.0  deltan.caug=0.76   mu1p.caug=2.5  mu2p.caug=20
    ncritp.caug=1.e19  alphap.caug=-3  betap.caug=-3  gammap.caug=0.0  deltap.caug=0.5
```

```
82.
83. #################################################################
84.
85. IMPACT  REGION=3  ANISO  E.SIDE  SELB  SIC4H0001  an1=3.44e6  an2=3.44e6
    bn1=2.58e7  bn2=2.58e7  ap1=3.5e6  ap2=3.5e6  bp1=1.7e7  bp2=1.7e7  opphe=0.106
86.
87. METHOD  NEWTON  AUTONR  dvmax=1e8  climit=1e-9  maxtraps=40  itlimit=40  ir.tol=1.e-
    40  cr.tol=1.e-40  ix.tol=1.e-40  px.tol=1.e-30  pr.tol=1.e-45  cx.tol=1.e-30
88.
89. OUTPUT  FLOWLINES
90.
91. LOG  outf=MOSFET_3300V_Breakdown.log
92.
93. SOLVE  init
94. SOLVE  vgate=0
95. SOLVE  vdrain=0.05  vstep=0.05  vfinal=2.00  name=drain  previous
96. SOLVE  vstep=2     vfinal=20    name=drain  previous
97. SOLVE  vstep=5     vfinal=100   name=drain  previous
98. SOLVE  vstep=50    vfinal=4000  name=drain  previous
99. SOLVE  vstep=10    vfinal=4100  name=drain  previous
100. SOLVE vstep=2.0   vfinal=4400  name=drain  compl=1e-21 cname=drain  previous
101.
102. SAVE  outf=MOSFET_3300V_Breakdown.str
103.
104. QUIT
```

Table 2.   Code walkthrough: Vertical D-MOSFET half-cell structure forward breakdown
J–V characteristics.

Line No:	Functionality
1	Configure ATLAS simulator to use 160-bit extended precision and utilize 32 cores of the CPU if hardware resources are available. The version of ATLAS to be used by the simulator is set to 5.18.3.R using the $-V$ option in the simflags command.
5	Initialize device structure mesh information.
7–34	X-axis and Y-axis mesh distribution.
38–40	Declare nitride, oxide and 4H-SiC as the material for the areas specified by the x and y coordinates.
44–46	Electrode specifications for the MOSFET (Aluminum source and drain electrode and polysilicon gate electrode).
50–61	Specify doping profile, type, and concentration for different areas of the MOSFET half-cell structure.
63	Save the device structure (*.str*) file on the local hard drive. The device structure can be viewed by opening the file via **TonyPlot** to troubleshoot/optimize the structure.
65	Specify material parameters for 4H-SiC. Detailed description of these parameters is available in the Silvaco$^{©}$ ATLAS manual. The values for these parameters can either be obtained via material research or from literature.

(Continued)

Table 2. (*Continued*)

Line No:	Functionality
69	Specify the various models to be included in the 4H-SiC MOSFET simulation.
71	Specify trapped charge density at the oxide–semiconductor interface.
73	Use contact statement to configure n-type polysilicon gate contact.
77	Specify mobility parameters for 4H-SiC. Detailed description of these parameters is available in the Silvaco© ATLAS manual. The values for these parameters can either be obtained via material research or from literature.
81	Specify anisotropic mobility parameters for 4H-SiC. Detailed description of these parameters is available in the Silvaco© ATLAS manual. The values for these parameters can either be obtained via material research or from literature.
85	Specify impact ionization parameters for 4H-SiC. This statement is mandatory to obtain device breakdown characteristics.
87	Specify the solver type and the tolerance values to be used during the simulation. This is an extremely critical statement which can alter the simulation outcome.
89	Include current flowlines in the output structure file.
91	Save the simulation log (**.log**) file on the local hard drive. The simulation results can be viewed by opening the file via **TonyPlot**.
93–94	Solve for the initial bias conditions followed by solving for zero gate voltage.
95–100	Positive sweep of drain voltage for steady-state forward breakdown J–V characteristics.
102	Save the post-forward-breakdown simulation device structure (**.str**) file on the local hard drive. Saving the file at this stage of the simulation will enable the user to visualize the variation in various electrothermal parameters within the device structure introduced due to the particular simulation. For example, in this simulation, user can view the electric field profile in the MOSFET during forward breakdown.
104	Terminate the simulation.

9.5.2.1.4. Forward breakdown simulation results

The forward breakdown J–V characteristics for the 3300 V SiC MOSFET is shown in Fig. 18. The data was obtained for lattice temperature values of 27°C, 75°C, 125°C, and 175°C at a constant gate to source voltage of 0 V. Breakdown voltage of 4341 V was obtained for the MOSFET structure at 27°C lattice temperature. An increase in drain to source leakage current density was observed when the lattice temperature was increased from

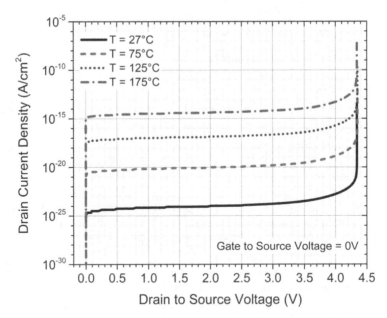

Fig. 18. Forward breakdown J–V characteristics for the SiC D-MOSFET half-cell structure on a semi-log scale.

ambient condition (27°C) to 175°C, which was similar to the results obtained for the diode simulation. Again, the breakdown simulation characteristics are dependent on the impact ionization coefficients used in the **IMPACT** statement.

To visualize the electric field distribution in the MOSFET half-cell structure, the electric field contour plot was extracted from the structure file saved at the end of breakdown simulation which corresponds to the last simulation step/bias voltage before the program terminated. The electric field distribution in the MOSFET half-cell structure is shown in Figs. 19(a) and 19(b).

It can be seen from the electric field profiles that a maximum electric field of 2.96 MV/cm exists at the P-base/N− drift interface. Moreover, abrupt increase in drain to source current density at the breakdown voltage indicates avalanche breakdown occurring in the intrinsic body diode formed at the P-base/N− drift junction which is the preferred mode of forward breakdown. The current flow path can be verified through the **Current Flowlines** profile from the structure file saved after the completion of simulation. The current flowlines profile shown in Fig. 20 clearly indicates current conduction through the P-base region into the source electrode without going through the N+ source region.

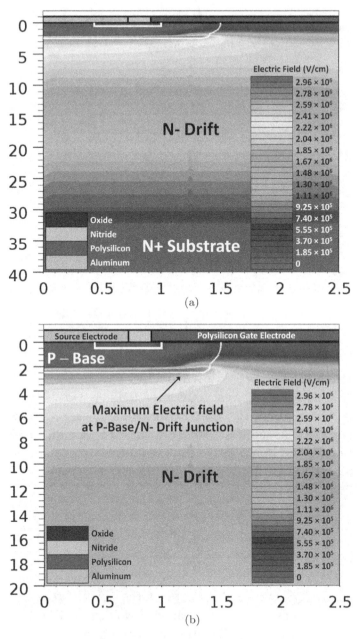

Fig. 19. (a) Contour plot of SiC D-MOSFET half-cell structure electric field profile during forward breakdown. (b) Contour plot of SiC D-MOSFET half-cell structure electric field profile during forward breakdown (zoomed-in view).

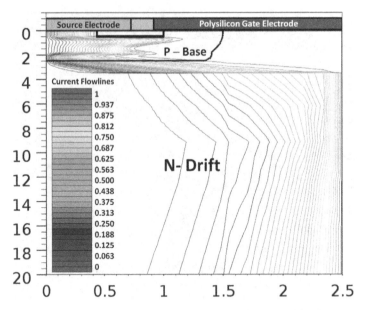

Fig. 20.   Current flowlines contour plot of SiC D-MOSFET half-cell structure during forward breakdown.

 If MOSFET breakdown occurs through the P-base and N+ source regions, current density waveform will not increase abruptly, instead it will increase with a positive slope. This can be related to BJT action taking place because of reach-through breakdown occurring due to the extension of depletion layer in the P-base region.

9.5.3.   Vertical D-MOSFET complete-cell structure

The MOSFET complete-cell structure was designed for a rated current density of $100 \, \text{A/cm}^2$ and blocking voltage of 3300 V. Since the rated blocking voltage is typically considered as 80% of the actual breakdown voltage, the MOSFET was designed for a breakdown voltage of 4200 V. The design equations used for the MOSFET structure can be found in the references. The drift region had a thickness of $30 \, \mu\text{m}$ based on the design equations and was uniformly doped with a donor concentration of $3.3 \times 10^{15} \, \text{cm}^{-3}$. The N+ source region was $0.5 \, \mu\text{m}$ deep and was heavily doped with a uniform donor concentration of $1.0 \times 10^{20} \, \text{cm}^{-3}$. The N+ substrate was $150 \, \mu\text{m}$ thick and was heavily doped with a uniform donor concentration of $1.0 \times 10^{20} \, \text{cm}^{-3}$. The P-base region was doped with an acceptor concentration of $4.5 \times 10^{17} \, \text{cm}^{-3}$

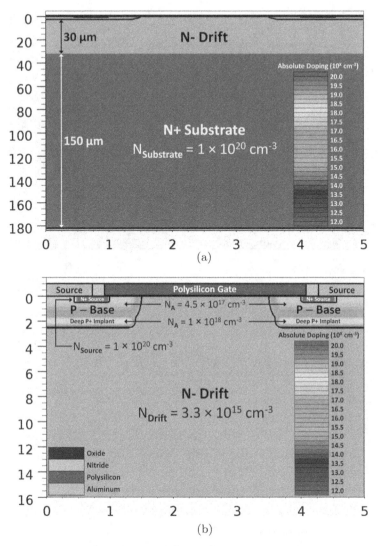

Fig. 21. (a) 3300 V SiC vertical D-MOSFET (active area $= 5\,\mu\mathrm{m}^2$) complete-cell structure designed in Silvaco© ATLAS. (b) 3300 V SiC vertical D-MOSFET (active area $= 5\,\mu\mathrm{m}^2$) complete-cell structure designed in Silvaco© ATLAS (zoomed-in view).

using a gaussian doping profile and had a width of $1.5\,\mu\mathrm{m}$ and maximum junction depth of $2\,\mu\mathrm{m}$. The P-base region dimensions were selected for a D-MOSFET channel length of $0.5\,\mu\mathrm{m}$. Due to the high blocking voltage, a deep P+ region with an acceptor concentration of $1.0 \times 10^{18}\,\mathrm{cm}^{-3}$ was formed using a Gaussian doping profile at a depth of $2.5\,\mu\mathrm{m}$ beneath the P-base region to restrict the electric field and prevent reach-through breakdown. In this MOSFET model, n-type dopant is assumed to be nitrogen and

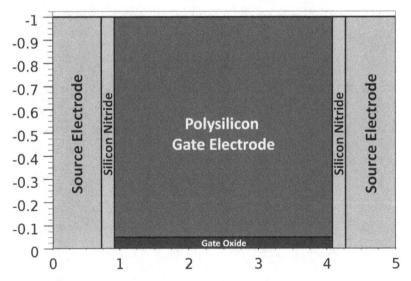

Fig. 22.   Enlarged view of the gate–source regions in the 3300 V SiC vertical D-MOSFET complete-cell structure.

p-type dopant is assumed to be Aluminum with corresponding ionization energies of 50 meV and 200 meV, respectively, which were used to account for incomplete ionization. Gate oxide thickness of 500 Å was used along with an interface charge density of $2.5 \times 10^{12}\,\mathrm{cm}^{-2}$ at the SiO_2/SiC interface.[7,8] The gate contact was made using n-type polysilicon and aluminum was used for source and drain ohmic contacts. The 2D MOSFET complete-cell structure was designed for an approximate active area of $5\,\mu\mathrm{m}^2$ where the X-dimension is $5\,\mu\mathrm{m}$ and the default Z-dimension is $1\,\mu\mathrm{m}$. Due to the large substrate thickness as compared to the drift layer, the complete-cell D-MOSFET device structure designed using Silvaco© ATLAS has been split into Figs. 21(a) and 21(b), respectively.

The zoomed-in image of gate–source region in the MOSFET complete-cell structure is shown in Fig. 22. Silicon nitride insulator is used between the gate and source electrode. Gate oxide thickness of 500 Å has been used in all the simulation models discussed in this chapter.

9.5.3.1.   *Steady-state simulation*

Steady-state/DC simulation helps in verifying the basic operation of the device model. This section will discuss the various steady-state simulations performed on the MOSFET complete-cell structure which includes forward conduction and forward blocking/breakdown (J–V) characteristics at 27°C, 75°C, 125°C, and 175°C lattice temperature, threshold voltage measurement,

MOSFET capacitance–voltage (*C–V*), and gate charge. Steady-state simulations help the user to refine the device model which includes optimization of the mesh profile and doping concentration adjustment to fine-tune the breakdown voltage.

9.5.3.1.1. Forward conduction *J–V* characteristics

The following code was used to simulate the MOSFET forward conduction drain to source current density versus voltage (*J–V*) characteristics at a gate to source voltage (V_{GS}) of +20 V and lattice temperature of 27°C. A brief explanation of the steady-state simulation program is provided in the code walkthrough (Table 3).

```
Sample code: Vertical D-MOSFET complete-cell structure forward conduction J-V characteristics
@ 27°C

1.   GO ATLAS SIMFLAGS ="-V 5.18.3.R -P 32 -160"
2.
3.   ##### 3300V D-MOSFET COMPLETE CELL FORWARD J-V @ 27C #####
4.
5.   MESH  WIDTH=1
6.
7.   ## X-MESH
8.
9.   X.MESH  loc=0.00    spac=0.08
10.  X.MESH  loc=1.00    spac=0.04
11.  X.MESH  loc=1.30    spac=0.025
12.  X.MESH  loc=1.50    spac=0.025
13.  X.MESH  loc=1.70    spac=0.15
14.  X.MESH  loc=3.20    spac=0.15
15.  X.MESH  loc=3.50    spac=0.025
16.  X.MESH  loc=3.70    spac=0.025
17.  X.MESH  loc=4.00    spac=0.04
18.  X.MESH  loc=5.00    spac=0.08
19.
20.  ## Y-MESH
21.
22.  Y.MESH  loc=-1.00   spac=0.94
23.  Y.MESH  loc=-0.06   spac=0.94
24.  Y.MESH  loc=-0.05   spac=0.025
25.  Y.MESH  loc=0.00    spac=0.025
26.  Y.MESH  loc=0.02    spac=0.098
27.  Y.MESH  loc=1.00    spac=0.098
28.  Y.MESH  loc=1.20    spac=0.1
29.  Y.MESH  loc=1.80    spac=0.1
30.  Y.MESH  loc=2.20    spac=0.1
31.  Y.MESH  loc=3.50    spac=2.50
32.  Y.MESH  loc=30.0    spac=5.0
33.  Y.MESH  loc=31.5    spac=0.25
34.  Y.MESH  loc=32.5    spac=0.25
35.  Y.MESH  loc=33.0    spac=20
36.  Y.MESH  loc=180.0   spac=20
37.  Y.MESH  loc=182.0   spac=1.0
38.  Y.MESH  loc=184.0   spac=1.0
39.
```

```
40. ##### DEFINING REGIONS
41.
42. REGION   num=1   y.max=0   material=Si3N4
43. REGION   num=2   x.min=0.91  x.max=4.09   y.min=-0.05  y.max=0  material=oxide
44. REGION   num=3   y.min=0   material=4H-SiC
45.
46. ##### DEFINING ELECTRODES
47.
48. ELECTRODE   name=source  x.min=0.0   x.max=0.75   y.max=0   material=aluminum
49. ELECTRODE   name=source  x.min=4.25  x.max=5.00   y.max=0   material=aluminum
50. ELECTRODE   name=gate   x.min=0.90  x.max=4.10   y.max=-0.05  material=polysilicon
51. ELECTRODE   name=drain   y.min=182   y.max=184   material=aluminum
52.
53. ##### DOPING DISTRIBUTION
54.
55. ## BULK DOPING
56. DOPING   uniform   n.type  conc=3.3e15   REGION=3
57.
58. ## N+ SOURCE DOPING
59. DOPING   uniform  n.type conc=1.e20  x.min=0.44  x.max=0.99  y.min=0  y.max=0.5
60. DOPING   uniform  n.type conc=1.e20  x.min=4.01  x.max=4.56  y.min=0  y.max=0.5
61.
62. ## P-BASE DOPING
63. DOPING   gauss   p.type  conc=4.5e17  x.min=0.0   x.max=1.3   junc=2.0  rat=0.1
64. DOPING   gauss   p.type  conc=4.5e17  x.min=3.7   x.max=5.0   junc=2.0  rat=0.1
65. DOPING   gauss   p.type  conc=1.0e18  x.min=0.0   x.max=1.3   junc=2.5  rat=0.2
    start=2.0
66. DOPING   gauss   p.type  conc=1.0e18  x.min=3.7   x.max=5.0   junc=2.5  rat=0.2
    start=2.0
67.
68. ## N+ SUBSTRATE DOPING
69. DOPING   uniform  n.type  conc=1.e20  y.min=32   y.max=182
70.
71. SAVE outf=MOSFET_3300V.str  master.out
72.
73. MATERIAL  material=4H-SiC  REGION=3  permittivity=9.76   eg300=3.26
    affinity=3.7 egalpha=3.3e-2  egbeta=1.e+5  nc300=1.7e+19  nv300=2.5e+19
    arichn=146 arichp=30 augn=3.e-29 augp=3.e-29 taun0=3.33e-6 taup0=6.7e-7
    nsrhn=3.e+17 nsrhp=3.e+17 edb=0.050  eab=0.200
74.
75. ## MODELS USED
76.
77. MODELS  REGION=3  MATERIAL=4H-SiC FERMIDIRAC ANALYTIC CONWELL FLDMOB SRH BGN
    AUGER INCOMPLETE TEMP=300  PRINT
78.
79. INTERFACE  REGION=2  charge=2.5e12  s.n=1.e4  s.p=1.e4  s.i
80.
81. CONTACT  NAME=GATE n.polysilicon
82.
83. ## MOBILITY
84.
85. MOBILITY  material=4H-SiC  REGION=3  vsatn=2.2e7  vsatp=2.2e7  betan=1.2
    betap=2  mu1n.caug=40  mu2n.caug=1136  ncritn.caug=2e17  alphan.caug=-3
    betan.caug=-3 gamman.caug=0.0 deltan.caug=0.76  mu1p.caug=20  mu2p.caug=125
    ncritp.caug=1.e19  alphap.caug=-3 betap.caug=-3 gammap.caug=0.0
    deltap.caug=0.5
86.
87. ######################### Anisotropic Mobility #########################
88.
89. MOBILITY  material=4H-SiC  REGION=3  n.angle=90 p.angle=90  vsatn=2.2e7
```

```
     mu2p.caug=20  ncritp.caug=1.e19  alphap.caug=-3  betap.caug=-3  gammap.caug=0.0
     deltap.caug=0.5
     vsatp=2.2e7  betan=1.2 betap=2  mu1n.caug=5  mu2n.caug=947  ncritn.caug=2e17
     alphan.caug=-3  betan.caug=-3  gamman.caug=0.0  deltan.caug=0.76  mu1p.caug=2.5
90.
91. ############################################################################
92.
93. IMPACT  REGION=3  ANISO  E.SIDE  SELB  SIC4H0001  an1=3.44e6  an2=3.44e6
     bn1=2.58e7  bn2=2.58e7  ap1=3.5e6  ap2=3.5e6  bp1=1.7e7  bp2=1.7e7 opphe=0.106
94.
95. METHOD  NEWTON  AUTONR  dvmax=1e8 climit=1e-9  maxtraps=40 itlimit=40
     ir.tol=1.e-40 cr.tol=1.e-40 ix.tol=1.e-40 px.tol=1.e-30 pr.tol=1.e-45
     cx.tol=1.e-30
96.
97. OUTPUT  FLOWLINES
98.
99. ## SOLVING INITIAL VALUE
100.
101. SOLVE  initial
102. SOLVE  vgate=4
103. SOLVE  vgate=6
104. SOLVE  vgate=8
105. SOLVE  vgate=10
106. SOLVE  vgate=12
107. SOLVE  vgate=14
108. SOLVE  vgate=16
109. SOLVE  vgate=18
110. SOLVE  vgate=20      outf=Vgs20
111.
112. LOAD  infile=Vgs20
113.
114. LOG  outf=MOSFET_Vgs20_27C.log
115.
116. SOLVE  vdrain=0.05     vstep=0.05     vfinal=1.00    name=drain
117. SOLVE  vstep=0.25      vfinal=10.0    name=drain
118.
119. SAVE  outf=MOSFET_Vgs20_27C.str
120.
121. QUIT
```

Table 3.   Code walkthrough: Vertical D-MOSFET complete-cell structure forward conduction J–V characteristics.

Line No:	Functionality
1	Configure ATLAS simulator to use 160-bit extended precision and utilize 32 cores of the CPU if hardware resources are available. The version of ATLAS to be used by the simulator is set to 5.18.3.R using the $-$V option in the simflags command.
5	Initialize device structure mesh information.
7–38	X-axis and Y-axis mesh distribution.
42–44	Declare nitride, oxide and 4H-SiC as the material for the areas specified by the x and y coordinates.
48–51	Electrode specifications for the MOSFET (Aluminum source and drain electrode and polysilicon gate electrode).

(*Continued*)

Table 3. (*Continued*)

Line No:	Functionality
55–69	Specify doping profile, type, and concentration for different areas of the MOSFET complete-cell structure.
71	Save the device structure (*.str*) file on the local hard drive. The device structure can be viewed by opening the file via *TonyPlot* to troubleshoot/optimize the structure.
73	Specify material parameters for 4H-SiC. Detailed description of these parameters is available in the Silvaco© ATLAS manual. The values for these parameters can either be obtained via material research or from literature.
77	Specify the various models to be included in the 4H-SiC MOSFET simulation.
79	Specify trapped charge density at the oxide–semiconductor interface.
81	Use contact statement to configure n-type polysilicon gate contact.
85	Specify mobility parameters for 4H-SiC. Detailed description of these parameters is available in the Silvaco© ATLAS manual. The values for these parameters can either be obtained via material research or from literature.
89	Specify anisotropic mobility parameters for 4H-SiC. Detailed description of these parameters is available in the Silvaco© ATLAS manual. The values for these parameters can either be obtained via material research or from literature.
93	Specify impact ionization parameters for 4H-SiC. This statement is mandatory to obtain device breakdown characteristics.
95	Specify the solver type and the tolerance values to be used during the simulation. This is an extremely critical statement which can alter the simulation outcome.
97	Include current flowlines in the output structure file.
101–110	Solve for the initial bias conditions followed by solving for increasing discrete gate voltages. The results are saved in a binary file after solving for the final required gate bias voltage.
112	Load the binary file saved in step 110.
114	Save the simulation log (*.log*) file on the local hard drive. The simulation results can be viewed by opening the file via *TonyPlot*.
116–117	Positive sweep of drain voltage for steady-state forward *J–V* characteristics.
119	Save the post-forward-bias simulation device structure (*.str*) file on the local hard drive. Saving the file at this stage of the simulation will enable the user to visualize the variation in various electrothermal parameters within the device structure introduced due to the particular simulation.
121	Terminate the simulation.

9.5.3.1.2.   Forward conduction simulation results

The forward conduction J–V characteristics for the 3300 V SiC MOSFET
are shown in Fig. 23. The data was obtained for lattice temperature values
of 27°C, 75°C, 125°C, and 175°C at a constant gate to source voltage of
+20 V. As the lattice temperature increases from 27°C to 175°C, the ON-
state resistance (R_{DSON}) of the MOSFET increases, which is evident from
the forward J–V graph. At an ON-state drain current density of 100 A/cm^2,
drain to source voltage drop of 1.5 V was observed across the MOSFET at
27°C device temperature which corresponds to a specific ON-state resistance
($R_{DSON, SP}$) of 15 m$\Omega \cdot$ cm^2, whereas at 175°C lattice temperature, drain to
source voltage drop increases to 6 V which corresponds to an $R_{DSON, SP}$ of
60 m$\Omega \cdot$cm^2. These results were exactly same as that obtained for the half-cell
structure simulation.

The current conduction in a vertical D-MOSFET complete-cell structure
can be visualized using the electron concentration contour plots extracted
from the forward J–V simulation shown in Figs. 24(a) and 24(b) (images
have been scaled to highlight the area of interest). The current conduction
path from drain to source can be seen Fig. 24(a), which also shows the
depletion region formed at the P-base/N-drift region p–n junction. The
zoomed-in version of electron concentration contour plot in Fig. 24(b) shows
high electron concentration in the P-base region underneath the gate oxide
which is the result of channel/inversion layer formation.

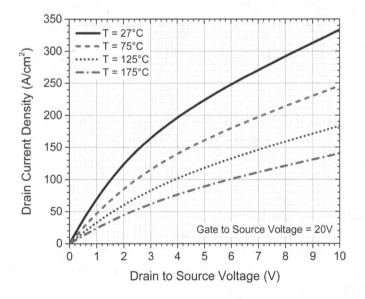

Fig. 23.   Forward J–V characteristics for the SiC D-MOSFET complete-cell structure.

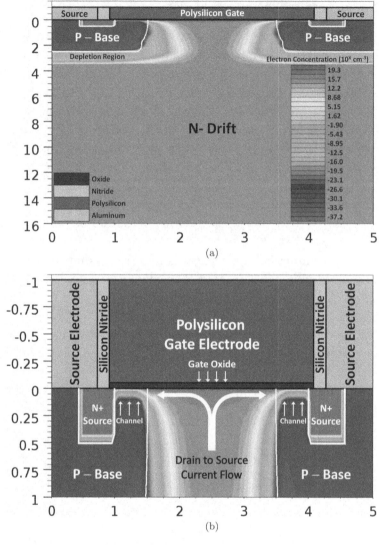

Fig. 24. (a) Contour plot of SiC D-MOSFET complete-cell structure electron concentration profile during forward conduction. (b) Contour plot of SiC D-MOSFET complete-cell structure electron concentration profile during forward conduction highlighting current conduction through the channel formed in the P-base region.

The current flow path during forward conduction can also be visualized by extracting the **Current Flowlines** profile from the structure file saved after the completion of simulation. The Current flowlines profile shown in Figs. 25(a) and 25(b) is a normalized contour plot which depicts the magnitude of current flow through the device structure. It can be observed in Figs. 25(a) and 25(b) that maximum current flow is occurring through the

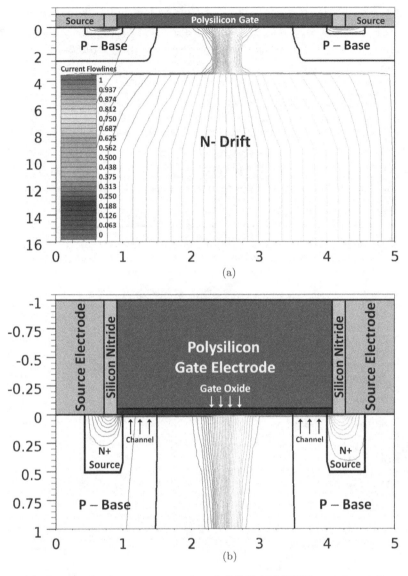

Fig. 25. (a) Current flowlines contour plot of SiC D-MOSFET complete-cell structure during forward conduction. (b) Current flowlines contour plot of SiC D-MOSFET complete-cell structure during forward conduction (zoomed-in view).

right half-cell of the MOSFET even though we expect to see uniform current sharing between both the half-cells. This is due to fact that in a complete-cell D-MOSFET structure, there are two conduction paths (through either half-cell) and since current flowlines are normalized values, software will select the maximum value to be used as the normalization factor. This effect was not seen in the half-cell simulation result discussed earlier since there is only one conduction path. As seen in the half-cell structure simulation, current flow occurs from drain to source via N− Drift region, JFET region, accumulation region, and the inversion layer/channel.

9.5.3.1.3.   Forward breakdown *J–V* characteristics

The following code was used to simulate the D-MOSFET complete-cell structure forward breakdown *J–V* characteristics at a gate to source voltage (V_{GS}) of 0 V and lattice temperature of 27°C. A brief explanation of the steady-state simulation program is provided in the code walkthrough (Table 4).

```
Sample code: Vertical D-MOSFET complete-cell structure forward breakdown J-V characteristics
@ 27°C
```

```
1.   GO ATLAS SIMFLAGS ="-V 5.18.3.R -P 32 -160"
2.
3.   ##### 3300V D-MOSFET COMPLETE CELL FORWARD BREAKDOWN J-V @ 27C #####
4.
5.   MESH  WIDTH=1
6.
7.   ## X-MESH
8.
9.   X.MESH  loc=0.00     spac=0.08
10. X.MESH  loc=1.00     spac=0.04
11. X.MESH  loc=1.30     spac=0.025
12. X.MESH  loc=1.50     spac=0.025
13. X.MESH  loc=1.70     spac=0.15
14. X.MESH  loc=3.20     spac=0.15
15. X.MESH  loc=3.50     spac=0.025
16. X.MESH  loc=3.70     spac=0.025
17. X.MESH  loc=4.00     spac=0.04
18. X.MESH  loc=5.00     spac=0.08
19.
20. ## Y-MESH
21.
22. Y.MESH  loc=-1.00    spac=0.94
23. Y.MESH  loc=-0.06    spac=0.94
24. Y.MESH  loc=-0.05    spac=0.025
25. Y.MESH  loc=0.00     spac=0.025
26. Y.MESH  loc=0.02     spac=0.098
27. Y.MESH  loc=1.00     spac=0.098
28. Y.MESH  loc=1.20     spac=0.1
29. Y.MESH  loc=1.80     spac=0.1
30. Y.MESH  loc=2.20     spac=0.1
31. Y.MESH  loc=3.50     spac=2.50
32. Y.MESH  loc=30.0     spac=5.0
33. Y.MESH  loc=31.5     spac=0.25
34. Y.MESH  loc=32.5     spac=0.25
35. Y.MESH  loc=33.0     spac=20
36. Y.MESH  loc=180.0    spac=20
37. Y.MESH  loc=182.0    spac=1.0
38. Y.MESH  loc=184.0    spac=1.0
39.
```

```
40. ##### DEFINING REGIONS
41.
42. REGION   num=1   y.max=0   material=Si3N4
43. REGION   num=2   x.min=0.91 x.max=4.09 y.min=-0.05 y.max=0  material=oxide
44. REGION   num=3   y.min=0   material=4H-SiC
45.
46. ##### DEFINING ELECTRODES
47.
48. ELECTRODE  name=source x.min=0.0  x.max=0.75 y.max=0    material=aluminum
49. ELECTRODE  name=source x.min=4.25 x.max=5.00 y.max=0    material=aluminum
50. ELECTRODE  name=gate   x.min=0.90 x.max=4.10 y.max=-0.05 material=polysilicon
51. ELECTRODE  name=drain  y.min=182  y.max=184  material=aluminum
52.
53. ##### DOPING DISTRIBUTION
54.
55. ## BULK DOPING
56. DOPING  uniform  n.type conc=3.3e15  REGION=3
57.
58. ## N+ SOURCE DOPING
59. DOPING  uniform n.type conc=1.e20 x.min=0.44 x.max=0.99 y.min=0 y.max=0.5
60. DOPING  uniform n.type conc=1.e20 x.min=4.01 x.max=4.56 y.min=0 y.max=0.5
61.
62. ## P-BASE DOPING
63. DOPING  gauss   p.type conc=4.5e17 x.min=0.0 x.max=1.3 junc=2.0   rat=0.1
64. DOPING  gauss   p.type conc=4.5e17 x.min=3.7 x.max=5.0 junc=2.0   rat=0.1
65. DOPING  gauss   p.type conc=1.0e18 x.min=0.0 x.max=1.3 junc=2.5   rat=0.2
    start=2.0
66. DOPING  gauss   p.type conc=1.0e18 x.min=3.7 x.max=5.0 junc=2.5   rat=0.2
    start=2.0
67.
68. ## N+ SUBSTRATE DOPING
69. DOPING  uniform n.type   conc=1.e20 y.min=32   y.max=182
70.
71. SAVE  outf=MOSFET_3300V.str  master.out
72.
73. MATERIAL  material=4H-SiC REGION=3  permittivity=9.76  eg300=3.26
    affinity=3.7  egalpha=3.3e-2  egbeta=1.e+5  nc300=1.7e+19 nv300=2.5e+19
    arichn=146  arichp=30  augn=3.e-29  augp=3.e-29  taun0=3.33e-6  taup0=6.7e-7
    nsrhn=3.e+17 nsrhp=3.e+17 edb=0.050 eab=0.200
74.
75. ## MODELS USED
76.
77. MODELS REGION=3  MATERIAL=4H-SiC  FERMIDIRAC ANALYTIC CONWELL FLDMOB SRH BGN
    AUGER INCOMPLETE TEMP=300  PRINT
78.
79. INTERFACE  REGION=2 charge=2.5e12  s.n=1.e4  s.p=1.e4  s.i
80.
81. CONTACT  NAME=GATE n.polysilicon
82.
83. ## MOBILITY
84.
85. MOBILITY  material=4H-SiC REGION=3 vsatn=2.2e7 vsatp=2.2e7 betan=1.2
    betap=2  mu1n.caug=40  mu2n.caug=1136 ncritn.caug=2e17 alphan.caug=-3
    betan.caug=-3 gamman.caug=0.0 deltan.caug=0.76   mu1p.caug=20 mu2p.caug=125
    ncritp.caug=1.e19 alphap.caug=-3 betap.caug=-3 gammap.caug=0.0
    deltap.caug=0.5
86.
87. ####################### Anisotropic Mobility #######################
88.
89. MOBILITY  material=4H-SiC  REGION=3 n.angle=90 p.angle=90 vsatn=2.2e7
```

```
     mu1p.caug=2.5  mu2p.caug=20  ncritp.caug=1.e19  alphap.caug=-3  betap.caug=-3
     gammap.caug=0.0  deltap.caug=0.5
     vsatp=2.2e7  betan=1.2 betap=2  mu1n.caug=5  mu2n.caug=947  ncritn.caug=2e17
     alphan.caug=-3  betan.caug=-3  gamman.caug=0.0  deltan.caug=0.76
90.
91. ############################################################################
92.
93. IMPACT  REGION=3  ANISO  E.SIDE  SELB  SIC4H0001  an1=3.44e6  an2=3.44e6
     bn1=2.58e7  bn2=2.58e7  ap1=3.5e6  ap2=3.5e6  bp1=1.7e7  bp2=1.7e7 opphe=0.106
94.
95. METHOD  NEWTON  AUTONR  dvmax=1e8 climit=1e-9  maxtraps=40 itlimit=40
     ir.tol=1.e-40 cr.tol=1.e-40 ix.tol=1.e-40 px.tol=1.e-30 pr.tol=1.e-45
     cx.tol=1.e-30
96.
97. OUTPUT  FLOWLINES
98.
99. LOG  outf=MOSFET_3300V_Breakdown.log
100.
101. SOLVE  init
102. SOLVE  vgate=0
103. SOLVE  vdrain=0.05  vstep=0.05  vfinal=2.00  name=drain    previous
104. SOLVE  vstep=2     vfinal=20    name=drain   previous
105. SOLVE  vstep=5     vfinal=100   name=drain   previous
106. SOLVE  vstep=50    vfinal=4000  name=drain   previous
107. SOLVE  vstep=10    vfinal=4100  name=drain   previous
108. SOLVE  vstep=2.0   vfinal=4400  name=drain   compl=1e-21  cname=drain    previous
109.
110. SAVE  outf=MOSFET_3300V_Breakdown.str
111.
112. QUIT
```

Table 4. Code walkthrough: Vertical D-MOSFET complete-cell structure forward breakdown *J–V* characteristics.

Line No:	Functionality
1	Configure ATLAS simulator to use 160-bit extended precision and utilize 32 cores of the CPU if hardware resources are available. The version of ATLAS to be used by the simulator is set to 5.18.3.R using the $-V$ option in the simflags command.
5	Initialize device structure mesh information.
7–38	X-axis and Y-axis mesh distribution.
42–44	Declare nitride, oxide and 4H-SiC as the material for the areas specified by the x and y coordinates.
48–51	Electrode specifications for the MOSFET (Aluminum source and drain electrode and polysilicon gate electrode).
55–69	Specify doping profile, type, and concentration for different areas of the MOSFET complete-cell structure.
71	Save the device structure (**.str**) file on the local hard drive. The device structure can be viewed by opening the file via **TonyPlot** to troubleshoot/optimize the structure.

(*Continued*)

Table 4.   (*Continued*)

Line No:	Functionality
73	Specify material parameters for 4H-SiC. Detailed description of these parameters is available in the Silvaco© ATLAS manual. The values for these parameters can either be obtained via material research or from literature.
77	Specify the various models to be included in the 4H-SiC MOSFET simulation.
79	Specify trapped charge density at the oxide–semiconductor interface.
81	Use contact statement to configure n-type polysilicon gate contact.
85	Specify mobility parameters for 4H-SiC. Detailed description of these parameters is available in the Silvaco© ATLAS manual. The values for these parameters can either be obtained via material research or from literature.
89	Specify anisotropic mobility parameters for 4H-SiC. Detailed description of these parameters is available in the Silvaco© ATLAS manual. The values for these parameters can either be obtained via material research or from literature.
93	Specify impact ionization parameters for 4H-SiC. This statement is mandatory to obtain device breakdown characteristics.
95	Specify the solver type and the tolerance values to be used during the simulation. This is an extremely critical statement which can alter the simulation outcome.
97	Include current flowlines in the output structure file.
99	Save the simulation log (`.log`) file on the local hard drive. The simulation results can be viewed by opening the file via **TonyPlot**.
101–102	Solve for the initial bias conditions followed by solving for zero gate voltage.
103–108	Positive sweep of drain voltage for steady-state forward breakdown J–V characteristics.
110	Save the post-forward-breakdown simulation device structure (`.str`) file on the local hard drive. Saving the file at this stage of the simulation will enable the user to visualize the variation in various electrothermal parameters within the device structure introduced due to the particular simulation.
112	Terminate the simulation.

9.5.3.1.4.   Forward breakdown simulation results

The forward breakdown J–V characteristics for the 3300 V SiC MOSFET complete-cell structure is shown in Fig. 26. The data was obtained for lattice temperature values of 27°C, 75°C, 125°C, and 175°C at a constant gate to source voltage of 0 V. Breakdown voltage of 4341 V was obtained for the

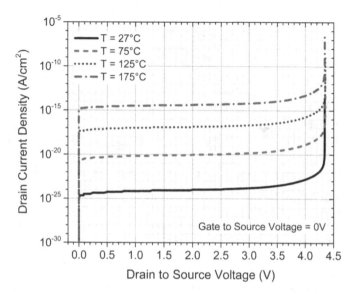

Fig. 26.   Forward breakdown *J–V* characteristics for the SiC D-MOSFET complete-cell structure on a semi-log scale.

MOSFET structure at 27°C lattice temperature. An increase in drain to source leakage current density was observed when the lattice temperature was increased from ambient condition (27°C) to 175°C, which was similar to the results obtained for the half-cell structure.

To visualize the electric field distribution in the MOSFET complete-cell structure, the electric field contour plot was extracted from the structure file saved at the end of breakdown simulation which corresponds to the last simulation step/bias voltage before the program terminated. The electric field distribution in the MOSFET complete-cell structure is shown in Figs. 27(a) and 27(b). The electric field profile shown in Fig. 27(b) highlights the spreading of electric field across the P-base regions, and maximum electric field of 2.96 MV/cm is observed at the edge of the P-base regions.

The current flowlines profile shown in Fig. 28 indicates device breakdown through the p–n junction formed at the P-base/N– drift interface. MOSFET breakdown through the intrinsic body diode can also be seen from the abrupt increase in drain to source current density in Fig. 26. As discussed before, slightly higher current is flowing through the right half-cell of the D-MOSFET structure based on the current flowlines profile.

A quantitative analysis of the electric field distribution in the D-MOSFET structure was performed by plotting the 1D electric field profiles as a function of device depth in Figs. 29(a), 29(b), and 29(c) (images have been scaled to highlight the region of interest). Electric field data was

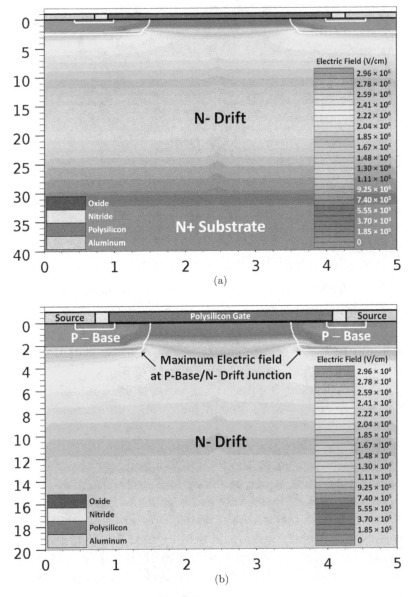

Fig. 27. (a) Contour plot of SiC D-MOSFET complete-cell structure electric field profile during forward breakdown. (b) Contour plot of SiC D-MOSFET complete-cell structure electric field profile during forward breakdown (zoomed-in view).

extracted for the following points: Edges of the P-base regions which are also the points of breakdown ($x = 1.0$ μm and $x = 4.0$ μm) and middle of the active area where the SiC/SiO$_2$ interface is exposed to blocking electric field ($x = 2.5$ μm) using the **cutline** feature in **TonyPlot**. Figure 29(a)

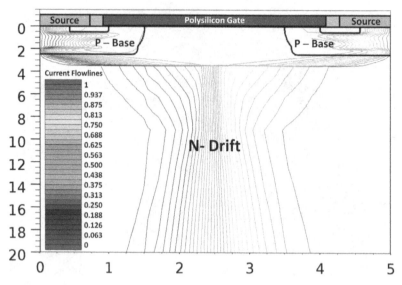

Fig. 28.   Current flowlines contour plot of SiC D-MOSFET complete-cell structure during forward breakdown.

shows the summary of electric field magnitude at the aforementioned points, whereas Figs. 29(b) and 29(c) focus on the electric field profiles pertaining to breakdown and oxide–semiconductor interface, respectively.

The 1D electric field profiles at the edge of P-base regions shown in Fig. 29(b) are superimposable, thereby indicating uniform field distribution. Breakdown electric field of 2.96 MV/cm was observed at the edge of both the P-base regions. Since the reliability of gate oxide is dependent on the magnitude of electric field at the SiC/SiO_2 interface, the 1D electric field profile of the gate oxide region is shown in Fig. 29(c). An electric field of 1.67 MV/cm was present in the gate oxide while the SiC/SiO_2 interface was exposed to 0.2 MV/cm. Based on literature review, the reliability of gate oxide is jeopardized once the electric field exceeds 7 MV/cm and since the obtained value of electric field is much lower than that, it can be inferred that there is sufficient shielding of the gate oxide by the P-base regions.[5]

 The magnitude of electric field in the gate oxide can also be obtained using the *Probe* feature in TonyPlot.

 The ratio of electric field in the gate oxide to the SiC/SiO_2 interface may not be the same as calculated using Gauss law. This could be due to the difference in the value of permittivity used internally by the software.

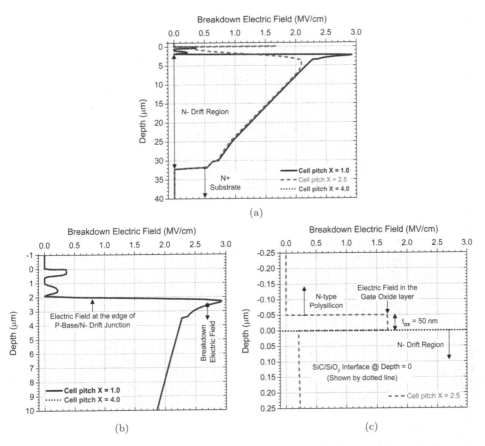

Fig. 29. (a) 1D electric field profile as a function of device depth at varying points across the D-MOSFET active area/cell pitch zoomed in for details (Breakdown electric field is shown by solid and dotted lines). (b) 1D electric field profile as a function of device depth at the edge of P-base regions zoomed in for details (Breakdown electric field shown by solid and dotted lines). (c) 1D electric field profile as a function of device depth in the middle of active area focusing on gate oxide layer and SiC/SiO$_2$ interface (zoomed-in view).

9.5.3.1.5. Threshold voltage measurement

There are different techniques which can be used to measure the threshold voltage of a power MOSFET. The simulation used to extract the threshold voltage of a 3300 V SiC D-MOSFET is based on a measurement technique which is typically used in power MOSFET datasheets. In this method, drain and gate terminals of the MOSFET are shorted together ($V_{GS} = V_{DS}$) and the drain to source voltage is increased up to a set value. The threshold voltage is measured at a drain current density value which has been derived from commercial SiC MOSFET datasheet value.[9] The following code was used to simulate the D-MOSFET complete-cell structure to extract the threshold voltage at a lattice temperature of 27°C. The simulation was repeated for lattice temperature values of 75°C, 125°C, and 175°C to understand the change in threshold voltage. A brief explanation of the simulation program is provided in the code walkthrough (Table 5).

```
Sample code: Vertical D-MOSFET complete-cell structure threshold voltage measurement @ 27°C

1.   GO ATLAS SIMFLAGS ="-V 5.18.3.R -P 32 -160"
2.
3.   ##### 3300V D-MOSFET COMPLETE CELL THRESHOLD VOLTAGE J-V @ 27C #####
4.
5.   MESH WIDTH=1
6.
7.   ## X-MESH
8.
9.   X.MESH  loc=0.00      spac=0.08
10.  X.MESH  loc=1.00      spac=0.04
11.  X.MESH  loc=1.30      spac=0.025
12.  X.MESH  loc=1.50      spac=0.025
13.  X.MESH  loc=1.70      spac=0.15
14.  X.MESH  loc=3.20      spac=0.15
15.  X.MESH  loc=3.50      spac=0.025
16.  X.MESH  loc=3.70      spac=0.025
17.  X.MESH  loc=4.00      spac=0.04
18.  X.MESH  loc=5.00      spac=0.08
19.
20.  ## Y-MESH
21.
22.  Y.MESH  loc=-1.00     spac=0.94
23.  Y.MESH  loc=-0.06     spac=0.94
24.  Y.MESH  loc=-0.05     spac=0.025
25.  Y.MESH  loc=0.00      spac=0.025
26.  Y.MESH  loc=0.02      spac=0.098
27.  Y.MESH  loc=1.00      spac=0.098
28.  Y.MESH  loc=1.20      spac=0.1
29.  Y.MESH  loc=1.80      spac=0.1
30.  Y.MESH  loc=2.20      spac=0.1
31.  Y.MESH  loc=3.50      spac=2.50
32.  Y.MESH  loc=30.0      spac=5.0
33.  Y.MESH  loc=31.5      spac=0.25
34.  Y.MESH  loc=32.5      spac=0.25
35.  Y.MESH  loc=33.0      spac=20
36.  Y.MESH  loc=180.0     spac=20
37.  Y.MESH  loc=182.0     spac=1.0
38.  Y.MESH  loc=184.0     spac=1.0
39.
40.  ##### DEFINING REGIONS
41.
42.  REGION  num=1  y.max=0    material=Si3N4
43.  REGION  num=2  x.min=0.91  x.max=4.09  y.min=-0.05  y.max=0  material=oxide
44.  REGION  num=3  y.min=0    material=4H-SiC
45.
46.  ##### DEFINING ELECTRODES
47.
48.  ELECTRODE  name=source  x.min=0.0   x.max=0.75  y.max=0   material=aluminum
49.  ELECTRODE  name=source  x.min=4.25  x.max=5.00  y.max=0   material=aluminum
50.  ELECTRODE  name=gate  x.min=0.90  x.max=4.10  y.max=-0.05  material=polysilicon
51.  ELECTRODE  name=drain   y.min=182  y.max=184    material=aluminum
```

```
52.
53. ##### DOPING DISTRIBUTION
54.
55. ## BULK DOPING
56. DOPING uniform  n.type  conc=3.3e15    REGION=3
57.
58. ## N+ SOURCE DOPING
59. DOPING uniform  n.type  conc=1.e20  x.min=0.44  x.max=0.99  y.min=0 y.max=0.5
60. DOPING uniform  n.type  conc=1.e20  x.min=4.01  x.max=4.56  y.min=0 y.max=0.5
61.
62. ## P-BASE DOPING
63. DOPING  gauss  p.type conc=4.5e17  x.min=0.0  x.max=1.3  junc=2.0   rat=0.1
64. DOPING  gauss  p.type conc=4.5e17  x.min=3.7  x.max=5.0  junc=2.0   rat=0.1
65. DOPING  gauss  p.type conc=1.0e18  x.min=0.0  x.max=1.3  junc=2.5   rat=0.2
    start=2.0
66. DOPING  gauss  p.type conc=1.0e18  x.min=3.7  x.max=5.0  junc=2.5   rat=0.2
    start=2.0
67.
68. ## N+ SUBSTRATE DOPING
69. DOPING  uniform  n.type  conc=1.e20  y.min=32   y.max=182
70.
71. SAVE  outf=MOSFET_3300V.str  master.out
72.
73. MATERIAL  material=4H-SiC  REGION=3  permittivity=9.76    eg300=3.26
    affinity=3.7  egalpha=3.3e-2  egbeta=1.e+5  nc300=1.7e+19 nv300=2.5e+19
    arichn=146  arichp=30  augn=3.e-29  augp=3.e-29  taun0=3.33e-6  taup0=6.7e-7
    nsrhn=3.e+17  nsrhp=3.e+17 edb=0.050  eab=0.200
74.
75. ## MODELS USED
76.
77. MODELS  REGION=3 MATERIAL=4H-SIC FERMIDIRAC ANALYTIC CONWELL FLDMOB SRH BGN
    AUGER INCOMPLETE TEMP=300  PRINT
78.
79. INTERFACE  REGION=2  charge=2.5e12  s.n=1.e4  s.p=1.e4  s.i
80.
81. CONTACT  NAME=GATE  n.polysilicon
82. CONTACT  NAME=GATE  COMMON=DRAIN
83.
84. ## MOBILITY
85.
86. MOBILITY  material=4H-SiC  REGION=3  vsatn=2.2e7  vsatp=2.2e7  betan=1.2
    betap=2  mu1n.caug=40  mu2n.caug=1136  ncritn.caug=2e17  alphan.caug=-3
    betan.caug=-3  gamman.caug=0.0  deltan.caug=0.76   mu1p.caug=20  mu2p.caug=125
    ncritp.caug=1.e19  alphap.caug=-3  betap.caug=-3  gammap.caug=0.0
    deltap.caug=0.5
87.
88. ######################### Anisotropic Mobility #########################
89.
90. MOBILITY  material=4H-SiC  REGION=3  n.angle=90 p.angle=90 vsatn=2.2e7
    vsatp=2.2e7  betan=1.2 betap=2  mu1n.caug=5  mu2n.caug=947  ncritn.caug=2e17
    alphan.caug=-3  betan.caug=-3  gamman.caug=0.0  deltan.caug=0.76
    mu1p.caug=2.5  mu2p.caug=20  ncritp.caug=1.e19  alphap.caug=-3  betap.caug=-3
    gammap.caug=0.0  deltap.caug=0.5
91.
92. ####################################################################
93.
94. IMPACT  REGION=3 ANISO  E.SIDE  SELB  SIC4H0001  an1=3.44e6  an2=3.44e6
    bn1=2.58e7 bn2=2.58e7  ap1=3.5e6  ap2=3.5e6 bp1=1.7e7  bp2=1.7e7 opphe=0.106
95.
```

```
96. METHOD  NEWTON  AUTONR  dvmax=1e8 climit=1e-9 maxtraps=40 itlimit=40
    ir.tol=1.e-40 cr.tol=1.e-40 ix.tol=1.e-40 px.tol=1.e-30 pr.tol=1.e-45
    cx.tol=1.e-30
97.
98. OUTPUT  FLOWLINES
99.
100. ## SOLVING INITIAL VALUE
101.
102. SOLVE  initial
103.
104. LOG  outf=MOSFET_Threshold_27C.log
105.
106. SOLVE  vdrain=0.02  vstep=0.02   vfinal=5.00   name=drain   previous
107.
108. SAVE  outf=MOSFET_ Threshold_27C.str
109.
110. QUIT
```

Table 5. Code walkthrough: Vertical D-MOSFET complete-cell structure threshold voltage measurement.

Line No:	Functionality
1	Configure ATLAS simulator to use 160-bit extended precision and utilize 32 cores of the CPU if hardware resources are available. The version of ATLAS to be used by the simulator is set to 5.18.3.R using the $-V$ option in the simflags command.
5	Initialize device structure mesh information.
7–38	X-axis and Y-axis mesh distribution.
42–44	Declare nitride, oxide and 4H-SiC as the material for the areas specified by the x and y coordinates.
48–51	Electrode specifications for the MOSFET (Aluminum source and drain electrode and polysilicon gate electrode).
55–69	Specify doping profile, type, and concentration for different areas of the MOSFET complete-cell structure.
71	Save the device structure (*.str*) file on the local hard drive. The device structure can be viewed by opening the file via **TonyPlot** to troubleshoot/optimize the structure.
73	Specify material parameters for 4H-SiC. Detailed description of these parameters is available in the Silvaco© ATLAS manual. The values for these parameters can either be obtained via material research or from literature.
77	Specify the various models to be included in the 4H-SiC MOSFET simulation.
79	Specify trapped charge density at the oxide–semiconductor interface.
81	Use contact statement to configure n-type polysilicon gate contact.

(*Continued*)

Table 5. (*Continued*)

Line No:	Functionality
82	Shorting of gate and drain electrodes.
86	Specify mobility parameters for 4H-SiC. Detailed description of these parameters is available in the Silvaco© ATLAS manual. The values for these parameters can either be obtained via material research or from literature.
90	Specify anisotropic mobility parameters for 4H-SiC. Detailed description of these parameters is available in the Silvaco© ATLAS manual. The values for these parameters can either be obtained via material research or from literature.
94	Specify impact ionization parameters for 4H-SiC. This statement is mandatory to obtain device breakdown characteristics.
96	Specify the solver type and the tolerance values to be used during the simulation. This is an extremely critical statement which can alter the simulation outcome.
98	Include current flowlines in the output structure file.
102	Solve for the initial bias conditions.
104	Save the simulation log (*.log*) file on the local hard drive. The simulation results can be viewed by opening the file via **TonyPlot**.
106	Positive sweep of drain voltage for threshold voltage measurement.
108	Save the post simulation device structure (*.str*) file on the local hard drive.
110	Terminate the simulation.

9.5.3.1.6. Threshold voltage measurement simulation results

The threshold measurement J–V characteristics for the 3300 V SiC MOSFET complete-cell structure at lattice temperature values of 27°C, 75°C, 125°C, and 175°C are shown in Figs. 30(a) and 30(b) on a linear and semi-log scale, respectively. Since the gate and drain terminals were shorted, the X-axis value is equal to V_{GS} and V_{DS}. The threshold voltage was extracted from the semi-log plot shown in Fig. 30(b) at the 20 mA/cm^2 data point. The reason behind the selection of the particular drain current density is as follows: A commercial SiC MOSFET datasheet was used as a reference in the calculation of the threshold voltage. The known value of threshold voltage was obtained from the datasheet along with the drain current value at which the measurement was specified.[3] Using the rated ON-state current of the commercial MOSFET at 27°C and assuming that the typical ON-state current density of MOSFET is 100 A/cm^2, current density corresponding to the drain current at which the threshold voltage was measured can be

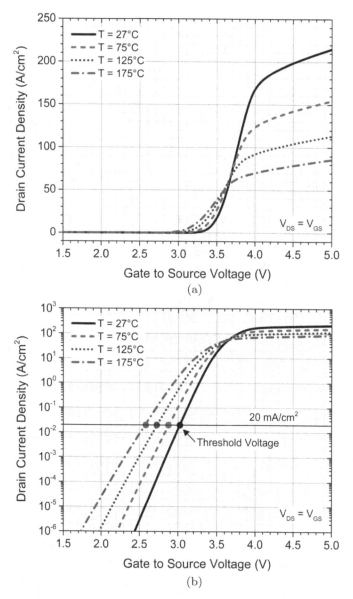

Fig. 30. (a) Threshold voltage measurement J–V characteristics for the SiC D-MOSFET complete-cell structure on a linear scale. (b) Threshold voltage measurement J–V characteristics for the SiC D-MOSFET complete-cell structure on a semi-log scale.

calculated. Since threshold voltage is measured at very low drain current, the current density value was calculated to be 20 mA/cm^2.

At 27°C lattice temperature, threshold voltage of 3.02 V was calculated for the 3300 V SiC D-MOSFET complete-cell structure which decreased to

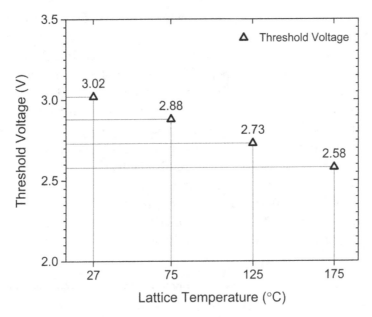

Fig. 31. Summary of 3300 V SiC D-MOSFET threshold voltage as a function of lattice temperature.

2.58 V at 175°C. The complete summary of threshold voltage and lattice temperature is shown in Fig. 31.

 It may be noted that the variation of threshold voltage with lattice temperature is dependent on device and simulation parameters and the user may see different results based on the device design and simulation parameters.

9.5.3.1.7. MOSFET capacitance–voltage characteristics

In the earlier discussion on MOS capacitance, it was found that the input capacitance (C_{ISS}) is more or less constant; however, the output capacitance (C_{OSS}) and reverse transfer capacitance (C_{RSS}) are highly nonlinear and vary as a function of applied drain bias voltage. This is due to the fact that the drain to source capacitance (C_{DS}) and gate to drain *miller* capacitance (C_{GD}) are dependent on semiconductor junction capacitance which are highly nonlinear in nature while gate to source capacitance (C_{GS}) is dependent on device structure. Silvaco© ATLAS can be used to extract MOSFET capacitance using AC simulation. Since 2D simulations are being discussed in this textbook, capacitance obtained from the simulation results is expressed as capacitance per unit length ($F/\mu m$). The approach used to simulate for MOSFET capacitance consists of injecting a high-frequency small signal AC voltage through the required device terminal at a fixed drain to source voltage. The results discussed in this section are based on simulations performed using an AC signal frequency of 1 MHz and voltage of 10 mV. In order to obtain capacitance per unit length versus drain voltage (C–V) characteristics, the same approach can be used, but instead of using a fixed drain to source voltage, the program code can be altered to ramp up the drain to source voltage till the desired magnitude.[8]

The following code was used to simulate and extract MOSFET input capacitance ($F/\mu m$) versus drain to source voltage (C–V) characteristics at a gate to source voltage (V_{GS}) of 0 V and lattice temperature of 27°C. A brief explanation of the simulation program is provided in the code walkthrough (Table 6).

```
Sample code: Vertical D-MOSFET complete-cell structure input capacitance C-V characteristics
@ 27°C

1.   GO ATLAS SIMFLAGS ="-V 5.18.3.R -P 32 -160"
2.
3.   ##### 3300V D-MOSFET COMPLETE CELL INPUT CAPACITANCE C-V @ 27C #####
4.
5.   MESH  WIDTH=1
6.
7.   ## X-MESH
8.
9.   X.MESH  loc=0.00     spac=0.08
10.  X.MESH  loc=1.00     spac=0.04
11.  X.MESH  loc=1.30     spac=0.025
12.  X.MESH  loc=1.50     spac=0.025
13.  X.MESH  loc=1.70     spac=0.15
14.  X.MESH  loc=3.20     spac=0.15
15.  X.MESH  loc=3.50     spac=0.025
16.  X.MESH  loc=3.70     spac=0.025
17.  X.MESH  loc=4.00     spac=0.04
18.  X.MESH  loc=5.00     spac=0.08
19.
20.  ## Y-MESH
21.
22.  Y.MESH  loc=-1.00    spac=0.94
23.  Y.MESH  loc=-0.06    spac=0.94
24.  Y.MESH  loc=-0.05    spac=0.025
25.  Y.MESH  loc=0.00     spac=0.025
26.  Y.MESH  loc=0.02     spac=0.098
27.  Y.MESH  loc=1.00     spac=0.098
28.  Y.MESH  loc=1.20     spac=0.1
29.  Y.MESH  loc=1.80     spac=0.1
30.  Y.MESH  loc=2.20     spac=0.1
31.  Y.MESH  loc=3.50     spac=2.50
32.  Y.MESH  loc=30.0     spac=5.0
33.  Y.MESH  loc=31.5     spac=0.25
34.  Y.MESH  loc=32.5     spac=0.25
35.  Y.MESH  loc=33.0     spac=20
```

```
36. Y.MESH   loc=180.0    spac=20
37. Y.MESH   loc=182.0    spac=1.0
38. Y.MESH   loc=184.0    spac=1.0
39.
40. ##### DEFINING REGIONS
41.
42. REGION  num=1  y.max=0   material=Si3N4
43. REGION  num=2  x.min=0.91  x.max=4.09  y.min=-0.05  y.max=0  material=oxide
44. REGION  num=3  y.min=0   material=4H-SiC
45.
46. ##### DEFINING ELECTRODES
47.
48. ELECTRODE  name=source  x.min=0.0   x.max=0.75  y.max=0   material=aluminum
49. ELECTRODE  name=source  x.min=4.25  x.max=5.00  y.max=0   material=aluminum
50. ELECTRODE  name=gate  x.min=0.90  x.max=4.10  y.max=-0.05  material=polysilicon
51. ELECTRODE  name=drain   y.min=182  y.max=184    material=aluminum
52.
53. ##### DOPING DISTRIBUTION
54.
55. ## BULK DOPING
56. DOPING  uniform  n.type  conc=3.3e15   REGION=3
57.
58. ## N+ SOURCE DOPING
59. DOPING  uniform  n.type  conc=1.e20  x.min=0.44  x.max=0.99  y.min=0  y.max=0.5
60. DOPING  uniform  n.type  conc=1.e20  x.min=4.01  x.max=4.56  y.min=0  y.max=0.5
61.
62. ## P-BASE DOPING
63. DOPING  gauss  p.type  conc=4.5e17  x.min=0.0  x.max=1.3  junc=2.0   rat=0.1
64. DOPING  gauss  p.type  conc=4.5e17  x.min=3.7  x.max=5.0  junc=2.0   rat=0.1
65. DOPING  gauss  p.type  conc=1.0e18  x.min=0.0  x.max=1.3  junc=2.5   rat=0.2
    start=2.0
66. DOPING  gauss  p.type  conc=1.0e18  x.min=3.7  x.max=5.0  junc=2.5   rat=0.2
    start=2.0
67.
68. ## N+ SUBSTRATE DOPING
69. DOPING  uniform  n.type  conc=1.e20  y.min=32   y.max=182
70.
71. SAVE  outf=MOSFET_3300V.str  master.out
72.
73. MATERIAL  material=4H-SiC  REGION=3  permittivity=9.76   eg300=3.26
    affinity=3.7   egalpha=3.3e-2   egbeta=1.e+5  nc300=1.7e+19  nv300=2.5e+19
    arichn=146  arichp=30  augn=3.e-29  augp=3.e-29  taun0=3.33e-6  taup0=6.7e-7
    nsrhn=3.e+17  nsrhp=3.e+17  edb=0.050  eab=0.200
74.
75. ## MODELS USED
76.
77. MODELS  REGION=3  MATERIAL=4H-SIC FERMIDIRAC ANALYTIC CONWELL FLDMOB SRH BGN
    AUGER INCOMPLETE TEMP=300  PRINT
78.
79. INTERFACE  REGION=2  charge=2.5e12  s.n=1.e4  s.p=1.e4  s.i
80.
81. CONTACT  NAME=GATE n.polysilicon
82.
83. ## MOBILITY
84.
85. MOBILITY  material=4H-SiC  REGION=3  vsatn=2.2e7  vsatp=2.2e7  betan=1.2
    betap=2  mu1n.caug=40  mu2n.caug=1136  ncritn.caug=2e17  alphan.caug=-3
    betan.caug=-3  gamman.caug=0.0  deltan.caug=0.76  mu1p.caug=20  mu2p.caug=125
    ncritp.caug=1.e19  alphap.caug=-3  betap.caug=-3  gammap.caug=0.0
    deltap.caug=0.5
```

```
86.
87. ######################### Anisotropic Mobility #########################
88.
89. MOBILITY  material=4H-SiC REGION=3  n.angle=90 p.angle=90 vsatn=2.2e7
    vsatp=2.2e7  betan=1.2 betap=2  mu1n.caug=5  mu2n.caug=947  ncritn.caug=2e17
    alphan.caug=-3  betan.caug=-3  gamman.caug=0.0  deltan.caug=0.76
    mu1p.caug=2.5  mu2p.caug=20  ncritp.caug=1.e19  alphap.caug=-3  betap.caug=-3
    gammap.caug=0.0 deltap.caug=0.5
90.
91. #########################################################################
92.
93. IMPACT  REGION=3  ANISO  E.SIDE  SELB  SIC4H0001  an1=3.44e6  an2=3.44e6
    bn1=2.58e7  bn2=2.58e7  ap1=3.5e6  ap2=3.5e6  bp1=1.7e7 bp2=1.7e7 opphe=0.106
94.
95. METHOD  NEWTON  AUTONR  dvmax=1e8 climit=1e-9  maxtraps=40 itlimit=40
    ir.tol=1.e-40 cr.tol=1.e-40 ix.tol=1.e-40 px.tol=1.e-30 pr.tol=1.e-45
    cx.tol=1.e-30
96.
97. OUTPUT  FLOWLINES
98.
99. ## SOLVING INITIAL VALUE
100.
101. SOLVE   initial
102. SOLVE   vgate=0
103.
104. LOG  outf=mosCissVds_27C.log  master
105.
106. SOLVE   name=gate  AC  FREQ=1e6  ANAME=gate  VSS=0.01  previous
107.
108. SOLVE  vdrain=0.5 vstep=0.5 vfinal=5 name=drain  AC  FREQ=1e6  ANAME=gate
    VSS=0.01   previous
109. SOLVE  vstep=5   vfinal=25   name=drain  AC  FREQ=1e6  ANAME=gate  VSS=0.01
    previous
110. SOLVE  vstep=25  vfinal=500  name=drain  AC  FREQ=1e6  ANAME=gate  VSS=0.01
    previous
111. SOLVE  vstep=50  vfinal=3500 name=drain  AC  FREQ=1e6  ANAME=gate  VSS=0.01
    previous
112.
113. QUIT
```

Table 6.   Code walkthrough: Vertical D-MOSFET complete-cell structure input capacitance C–V characteristics.

Line No:	Functionality
1	Configure ATLAS simulator to use 160-bit extended precision and utilize 32 cores of the CPU if hardware resources are available. The version of ATLAS to be used by the simulator is set to 5.18.3.R using the $-$V option in the simflags command.
5	Initialize device structure mesh information.
7–38	X-axis and Y-axis mesh distribution.
42–44	Declare nitride, oxide and 4H-SiC as the material for the areas specified by the x and y coordinates.

(Continued)

Table 6. (*Continued*)

Line No:	Functionality
48–51	Electrode specifications for the MOSFET (Aluminum source and drain electrode and polysilicon gate electrode).
55–69	Specify doping profile, type, and concentration for different areas of the MOSFET complete-cell structure.
71	Save the device structure (*.str*) file on the local hard drive. The device structure can be viewed by opening the file via *TonyPlot* to troubleshoot/optimize the structure.
73	Specify material parameters for 4H-SiC. Detailed description of these parameters is available in the Silvaco© ATLAS manual. The values for these parameters can either be obtained via material research or from literature.
77	Specify the various models to be included in the 4H-SiC MOSFET simulation.
79	Specify trapped charge density at the oxide–semiconductor interface.
81	Use contact statement to configure n-type polysilicon gate contact.
85	Specify mobility parameters for 4H-SiC. Detailed description of these parameters is available in the Silvaco© ATLAS manual. The values for these parameters can either be obtained via material research or from literature.
89	Specify anisotropic mobility parameters for 4H-SiC. Detailed description of these parameters is available in the Silvaco© ATLAS manual. The values for these parameters can either be obtained via material research or from literature.
93	Specify impact ionization parameters for 4H-SiC. This statement is mandatory to obtain device breakdown characteristics.
95	Specify the solver type and the tolerance values to be used during the simulation. This is an extremely critical statement which can alter the simulation outcome.
97	Include current flowlines in the output structure file.
101–102	Solve for the initial bias conditions followed by solving for zero gate voltage.
104	Save the simulation log (*.log*) file on the local hard drive. The simulation results can be viewed by opening the file via *TonyPlot*.
106	Solve for gate bias under small signal AC condition. 10 mV signal @ 1 MHz frequency injected into the gate electrode.
108–111	Positive sweep of drain voltage while applying AC signal to the gate electrode and performing AC analysis at each drain bias voltage step.
113	Terminate the simulation.

The only difference between the program code for the simulation and extraction of input and output capacitance is the device terminal where the small signal AC analysis is performed. Simulation of input capacitance requires AC signal to be injected into the gate terminal, whereas simulation of output capacitance requires AC signal to be injected into the drain terminal.[8] The critical lines of code have been highlighted in the code walkthrough Tables 6 and 7. The following code was used to simulate and extract MOSFET output capacitance (F/μm) versus drain to source voltage (*C–V*) characteristics at a gate to source voltage (V_{GS}) of 0 V and lattice temperature of 27°C. A brief explanation of the simulation program is provided in the code walkthrough (Table 7).

```
Sample code: Vertical D-MOSFET complete-cell structure output capacitance C-V characteristics
@ 27°C

1.   GO ATLAS SIMFLAGS ="-V 5.18.3.R -P 32 -160"
2.
3.   ##### 3300V D-MOSFET COMPLETE CELL OUTPUT CAPACITANCE C-V @ 27C #####
4.
5.   MESH  WIDTH=1
6.
7.   ## X-MESH
8.
9.   X.MESH  loc=0.00    spac=0.08
10.  X.MESH  loc=1.00    spac=0.04
11.  X.MESH  loc=1.30    spac=0.025
12.  X.MESH  loc=1.50    spac=0.025
13.  X.MESH  loc=1.70    spac=0.15
14.  X.MESH  loc=3.20    spac=0.15
15.  X.MESH  loc=3.50    spac=0.025
16.  X.MESH  loc=3.70    spac=0.025
17.  X.MESH  loc=4.00    spac=0.04
18.  X.MESH  loc=5.00    spac=0.08
19.
20.  ## Y-MESH
21.
22.  Y.MESH  loc=-1.00   spac=0.94
23.  Y.MESH  loc=-0.06   spac=0.94
24.  Y.MESH  loc=-0.05   spac=0.025
25.  Y.MESH  loc=0.00    spac=0.025
26.  Y.MESH  loc=0.02    spac=0.098
27.  Y.MESH  loc=1.00    spac=0.098
28.  Y.MESH  loc=1.20    spac=0.1
29.  Y.MESH  loc=1.80    spac=0.1
30.  Y.MESH  loc=2.20    spac=0.1
31.  Y.MESH  loc=3.50    spac=2.50
32.  Y.MESH  loc=30.0    spac=5.0
33.  Y.MESH  loc=31.5    spac=0.25
34.  Y.MESH  loc=32.5    spac=0.25
35.  Y.MESH  loc=33.0    spac=20
36.  Y.MESH  loc=180.0   spac=20
37.  Y.MESH  loc=182.0   spac=1.0
38.  Y.MESH  loc=184.0   spac=1.0
39.
```

```
40. ##### DEFINING REGIONS
41.
42. REGION  num=1  y.max=0  material=Si3N4
43. REGION  num=2  x.min=0.91  x.max=4.09  y.min=-0.05  y.max=0  material=oxide
44. REGION  num=3  y.min=0  material=4H-SiC
45.
46. ##### DEFINING ELECTRODES
47.
48. ELECTRODE  name=source  x.min=0.0  x.max=0.75  y.max=0  material=aluminum
49. ELECTRODE  name=source  x.min=4.25  x.max=5.00  y.max=0  material=aluminum
50. ELECTRODE  name=gate  x.min=0.90  x.max=4.10  y.max=-0.05  material=polysilicon
51. ELECTRODE  name=drain  y.min=182  y.max=184  material=aluminum
52.
53. ##### DOPING DISTRIBUTION
54.
55. ## BULK DOPING
56. DOPING  uniform  n.type  conc=3.3e15  REGION=3
57.
58. ## N+ SOURCE DOPING
59. DOPING  uniform  n.type conc=1.e20  x.min=0.44  x.max=0.99  y.min=0  y.max=0.5
60. DOPING  uniform  n.type conc=1.e20  x.min=4.01  x.max=4.56  y.min=0  y.max=0.5
61.
62. ## P-BASE DOPING
63. DOPING  gauss  p.type conc=4.5e17  x.min=0.0  x.max=1.3  junc=2.0  rat=0.1
64. DOPING  gauss  p.type conc=4.5e17  x.min=3.7  x.max=5.0  junc=2.0  rat=0.1
65. DOPING  gauss  p.type conc=1.0e18  x.min=0.0  x.max=1.3  junc=2.5  rat=0.2
    start=2.0
66. DOPING  gauss  p.type conc=1.0e18  x.min=3.7  x.max=5.0  junc=2.5  rat=0.2
    start=2.0
67.
68. ## N+ SUBSTRATE DOPING
69. DOPING  uniform  n.type  conc=1.e20  y.min=32  y.max=182
70.
71. SAVE  outf=MOSFET_3300V.str  master.out
72.
73. MATERIAL  material=4H-SiC REGION=3  permittivity=9.76  eg300=3.26
    affinity=3.7  egalpha=3.3e-2  egbeta=1.e+5  nc300=1.7e+19  nv300=2.5e+19
    arichn=146  arichp=30  augn=3.e-29  augp=3.e-29  taun0=3.33e-6  taup0=6.7e-7
    nsrhn=3.e+17  nsrhp=3.e+17  edb=0.050  eab=0.200
74.
75. ## MODELS USED
76.
77. MODELS  REGION=3 MATERIAL=4H-SIC FERMIDIRAC ANALYTIC CONWELL FLDMOB SRH BGN
    AUGER INCOMPLETE TEMP=300  PRINT
78.
79. INTERFACE  REGION=2 charge=2.5e12  s.n=1.e4  s.p=1.e4  s.i
80.
81. CONTACT  NAME=GATE  n.polysilicon
82.
83. ## MOBILITY
84.
85. MOBILITY  material=4H-SiC REGION=3  vsatn=2.2e7  vsatp=2.2e7  betan=1.2
    betap=2  mu1n.caug=40  mu2n.caug=1136  ncritn.caug=2e17  alphan.caug=-3
    betan.caug=-3  gamman.caug=0.0  deltan.caug=0.76  mu1p.caug=20  mu2p.caug=125
    ncritp.caug=1.e19  alphap.caug=-3  betap.caug=-3  gammap.caug=0.0
    deltap.caug=0.5
86.
87. ####################### Anisotropic Mobility #######################
88.
```

```
89. MOBILITY  material=4H-SiC  REGION=3  n.angle=90 p.angle=90 vsatn=2.2e7
    vsatp=2.2e7  betan=1.2 betap=2  mu1n.caug=5  mu2n.caug=947  ncritn.caug=2e17
    alphan.caug=-3  betan.caug=-3  gamman.caug=0.0  deltan.caug=0.76
    mu1p.caug=2.5  mu2p.caug=20  ncritp.caug=1.e19  alphap.caug=-3  betap.caug=-3
    gammap.caug=0.0  deltap.caug=0.5
90.
91. ##########################################################################
92.
93. IMPACT  REGION=3  ANISO  E.SIDE  SELB  SIC4H0001  an1=3.44e6  an2=3.44e6
    bn1=2.58e7  bn2=2.58e7  ap1=3.5e6  ap2=3.5e6  bp1=1.7e7  bp2=1.7e7  opphe=0.106
94.
95. METHOD  NEWTON  AUTONR  dvmax=1e8 climit=1e-9  maxtraps=40 itlimit=40
    ir.tol=1.e-40 cr.tol=1.e-40 ix.tol=1.e-40 px.tol=1.e-30 pr.tol=1.e-45
    cx.tol=1.e-30
96.
97. OUTPUT  FLOWLINES
98.
99. ## SOLVING INITIAL VALUE
100.
101. SOLVE  initial
102. SOLVE  vgate=0
103.
104. LOG  outf=mosCossVds_27C.log  master
105.
106. SOLVE  name=drain  AC  FREQ=1e6  ANAME=drain  VSS=0.01  previous
107.
108. SOLVE  vdrain=0.5 vstep=0.5  vfinal=5  name=drain  AC  FREQ=1e6  ANAME=drain
     VSS=0.01    previous
109. SOLVE  vstep=5  vfinal=25   name=drain  AC  FREQ=1e6  ANAME=drain  VSS=0.01
     previous
110. SOLVE  vstep=25  vfinal=500  name=drain  AC  FREQ=1e6  ANAME=drain  VSS=0.01
     previous
111. SOLVE  vstep=50  vfinal=3500 name=drain  AC  FREQ=1e6  ANAME=drain  VSS=0.01
     previous
112.
113. QUIT
```

Table 7. Code walkthrough: Vertical D-MOSFET complete-cell structure output capacitance C–V characteristics.

Line No:	Functionality
1	Configure ATLAS simulator to use 160-bit extended precision and utilize 32 cores of the CPU if hardware resources are available. The version of ATLAS to be used by the simulator is set to 5.18.3.R using the $-V$ option in the simflags command.
5	Initialize device structure mesh information.
7–38	X-axis and Y-axis mesh distribution.
42–44	Declare nitride, oxide and 4H-SiC as the material for the areas specified by the x and y coordinates.
48–51	Electrode specifications for the MOSFET (Aluminum source and drain electrode and polysilicon gate electrode).

(Continued)

Table 7. (*Continued*)

Line No:	Functionality
55–69	Specify doping profile, type, and concentration for different areas of the MOSFET complete-cell structure.
71	Save the device structure (**.str**) file on the local hard drive. The device structure can be viewed by opening the file via **TonyPlot** to troubleshoot/optimize the structure.
73	Specify material parameters for 4H-SiC. Detailed description of these parameters is available in the Silvaco© ATLAS manual. The values for these parameters can either be obtained via material research or from literature.
77	Specify the various models to be included in the 4H-SiC MOSFET simulation.
79	Specify trapped charge density at the oxide–semiconductor interface.
81	Use Contact statement to configure n-type polysilicon gate contact.
85	Specify mobility parameters for 4H-SiC. Detailed description of these parameters is available in the Silvaco© ATLAS manual. The values for these parameters can either be obtained via material research or from literature.
89	Specify anisotropic mobility parameters for 4H-SiC. Detailed description of these parameters is available in the Silvaco© ATLAS manual. The values for these parameters can either be obtained via material research or from literature.
93	Specify impact ionization parameters for 4H-SiC. This statement is mandatory to obtain device breakdown characteristics.
95	Specify the solver type and the tolerance values to be used during the simulation. This is an extremely critical statement which can alter the simulation outcome.
97	Include current flowlines in the output structure file.
101–102	Solve for the initial bias conditions followed by solving for zero gate voltage.
104	Save the simulation log (**.log**) file on the local hard drive. The simulation results can be viewed by opening the file via **TonyPlot**.
106	Solve for drain bias under small signal AC condition. 10 mV signal @ 1 MHz frequency injected into the drain electrode.
108–111	Positive sweep of drain voltage while applying AC signal to the drain electrode and performing AC analysis at each drain bias voltage step.
113	Terminate the simulation.

9.5.3.1.8. MOSFET capacitance–voltage simulation results

The two log files obtained from the input and output capacitance simulation programs can be used to extract the gate to source (C_{GS}), gate to drain (C_{GD}), and drain to source capacitance (C_{DS}). The log file obtained from the input capacitance simulation (*mosCissVds_27C.log*) will provide C_{GS} and C_{GD} data while the log file obtained from the output simulation (*mosCossVds_27C.log*) will provide C_{DS} data in F/μm as a function of drain to source bias voltage (V_{DS}). The C–V characteristics for the 3300 V SiC MOSFET complete-cell structure is shown in Fig. 32. The capacitance data shown in Fig. 32 is expressed as C_{ISS}, C_{OSS}, and C_{RSS} and was obtained for a lattice temperature value of 27°C and gate to source voltage (V_{GS}) of 0 V using a 10 mV AC signal at 1 MHz frequency. Even though the MOSFET structure was simulated up to V_{DS} = 3500 V, the graph has been plotted up to V_{DS} = 2500 V which is approximately 75% of the rated voltage. Due to the miniature cell dimension, the capacitance data has a unit of nF/μm.

It can be seen from the C–V data that C_{ISS} is almost constant throughout the drain to source voltage (V_{DS}) range and although C_{ISS} is the sum of C_{GS} and C_{GD}, the nonlinearity in C_{GD} does not affect C_{ISS} since C_{GS} is several orders higher in magnitude.

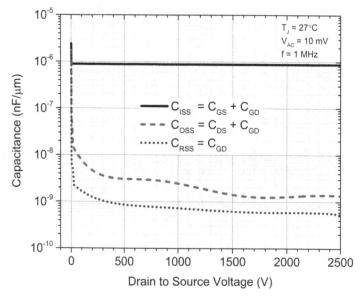

Fig. 32. Capacitance C–V characteristics for the SiC D-MOSFET complete-cell structure on a semi-log scale.

The waveforms obtained for C_{GD} and C_{DS} may have significant noise and variations throughout the drain to source voltage sweep during C–V simulation. It is highly recommended to use the curve smoothing algorithms present in a data processing software.

9.5.3.2. *Mixed-Mode transient simulation*

SiC MOSFET is the switching device of choice for applications involving high-voltage and high-current power electronic circuits. In a switching circuit, the power semiconductor device (in this case, SiC MOSFET) undergoes rapid turn-ON and turn-OFF based on the switching frequency and duty cycle. In a steady-state/DC circuit, the only loss occurring in the semiconductor device is due to ON-state power dissipation, also known as conduction loss. However in a switching circuit, when the device alternates rapidly between ON-state and OFF-state, switching losses also come into play along with the conduction loss and contribute to overall power dissipation and junction temperature rise. Switching loss occurs due to the voltage–current crossover when the device transitions from one state to the other. Since SiC MOSFET will be an integral part of a high-voltage power electronic system, it is important to understand device behavior under switching/transient condition. In this section, the 3300 V SiC D-MOSFET complete-cell structure is simulated under transient condition using various switching circuits at an ambient lattice temperature of 27°C. Except for gate charge simulation, all the simulations include non-isothermal lattice heating models to understand heat generation within the device structure under switching condition.

9.5.3.2.1. Gate charge simulation

The significance of MOSFET capacitance has been discussed in this chapter. To understand the switching behavior of the power MOSFET, it is necessary to understand the MOSFET turn-ON process. The turn-ON event of the MOSFET is associated with the charging of the input capacitance (C_{ISS}) which consists of gate to source (C_{GS}) and gate to drain *Miller* capacitance. The charge required to turn-ON the MOSFET is available in a commercial device datasheet and specified as gate to source (Q_{GS}), gate to drain (Q_{GD}), and total gate charge (Q_G). MOSFET Gate charge simulation can be performed in Silvaco© ATLAS using the test circuit shown in Fig. 33. Voltage source **VDC** is used to set the drain to source voltage to 2500 V (75% of rated

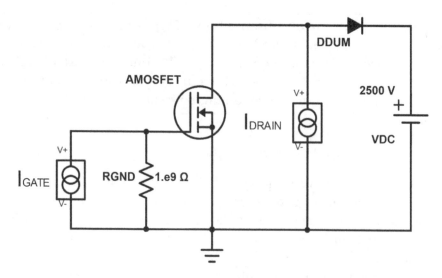

Fig. 33.   Test circuit used for MOSFET gate charge simulation.

blocking voltage 3300 V), while current source $\mathbf{I_{DRAIN}}$ sets the drain current magnitude to a value at which the gate turn-ON needs to be simulated. Diode (**DDUM**) ensures constant current flow through the MOSFET (**AMOSFET**) by preventing current flow from **VDC** into the MOSFET while permitting current from $\mathbf{I_{DRAIN}}$ into **VDC**. To reduce the simulation time, a built-in ideal diode model has been used in this simulation. A 10^9 Ω resistor (**RGND**) provides high impedance path from gate to ground, and current source $\mathbf{I_{GATE}}$ sets the gate current value at which gate turn-ON needs to be simulated. The test circuit was simulated without the inclusion of lattice heating models using a constant gate current of 1 $\mu A/\mu m$ and turn-ON drain current densities of 100 A/cm^2 and 500 A/cm^2. Drain current of 5 μA and 25 μA corresponded to the current densities of 100 A/cm^2 and 500 A/cm^2, respectively.[8]

The following code was used to simulate the 3300 V SiC MOSFET complete-cell structure gate charging for an ON-state current density of 100 A/cm^2 and constant gate current of 1 $\mu A/\mu m$. A brief explanation of the simulation program is provided in the code walkthrough (Table 8).

```
Sample code: Vertical D-MOSFET complete-cell structure gate charging simulation @ 100 A/cm²

1.  GO ATLAS SIMFLAGS ="-V 5.18.3.R -P 32 -160"
2.
3.  ##### 3300V D-MOSFET COMPLETE CELL GATE CHARGE @ 100 A/cm2 #####
4.
5.  MESH  WIDTH=1
```

```
6.
7.  ## X-MESH
8.
9.  X.MESH  loc=0.00    spac=0.08
10. X.MESH  loc=1.00    spac=0.04
11. X.MESH  loc=1.30    spac=0.025
12. X.MESH  loc=1.50    spac=0.025
13. X.MESH  loc=1.70    spac=0.15
14. X.MESH  loc=3.20    spac=0.15
15. X.MESH  loc=3.50    spac=0.025
16. X.MESH  loc=3.70    spac=0.025
17. X.MESH  loc=4.00    spac=0.04
18. X.MESH  loc=5.00    spac=0.08
19.
20. ## Y-MESH
21.
22. Y.MESH  loc=-1.00   spac=0.94
23. Y.MESH  loc=-0.06   spac=0.94
24. Y.MESH  loc=-0.05   spac=0.025
25. Y.MESH  loc=0.00    spac=0.025
26. Y.MESH  loc=0.02    spac=0.098
27. Y.MESH  loc=1.00    spac=0.098
28. Y.MESH  loc=1.20    spac=0.1
29. Y.MESH  loc=1.80    spac=0.1
30. Y.MESH  loc=2.20    spac=0.1
31. Y.MESH  loc=3.50    spac=2.50
32. Y.MESH  loc=30.0    spac=5.0
33. Y.MESH  loc=31.5    spac=0.25
34. Y.MESH  loc=32.5    spac=0.25
35. Y.MESH  loc=33.0    spac=20
36. Y.MESH  loc=180.0   spac=20
37. Y.MESH  loc=182.0   spac=1.0
38. Y.MESH  loc=184.0   spac=1.0
39.
40. ##### DEFINING REGIONS
41.
42. REGION  num=1  y.max=0   material=Si3N4
43. REGION  num=2  x.min=0.91  x.max=4.09   y.min=-0.05  y.max=0  material=oxide
44. REGION  num=3  y.min=0   material=4H-SiC
45.
46. ##### DEFINING ELECTRODES
47.
48. ELECTRODE  name=source  x.min=0.0   x.max=0.75  y.max=0   material=aluminum
49. ELECTRODE  name=source  x.min=4.25  x.max=5.00  y.max=0   material=aluminum
50. ELECTRODE  name=gate    x.min=0.90  x.max=4.10  y.max=-0.05 material=polysilicon
51. ELECTRODE  name=drain   y.min=182  y.max=184    material=aluminum
52.
53. ##### DOPING DISTRIBUTION
54.
55. ## BULK DOPING
56. DOPING  uniform   n.type conc=3.3e15    REGION=3
57.
58. ## N+ SOURCE DOPING
59. DOPING  uniform  n.type conc=1.e20  x.min=0.44  x.max=0.99  y.min=0  y.max=0.5
60. DOPING  uniform  n.type conc=1.e20  x.min=4.01  x.max=4.56  y.min=0  y.max=0.5
61.
62. ## P-BASE DOPING
63. DOPING  gauss  p.type conc=4.5e17  x.min=0.0  x.max=1.3  junc=2.0  rat=0.1
64. DOPING  gauss  p.type conc=4.5e17  x.min=3.7  x.max=5.0  junc=2.0  rat=0.1
```

```
65. DOPING  gauss  p.type conc=1.0e18  x.min=0.0  x.max=1.3  junc=2.5  rat=0.2
    start=2.0
66. DOPING  gauss  p.type conc=1.0e18  x.min=3.7  x.max=5.0  junc=2.5  rat=0.2
    start=2.0
67.
68. ## N+ SUBSTRATE DOPING
69. DOPING  uniform   n.type conc=1.e20  y.min=32  y.max=182
70.
71. SAVE  outf=MOSFET_3300V.str  master.out
72.
73. ##### STEADY STATE SIMULATION CIRCUIT #####
74.
75. GO ATLAS SIMFLAGS="-V 5.18.3.R -P 32 -160"
76.
77. .BEGIN
78.
79. VDC      1    0    0
80. DDUM     2    1    IDEAL
81. IDRAIN   0    2    0
82. AMOSFET  2=DRAIN  3=GATE   0=SOURCE   infile=MOSFET_3300V.str   width=1
83. RGND     3    0    1.E9
84. IGATE    0    3    0
85.
86. .MODEL  IDEAL D()
87.
88. .NODESET  v(1)=0  v(2)=0  v(3)=0
89. .NUMERIC  imaxdc=100
90. .LOG      outfile=MOSFET_DC_log
91. .SAVE     outfile=MOSFET_DC_Bias
92. .OPTIONS FULLN  print  noshift  relpot
93.
94. .DC  IDRAIN  0     1e-9   1e-11
95. .DC  IDRAIN  1e-9  1e-8   1e-9
96. .DC  IDRAIN  1e-8  1e-7   1e-8
97. .DC  IDRAIN  1e-7  1e-6   1e-7
98. .DC  IDRAIN  1e-6  5e-6   1e-6
99.
100. .DC   VDC  0.    10.    0.25
101. .DC   VDC  10.   100.   10.
102. .DC   VDC  100.  2500.  50.
103.
104. .END
105.
106. ##### MATERIAL PROPERTIES #####
107.
108. MATERIAL  DEVICE=AMOSFET  MATERIAL=4H-SiC region=3  permittivity=9.76
     eg300=3.26   affinity=3.7   egalpha=3.3e-2  egbeta=1.e+5  nc300=1.7e+19
     nv300=2.5e+19  arichn=146  arichp=30  augn=3.e-29  augp=3.e-29   taun0=3.33e-6
     taup0=6.7e-7  nsrhn=3.e+17  nsrhp=3.e+17  edb=0.050  eab=0.200
109.
110. ##### MODELS USED #####
111.
112. MODELS  DEVICE=AMOSFET REGION=3 MATERIAL=4H-SIC FERMIDIRAC ANALYTIC CONWELL
     FLDMOB SRH BGN AUGER INCOMPLETE PRINT
113.
114. INTERFACE  DEVICE=AMOSFET region=2 charge=2.5e12 s.n=1.e4 s.p=1.e4  s.i
115.
116. CONTACT  DEVICE=AMOSFET NAME=GATE n.polysilicon
117.
```

```
118. MOBILITY  DEVICE=AMOSFET  material=4H-SiC region=3  vsatn=2.2e7  vsatp=2.2e7
     betan=1.2 betap=2  mu1n.caug=40  mu2n.caug=1136  ncritn.caug=2e17
     alphan.caug=-3  betan.caug=-3  gamman.caug=0.0  deltan.caug=0.76  mu1p.caug=20
     mu2p.caug=125  ncritp.caug=1.e19  alphap.caug=-3  betap.caug=-3
     gammap.caug=0.0  deltap.caug=0.5
119.
120. MOBILITY  DEVICE=AMOSFET  material=4H-SiC region=3  n.angle=90  p.angle=90
     vsatn=2.2e7  vsatp=2.2e7  betan=1.2 betap=2  mu1n.caug=5  mu2n.caug=947
     ncritn.caug=2e17  alphan.caug=-3  betan.caug=-3  gamman.caug=0.0
     deltan.caug=0.76  mu1p.caug=2.5  mu2p.caug=20  ncritp.caug=1.e19
     alphap.caug=-3  betap.caug=-3  gammap.caug=0.0  deltap.caug=0.5
121.
122. IMPACT  DEVICE=AMOSFET  REGION=3  ANISO  E.SIDE  SELB  SIC4H0001  an1=3.44e6
     an2=3.44e6  bn1=2.58e7  bn2=2.58e7  ap1=3.5e6  ap2=3.5e6  bp1=1.7e7  bp2=1.7e7
     opphe=0.106
123.
124. METHOD  NEWTON  AUTONR  dvmax=1e8 climit=1e-9  maxtraps=40 itlimit=40
     ir.tol=1.e-35 cr.tol=1.e-35 ix.tol=1.e-35 px.tol=1.e-30 pr.tol=1.e-45
     cx.tol=1.e-30
125.
126. GO ATLAS SIMFLAGS="-V 5.18.3.R -P 32 -160"
127.
128. ##### TRANSIENT SIMULATION CIRCUIT #####
129.
130. .BEGIN
131.
132. VDC      1    0    2500
133. DDUM     2    1    IDEAL
134. IDRAIN   0    2    5E-6
135. AMOSFET  2=DRAIN  3=GATE  0=SOURCE  infile=MOSFET_3300V.str   width=1
136. RGND     3    0    1.E9
137. IGATE    0    3    0   PULSE  0  1e-6  2e-8  1e-10  1e-10  100e-1  200e-1
138.
139. .MODEL  IDEAL D()
140.
141. .NUMERIC  imaxtr=100  dtmax=5.e-9
142. .OPTIONS  FULLN  print  noshift  relpot  write=20
143. .LOAD      infile=MOSFET_DC_Bias
144. .SAVE      master=MOSFET_GC
145. .LOG       outfile=MOSFET_GATE_CHARGE.log
146. .SAVE      outfile=MOSFET_GATE_CHARGE.str
147.
148. .TRAN  1ns  120ns
149.
150. .END
151.
152. ##### MATERIAL PROPERTIES #####
153.
154. MATERIAL  DEVICE=AMOSFET  material=4H-SiC  REGION=3  permittivity=9.76
     eg300=3.26  affinity=3.7  egalpha=3.3e-2  egbeta=1.e+5  nc300=1.7e+19
     nv300=2.5e+19  arichn=146  arichp=30  augn=3.e-29  augp=3.e-29  taun0=3.33e-6
     taup0=6.7e-7  nsrhn=3.e+17  nsrhp=3.e+17  edb=0.050  eab=0.200
155.
156. ##### MODELS USED #####
157.
158. MODELS  DEVICE=AMOSFET  REGION=3 MATERIAL=4H-SIC FERMIDIRAC ANALYTIC CONWELL
     FLDMOB SRH BGN AUGER INCOMPLETE PRINT
159.
160. INTERFACE  DEVICE=AMOSFET  REGION=2  charge=2.5e12  s.n=1.e4  s.p=1.e4  s.i
161.
```

```
162. CONTACT  DEVICE=AMOSFET  NAME=GATE n.polysilicon
163.
164. MOBILITY  DEVICE=AMOSFET  material=4H-SiC  REGION=3  vsatn=2.2e7  vsatp=2.2e7
     betan=1.2 betap=2 mu1n.caug=40 mu2n.caug=1136 ncritn.caug=2e17
     alphan.caug=-3 betan.caug=-3 gamman.caug=0.0 deltan.caug=0.76  mu1p.caug=20
     mu2p.caug=125 ncritp.caug=1.e19 alphap.caug=-3 betap.caug=-3
     gammap.caug=0.0 deltap.caug=0.5
165.
166. MOBILITY  DEVICE=AMOSFET  material=4H-SiC  REGION=3  n.angle=90 p.angle=90
     vsatn=2.2e7 vsatp=2.2e7  betan=1.2 betap=2 mu1n.caug=5 mu2n.caug=947
     ncritn.caug=2e17 alphan.caug=-3 betan.caug=-3 gamman.caug=0.0
     deltan.caug=0.76  mu1p.caug=2.5 mu2p.caug=20 ncritp.caug=1.e19
     alphap.caug=-3 betap.caug=-3 gammap.caug=0.0 deltap.caug=0.5
167.
168. IMPACT  DEVICE=AMOSFET  REGION=3  ANISO  E.SIDE  SELB  SIC4H0001  an1=3.44e6
     an2=3.44e6 bn1=2.58e7 bn2=2.58e7 ap1=3.5e6 ap2=3.5e6 bp1=1.7e7 bp2=1.7e7
     opphe=0.106
169.
170. METHOD  NEWTON  AUTONR  dvmax=1e8  climit=1e-9  maxtraps=40 itlimit=40
     ir.tol=1.e-35 cr.tol=1.e-35 ix.tol=1.e-35 px.tol=1.e-30 pr.tol=1.e-45
     cx.tol=1.e-30
171.
172. GO ATLAS SIMFLAGS="-V 5.18.3.R -P 32 -160"
173.
174. QUIT
```

Table 8.   Code walkthrough: Vertical D-MOSFET complete-cell structure gate charging simulation during MOSFET turn-ON.

Line No:	Functionality
1	Configure ATLAS simulator to use 160-bit extended precision and utilize 32 cores of the CPU if hardware resources are available. The version of ATLAS to be used by the simulator is set to 5.18.3.R using the -V option in the simflags command.
5	Initialize device structure mesh information.
7–38	X-axis and Y-axis mesh distribution.
42–44	Declare nitride, oxide, and 4H-SiC as the material for the areas specified by the x and y coordinates.
48–51	Electrode specifications for the MOSFET (Aluminum source and drain electrode and polysilicon gate electrode).
55–69	Specify doping profile, type, and concentration for different areas of the MOSFET complete-cell structure.
71	Save the device structure (**.str**) file on the local hard drive. The device structure can be viewed by opening the file via **TonyPlot** to troubleshoot/optimize the structure.
75	Initialize ATLAS simulator using GO ATLAS command (same as line 1).
77	Initialize the starting of SPICE-like code in Mixed-Mode steady-state simulation.

(Continued)

Table 8. (*Continued*)

Line No:	Functionality
79–84	Gate charge simulation test circuit description in SPICE-like format.
86	Invoke ideal diode model.
88	Declare the initial node voltage for the gate charge simulation test circuit nodes.
89	Set the maximum number of mixed circuit-device iterations to be performed during steady-state analysis (**imaxdc**) to 100.
90	Save log file after steady-state simulation completion.
91	Save file with bias information which will be used for transient simulation.
92	Specify Mixed-Mode steady-state simulation conditions. Full Newton solution method (**FULLN**), disable the shift of voltage for ATLAS devices (**noshift**), and enable the use of relative convergence criteria for potential especially when large voltage biases are involved (**relpot**).
94–98	Ramp up drain current to attain steady-state condition, i.e. 5 μA. This is split into multiple steps.
100–102	Ramp up DC voltage to attain steady-state condition, i.e. VDC = 2500 V. This is split into multiple steps.
104	Initialize the ending of SPICE-like code in Mixed-Mode steady-state simulation.
108	Specify material parameters for 4H-SiC. Detailed description of these parameters is available in the Silvaco$^©$ ATLAS manual. The values for these parameters can either be obtained via material research or from literature.
112	Specify the various models to be included in the 4H-SiC MOSFET simulation.
114	Specify trapped charge density at the oxide–semiconductor interface.
116	Use contact statement to configure n-type polysilicon gate contact.
118	Specify mobility parameters for 4H-SiC. Detailed description of these parameters is available in the Silvaco$^©$ ATLAS manual. The values for these parameters can either be obtained via material research or from literature.
120	Specify anisotropic mobility parameters for 4H-SiC. Detailed description of these parameters is available in the Silvaco$^©$ ATLAS manual. The values for these parameters can either be obtained via material research or from literature.
122	Specify impact ionization parameters for 4H-SiC. This statement is mandatory to obtain device breakdown characteristics.
124	Specify the solver type and the tolerance values to be used during the simulation. This is an extremely critical statement which can alter the simulation outcome.

(*Continued*)

Table 8.   (*Continued*)

Line No:	Functionality
126	Initialize ATLAS simulator using GO ATLAS command (same as line 1) for steady-state bias point simulation.
130	Initialize the starting of SPICE-like code in Mixed-Mode transient simulation.
132–137	Gate charge simulation test circuit description in SPICE-like format. The magnitude of DC voltage source is initialized at 2500 V and drain current source is initialized at 5 μA which is the result obtained from the earlier steady-state simulation. Transient parameters have been added to the Gate current source to generate a square wave.
139	Invoke ideal diode model.
141	Set the maximum number of mixed circuit-device iterations to be performed during transient analysis (**imaxtr**) to 100 and the maximum transient simulation time step (**dtmax**) to 5 ns.
142	Specify Mixed-Mode transient simulation conditions. Full Newton solution method for transient simulation (**FULLN**), disable the shift of voltage for ATLAS devices (**noshift**), enable the use of relative convergence criteria for potential especially when large voltage biases are involved (**relpot**), and write structure file after every 20 time-step iterations.
143	Load the steady-state simulations results saved in line 91.
144	Save the structure file after every 20 time-step iterations specified in line 142.
145	Save log file after the completion of transient simulation.
146	Save the structure file after the completion of transient simulation.
148	Specify the initial time interval of 1 ns and total simulation time of 120 ns.
150	Initialize the ending of SPICE-like code in Mixed-Mode transient simulation.
154–170	Same as line 108 to line 124.
172	Initialize ATLAS simulator using GO ATLAS command (same as line 1) for transient simulation.
174	Terminate the simulation.

9.5.3.2.2.   Gate charge simulation results

The gate charge simulation was performed for drain current densities of 100 A/cm^2 and 500 A/cm^2. The simulation time was selected such that the final gate voltage was 20 V. Since it is not easy to predict the final gate voltage under constant gate current drive, it is recommended to run the simulation first for a much larger time and then re-run the simulation based on the required final gate voltage. The summary of gate voltage waveform is shown in Figs. 34(a) and 34(b). Figure 34(b) is a zoomed-in version of

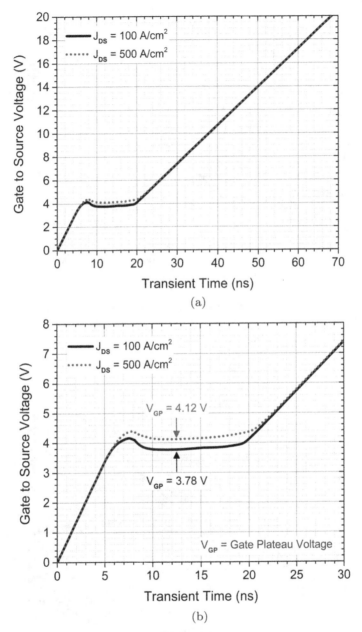

Fig. 34. (a) Gate voltage waveforms pertaining to 100 A/cm² (solid) and 500 A/cm² (dotted) turn-ON drain current density for a constant gate current of 1 μA/μm. (b) Gate voltage waveforms pertaining to 100 A/cm² (solid) and 500 A/cm² (dotted) turn-ON drain current density for a constant gate current of 1 μA/μm zoomed in to highlight gate plateau voltage.

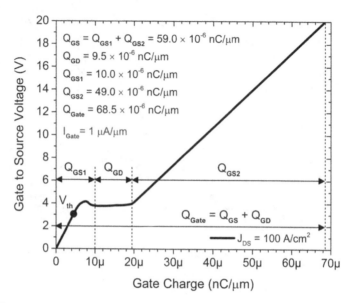

Fig. 35.   Gate voltage versus gate charge waveform pertaining to $100 \ \mathrm{A/cm^2}$ turn-ON drain current density for a constant gate current of $1 \ \mu\mathrm{A}/\mu\mathrm{m}$.

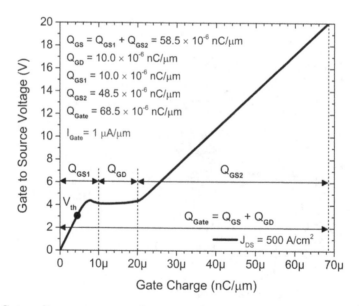

Fig. 36.   Gate voltage versus gate charge waveform pertaining to $500 \ \mathrm{A/cm^2}$ turn-ON drain current density for a constant gate current of $1 \ \mu\mathrm{A}/\mu\mathrm{m}$.

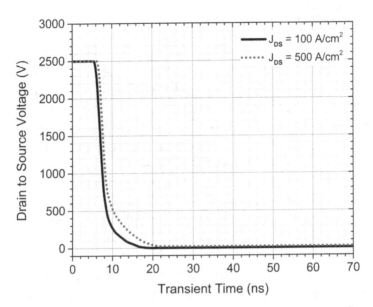

Fig. 37. Drain to source voltage waveforms pertaining to 100 A/cm² (solid) and 500 A/cm² (dotted) turn-ON drain current density for a constant gate current drive of 1 μA/μm.

Fig. 34(a) to highlight the impact of turn-ON drain current density on the gate plateau voltage (V_{GP}). The difference in gate plateau voltage can be explained based on the detailed analysis of MOSFET turn-ON process, which is out of scope of this textbook.

In order to extract the gate charge, the time axis of Fig. 34(a) was multiplied by the constant gate current magnitude of 1 μA/μm to obtain gate charge in C/μm. The gate to source voltage versus gate charge waveforms pertaining to drain current densities of 100 A/cm² and 500 A/cm² are shown in Figs. 35 and 36, respectively. Due to the miniature cell dimensions, the gate charge has been specified in nC/μm.

The gate to source capacitor charge (Q_{GS}) is split into phases Q_{GS1} and Q_{GS2}. It can be seen from Figs. 35 and 36 that the increase in turn-ON drain current density does not affect the total gate charge (Q_{Gate}); however, it does affect the distribution of charge between the gate to source and gate to drain *Miller* capacitance. The drain to source voltage waveforms during MOSFET turn-ON under varying drain current density is shown in Fig. 37.

9.5.3.2.3. Resistive switching simulation

In general, transient simulation is much more complicated than steady-state simulation, especially when the device being simulated is a SiC MOSFET. Resistive switching is a relatively simple circuit which can be used to understand MOSFET switching and can be used as a reference for more complicated circuits. Resistive switching simulation was carried out in Silvaco© ATLAS using the circuit shown in Fig. 38. The circuit consists of DC voltage source (**VDC**) which sets the drain to source voltage to the rated value of 3300 V. A 33 Ω resistor (**RSERIES**) is used to set the ON-state drain current to 100 A. It is obvious that a MOSFET cell with active area of 5 μm^2 cannot handle 100 A of current due to an unrealistic current density of 2×10^9 A/cm^2. Hence, a scaling factor (using ***width*** parameter) of 4×10^6 was used to reduce the current to 25 μA which corresponds to 500 A/cm^2 drain current density. A gate to ground resistor (**RGND**) of 10^{20} Ω was used to provide high impedance ground path and a series gate resistor (**RGATE**) of 10 Ω was used in series with the gate and gate voltage source (**VGATE**). Gate to source voltage of 0/20 V was used to drive the MOSFET at 100 kHz switching frequency and 50% duty cycle.[10] To limit the simulation time, only four switching cycles were simulated.

The following code was used to simulate the 3300 V SiC MOSFET complete-cell structure in a resistive switching circuit for an ON-state current

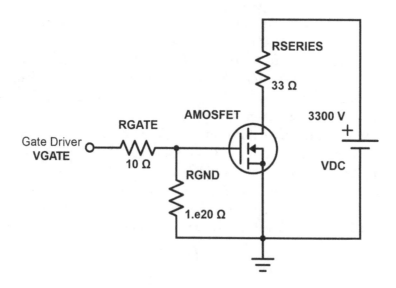

Fig. 38.   MOSFET resistive switching circuit.

density of 500 A/cm^2. A brief explanation of the simulation program is provided in the code walkthrough (Table 9).

```
Sample code: Vertical D-MOSFET complete-cell structure resistive switching simulation
@ 500 A/cm²

1.  GO ATLAS SIMFLAGS ="-V 5.18.3.R -P 32 -160"
2.
3.  ##### 3300V D-MOSFET COMPLETE RESISTIVE SWITCHING @ 500 A/cm2 #####
4.
5.  MESH
6.
7.  ## X-MESH
8.
9.  X.MESH  loc=0.00    spac=0.08
10. X.MESH  loc=1.00    spac=0.04
11. X.MESH  loc=1.30    spac=0.025
12. X.MESH  loc=1.50    spac=0.025
13. X.MESH  loc=1.70    spac=0.15
14. X.MESH  loc=3.20    spac=0.15
15. X.MESH  loc=3.50    spac=0.025
16. X.MESH  loc=3.70    spac=0.025
17. X.MESH  loc=4.00    spac=0.04
18. X.MESH  loc=5.00    spac=0.08
19.
20. ## Y-MESH
21.
22. Y.MESH  loc=-1.00   spac=0.94
23. Y.MESH  loc=-0.06   spac=0.94
24. Y.MESH  loc=-0.05   spac=0.025
25. Y.MESH  loc=0.00    spac=0.025
26. Y.MESH  loc=0.02    spac=0.098
27. Y.MESH  loc=1.00    spac=0.098
28. Y.MESH  loc=1.20    spac=0.1
29. Y.MESH  loc=1.80    spac=0.1
30. Y.MESH  loc=2.20    spac=0.1
31. Y.MESH  loc=3.50    spac=2.50
32. Y.MESH  loc=30.0    spac=5.0
33. Y.MESH  loc=31.5    spac=0.25
34. Y.MESH  loc=32.5    spac=0.25
35. Y.MESH  loc=33.0    spac=20
36. Y.MESH  loc=180.0   spac=20
37. Y.MESH  loc=182.0   spac=1.0
38. Y.MESH  loc=184.0   spac=1.0
39.
40. ##### DEFINING REGIONS
41.
42. REGION  num=1  y.max=0    material=Si3N4
43. REGION  num=2  x.min=0.91  x.max=4.09   y.min=-0.05  y.max=0  material=oxide
44. REGION  num=3  y.min=0    material=4H-SiC
45.
46. ##### DEFINING ELECTRODES
47.
48. ELECTRODE   name=source  x.min=0.0   x.max=0.75  y.max=0  material=aluminum
49. ELECTRODE   name=source  x.min=4.25  x.max=5.00  y.max=0  material=aluminum
50. ELECTRODE   name=gate  x.min=0.90  x.max=4.10  y.max=-0.05  material=polysilicon
51. ELECTRODE   name=drain   y.min=182  y.max=184     material=aluminum
52.
53. ##### DOPING DISTRIBUTION
```

```
54.
55. ## BULK DOPING
56. DOPING  uniform  n.type  conc=3.3e15  REGION=3
57.
58. ## N+ SOURCE DOPING
59. DOPING  uniform  n.type conc=1.e20  x.min=0.44  x.max=0.99  y.min=0  y.max=0.5
60. DOPING  uniform  n.type conc=1.e20  x.min=4.01  x.max=4.56  y.min=0  y.max=0.5
61.
62. ## P-BASE DOPING
63. DOPING  gauss  p.type conc=4.5e17  x.min=0.0   x.max=1.3  junc=2.0  rat=0.1
64. DOPING  gauss  p.type conc=4.5e17  x.min=3.7   x.max=5.0  junc=2.0  rat=0.1
65. DOPING  gauss  p.type conc=1.0e18  x.min=0.0   x.max=1.3  junc=2.5  rat=0.2
    start=2.0
66. DOPING  gauss  p.type conc=1.0e18  x.min=3.7   x.max=5.0  junc=2.5  rat=0.2
    start=2.0
67.
68. ## N+ SUBSTRATE DOPING
69. DOPING  uniform   n.type   conc=1.e20   y.min=32   y.max=182
70.
71. SAVE  outf=Resistive_DMOS_Structure.str  master.out
72.
73. ##### STEADY STATE SIMULATION CIRCUIT #####
74.
75. GO ATLAS SIMFLAGS="-V 5.18.3.R -P 32 -160"
76.
77. .BEGIN
78.
79. VDC      1    0    0
80. RSERIES  1    2    33
81. AMOSFET  2=drain  3=gate   0=source  infile=Resistive_DMOS_Structure.str
    width=4.e6
82. RGND     3    0    1e20
83. RGATE    3    4    10
84. VGATE    4    0    0
85.
86. .NODESET  v(1)=0  v(2)=0  v(3)=0  v(4)=0
87. .NUMERIC  imaxdc=100
88. .LOG      outfile=Resistive_DMOS_DC_log
89. .SAVE     outfile=Resistive_DMOS_DC_Bias
90. .OPTIONS  m2ln  print  noshift  relpot
91.
92. .DC  VDC  0.     10.     0.5
93. .DC  VDC  10.    50.     5.
94. .DC  VDC  50.    100.    10.
95. .DC  VDC  100.   1000.   50.
96. .DC  VDC  1000.  3300.   100.
97.
98. .END
99.
100. CONTACT  DEVICE=AMOSFET  NAME=GATE   n.polysilicon  EXT.ALPHA=10
101. CONTACT  DEVICE=AMOSFET  NAME=SOURCE              EXT.ALPHA=10
102. CONTACT  DEVICE=AMOSFET  NAME=DRAIN               EXT.ALPHA=10
103.
104. THERMCONTACT DEVICE=AMOSFET  num=4  x.min=0  x.max=5  y.min=0.0  y.max=182
     alpha=10   ext.temp=300
105.
106. INTERFACE  DEVICE=AMOSFET  REGION=2  charge=2.5e12  s.n=1.e4  s.p=1.e4  s.i
107.
108. MATERIAL  DEVICE=AMOSFET  material=4H-SiC  REGION=3  permittivity=9.76
     eg300=3.26   affinity=3.7   egalpha=3.3e-2   egbeta=1.e+5  nc300=1.7e+19
```

```
     nv300=2.5e+19  arichn=146  arichp=30  augn=3.e-29  augp=3.e-29   taun0=3.33e-6
     taup0=6.7e-7  nsrhn=3.e+17  nsrhp=3.e+17  edb=0.050  eab=0.200  tcon.polyn
     tc.a=0.137534   tc.b=4.9662e-4   tc.c=0.000000354  hc.a=2.35  hc.b=1.75e-3
     hc.c=1.e-9  hc.d=-6.6e4
109.
110. MODELS  DEVICE=AMOSFET  REGION=3 MATERIAL=4H-SiC FERMIDIRAC ANALYTIC CONWELL
     FLDMOB SRH BGN AUGER INCOMPLETE  LAT.TEMP  JOULE.HEAT  GR.HEAT  PRINT
111.
112. MOBILITY  DEVICE=AMOSFET  material=4H-SiC REGION=3  vsatn=2.2e7 vsatp=2.2e7
     betan=1.2 betap=2  mu1n.caug=40  mu2n.caug=1136  ncritn.caug=2e17
     alphan.caug=-3 betan.caug=-3 gamman.caug=0.0 deltan.caug=0.76   mu1p.caug=20
     mu2p.caug=125 ncritp.caug=1.e19 alphap.caug=-3 betap.caug=-3
     gammap.caug=0.0 deltap.caug=0.5
113.
114. MOBILITY  DEVICE=AMOSFET  material=4H-SiC REGION=3  n.angle=90 p.angle=90
     vsatn=2.2e7 vsatp=2.2e7  betan=1.2 betap=2  mu1n.caug=5  mu2n.caug=947
     ncritn.caug=2e17  alphan.caug=-3  betan.caug=-3  gamman.caug=0.0
     deltan.caug=0.76   mu1p.caug=2.5 mu2p.caug=20  ncritp.caug=1.e19
     alphap.caug=-3 betap.caug=-3 gammap.caug=0.0 deltap.caug=0.5
115.
116. IMPACT  DEVICE=AMOSFET  REGION=3  ANISO  E.SIDE  SELB  SIC4H0001  an1=3.44e6
     an2=3.44e6  bn1=2.58e7  bn2=2.58e7  ap1=3.5e6  ap2=3.5e6  bp1=1.7e7  bp2=1.7e7
     opphe=0.106
117.
118. METHOD  BLOCK climit=1.e-9  maxtraps=40  itlimit=50    max.temp=1000  dvmax=1.e8
     ix.tol=1.e-35  ir.tol=1.e-35  px.tol=1.e-35  pr.tol=1.e-30  cx.tol=1.e-45
     cr.tol=1.e-30
119.
120. GO ATLAS SIMFLAGS="-V 5.18.3.R -P 32 -160"
121.
122. ##### TRANSIENT SIMULATION CIRCUIT #####
123.
124. .BEGIN
125.
126. VDC        1    0    3300
127. RSERIES    1    2    33
128. AMOSFET    2=drain   3=gate    0=source  infile=Resistive_DMOS_Structure.str
     width=4.e6
129. RGND       3    0    1e20
130. RGATE      3    4    10
131. VGATE      4    0    0    PULSE  0   20   5us    50ns    50ns    5us    10.1us
132.
133. .NUMERIC  imaxtr=100
134. .OPTIONS  m2ln.tr  print  relpot  write=50
135. .LOAD     infile=Resistive_DMOS_DC_Bias
136. .SAVE     master=Resistive_DMOS_Transient
137. .LOG      outfile=Resistive_DMOS_500.log
138. .SAVE     outfile=Resistive_DMOS.str
139.
140. .TRAN  0.1ns  45.4us
141.
142. .END
143.
144. CONTACT  DEVICE=AMOSFET  NAME=GATE   n.polysilicon  EXT.ALPHA=10
145. CONTACT  DEVICE=AMOSFET  NAME=SOURCE              EXT.ALPHA=10
146. CONTACT  DEVICE=AMOSFET  NAME=DRAIN               EXT.ALPHA=10
147.
148. THERMCONTACT DEVICE=AMOSFET num=4  x.min=0  x.max=5  y.min=0.0  y.max=182
     alpha=10  ext.temp=300
149.
```

```
150. INTERFACE  REGION=2 charge=2.5e12  s.n=1.e4  s.p=1.e4  s.i
151.
152. MATERIAL  material=4H-SiC  REGION=3  permittivity=9.76   eg300=3.26
     affinity=3.7   egalpha=3.3e-2   egbeta=1.e+5  nc300=1.7e+19  nv300=2.5e+19
     arichn=146  arichp=30  augn=3.e-29  augp=3.e-29  taun0=3.33e-6  taup0=6.7e-7
     nsrhn=3.e+17  nsrhp=3.e+17  edb=0.050   eab=0.200  tcon.polyn  tc.a=0.137534
     tc.b=4.9662e-4   tc.c=0.000000354  hc.a=2.35  hc.b=1.75e-3  hc.c=1.e-9  hc.d=-
     6.6e4
153.
154. MODELS  DEVICE=AMOSFET REGION=3 MATERIAL=4H-SiC FERMIDIRAC ANALYTIC CONWELL
     FLDMOB SRH BGN AUGER INCOMPLETE LAT.TEMP JOULE.HEAT  GR.HEAT PRINT
155.
156. MOBILITY  material=4H-SiC  REGION=3  vsatn=2.2e7  vsatp=2.2e7  betan=1.2
     betap=2  mu1n.caug=40  mu2n.caug=1136  ncritn.caug=2e17  alphan.caug=-3
     betan.caug=-3  gamman.caug=0.0  deltan.caug=0.76   mu1p.caug=20  mu2p.caug=125
     ncritp.caug=1.e19  alphap.caug=-3  betap.caug=-3  gammap.caug=0.0
     deltap.caug=0.5
157.
158. MOBILITY  material=4H-SiC  REGION=3  n.angle=90  p.angle=90  vsatn=2.2e7
     vsatp=2.2e7  betan=1.2 betap=2  mu1n.caug=5  mu2n.caug=947  ncritn.caug=2e17
     alphan.caug=-3  betan.caug=-3  gamman.caug=0.0  deltan.caug=0.76
     mu1p.caug=2.5  mu2p.caug=20  ncritp.caug=1.e19  alphap.caug=-3  betap.caug=-3
     gammap.caug=0.0  deltap.caug=0.5
159.
160. IMPACT  DEVICE=AMOSFET  REGION=3  ANISO  E.SIDE  SELB  SIC4H0001  an1=3.44e6
     an2=3.44e6  bn1=2.58e7  bn2=2.58e7  ap1=3.5e6  ap2=3.5e6  bp1=1.7e7  bp2=1.7e7
     opphe=0.106
161.
162. METHOD  BLOCK.TRAN  climit=1.e-9  maxtraps=100  itlimit=100   dvmax=1.e8
     ix.tol=1.e-35  ir.tol=1.e-35  px.tol=1.e-35  pr.tol=1.e-30  cx.tol=1.e-45
     cr.tol=1.e-30
163.
164. OUTPUT  FLOWLINES  E.MOBILITY
165.
166. GO ATLAS SIMFLAGS="-V 5.18.3.R -P 32 -160"
167.
168. QUIT
```

Table 9. Code walkthrough: Vertical D-MOSFET complete-cell structure resistive switching.

Line No:	Functionality
1	Configure ATLAS simulator to use 160-bit extended precision and utilize 32 cores of the CPU if hardware resources are available. The version of ATLAS to be used by the simulator is set to 5.18.3.R using the $-V$ option in the simflags command.
5	Initialize device structure mesh information.
7–38	X-axis and Y-axis mesh distribution.
42–44	Declare nitride, oxide, and 4H-SiC as the material for the areas specified by the x and y coordinates.
48–51	Electrode specifications for the MOSFET (Aluminum source and drain electrode and polysilicon gate electrode).

(Continued)

Table 9. (*Continued*)

Line No:	Functionality
55–69	Specify doping profile, type, and concentration for different areas of the MOSFET complete-cell structure.
71	Save the device structure (**.str**) file on the local hard drive. The device structure can be viewed by opening the file via **TonyPlot** to troubleshoot/optimize the structure.
75	Initialize ATLAS simulator using GO ATLAS command (same as line 1).
77	Initialize the starting of SPICE-like code in Mixed-Mode steady-state simulation.
79–84	Resistive switching circuit description in SPICE-like format. Width parameter with a value of 4×10^6 has been used for the MOSFET structure.
86	Declare the initial node voltage for the resistive switching circuit nodes.
87	Set the maximum number of mixed circuit-device iterations to be performed during steady-state analysis (**imaxdc**) to 100.
88	Save log file after steady-state simulation completion.
89	Save file with bias information which will be used for transient simulation.
90	Specify Mixed-Mode steady-state simulation conditions. Modified two-level Newton solution method (**m2ln**), disable the shift of voltage for ATLAS devices (**noshift**), and enable the use of relative convergence criteria for potential especially when large voltage biases are involved (**relpot**).
92–96	Ramp up DC voltage to attain steady-state condition, i.e. VDC = 3300 V. This is split into multiple steps.
98	Initialize the ending of SPICE-like code in Mixed-Mode steady-state simulation.
100–102	Use contact statement to configure n-type polysilicon gate contact and specify heat transfer coefficient (**ext.alpha**) values.
104	Specify the thermal boundary for the MOSFET. Parameters includes boundary dimensions, heat transfer coefficient (**alpha**), and temperature of the thermal boundary (**ext.temp**) which is typically at 300 K.
106	Specify trapped charge density at the oxide–semiconductor interface.
108	Specify material parameters for 4H-SiC. Detailed description of these parameters is available in the Silvaco© ATLAS manual. The values for these parameters can either be obtained via material research or from literature.
110	Specify the various models to be included in the 4H-SiC MOSFET simulation.
112	Specify mobility parameters for 4H-SiC. Detailed description of these parameters is available in the Silvaco© ATLAS manual. The values for these parameters can either be obtained via material research or from literature.

(*Continued*)

Table 9.   (*Continued*)

Line No:	Functionality
114	Specify anisotropic mobility parameters for 4H-SiC. Detailed description of these parameters is available in the Silvaco© ATLAS manual. The values for these parameters can either be obtained via material research or from literature.
116	Specify impact ionization parameters for 4H-SiC. This statement is mandatory to obtain device breakdown characteristics.
118	Specify the solver type and the tolerance values to be used during the simulation. This is an extremely critical statement which can alter the simulation outcome.
120	Initialize ATLAS simulator using GO ATLAS command (same as line 1) for steady-state bias point simulation.
124	Initialize the starting of SPICE-like code in Mixed-Mode transient simulation.
126–131	Resistive switching circuit description in SPICE-like format. Width parameter with a value of 4×10^6 has been used for the MOSFET structure. The magnitude of DC voltage source is initialized at 3300 V, result obtained from the earlier steady-state simulation. Transient parameters have been added to the gate voltage source to generate a square wave.
133	Set the maximum number of mixed circuit-device iterations to be performed during transient analysis (***imaxtr***) to 100
134	Specify Mixed-Mode transient simulation conditions. Modified two-level Newton solution method for transient simulation (***m2ln.tr***), disable the shift of voltage for ATLAS devices (***noshift***), enable the use of relative convergence criteria for potential especially when large voltage biases are involved (***relpot***), and write structure file after every 50 time-step iterations.
135	Load the steady-state simulations results saved in line 89.
136	Save the structure file after every 50 time-step iterations specified in line 134.
137	Save log file after the completion of transient simulation.
138	Save the structure file after the completion of transient simulation.
140	Specify the initial time interval of 0.1 ns and total simulation time of 45.4 μs.
142	Initialize the ending of SPICE-like code in Mixed-Mode transient simulation.
144–160	Same as line 100 to line 116.
162	Specify the transient Block Newton solver type (***BLOCK.TRAN***) and the tolerance values to be used during the simulation.
164	Include current flowlines (***FLOWLINES***) and Electron Mobility (***E.MOBILITY***) in the output structure file.
166	Initialize ATLAS simulator using GO ATLAS command (same as line 1) for transient simulation.
168	Terminate the simulation.

9.5.3.2.4.   Resistive switching simulation results

The resistive switching simulation was performed on a 3300 V SiC D-MOSFET complete-cell structure at an ON-state drain current density 500 A/cm^2. The drain to source voltage (V_{DS}) and current density (J_{DS}) waveforms are shown in Fig. 39 and the power dissipation density (P_{RES}) and lattice temperature waveforms are shown in Fig. 40. During ON-state conduction, maximum drain to source voltage drop of 23 V was observed across the MOSFET at 500 A/cm^2 conduction current density, which corresponded to power dissipation density of 1.5 kW/cm^2. Peak switching power dissipation of 412 kW/cm^2 was observed during turn-ON and turn-OFF instant.

When the switching frequency used in power electronic circuits is high, the OFF-state time interval is not sufficient enough for the heat generated within the device to dissipate to ambient/heat sink which results in gradual build up of lattice temperature over the course of time. This effect can be observed in the lattice temperature waveform in Fig. 40. Maximum lattice temperature of 324 K was observed at the end of four switching cycles. The lattice temperature profiles of the D-MOSFET structure during initial

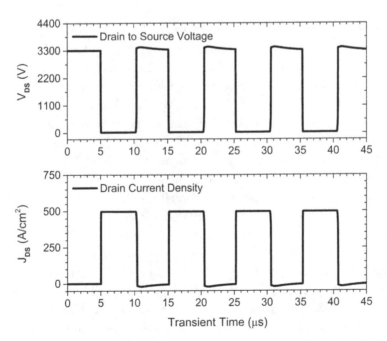

Fig. 39.   Drain to source voltage (above) and drain current density (below) waveforms during resistive switching simulation.

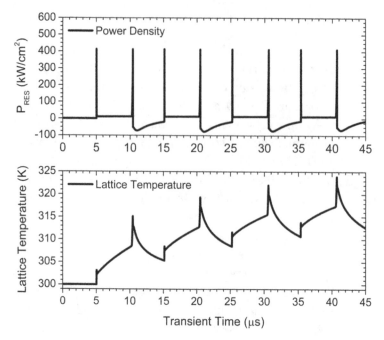

Fig. 40. Power dissipation density (above) and lattice temperature (below) waveforms during resistive switching simulation.

turn-ON of the device (at approximately $t = 5$ μs) are shown in Figs. 41(a) and 41(b), respectively. It can be seen from Fig. 41(b), turn-ON of the MOSFET is accompanied by the formation of thermal hot-spot in the JFET region which had a peak temperature 303 K.

The formation of thermal hot-spot in the JFET region during MOSFET turn-ON can be attributed to the initial current constriction due to the depletion layers formed at the P-base/N− drift regions interface. This can be validated through the electron concentration profiles shown in Figs. 42(a) and 42(b) which were recorded during initial MOSFET turn-ON. A direct comparison of Figs. 42(a) and 42(b) correlates the formation of hot-spot to the area associated with maximum current constriction.

Since the resistive switching simulation was run only for four switching cycles, the lattice heating profile was extracted for the peak lattice temperature attained during the simulation. The lattice temperature profiles corresponding to the final device turn-OFF (at approximately $t = 40$ μs) are shown in Figs. 43(a) and 43(b). It may be noted that the maximum value for lattice temperature in Fig. 40 is 324 K; however, the contour plots in Figs. 43(a) and 43(b) only show 322 K. This is due to the value selected for the number of iterations after which a structure file gets saved during

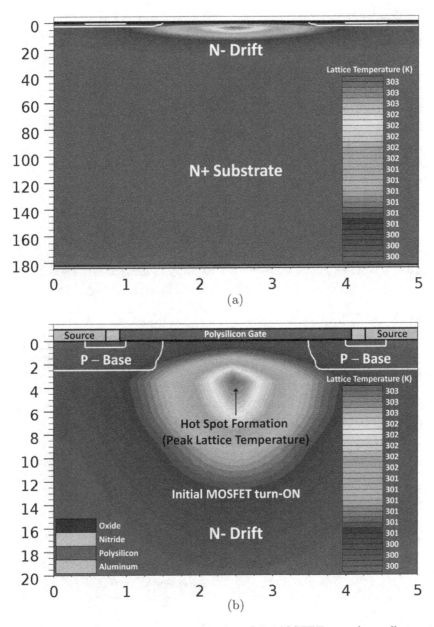

Fig. 41. (a) Lattice temperature contour plot of D-MOSFET complete-cell structure recorded at initial turn-ON time instant during resistive switching simulation. (b) Lattice temperature contour plot of D-MOSFET complete-cell structure recorded at initial turn-ON time instant during resistive switching simulation (zoomed-in view).

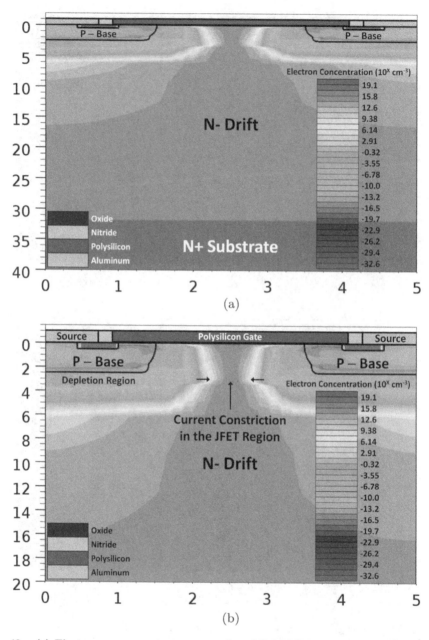

Fig. 42. (a) Electron concentration contour plot of D-MOSFET complete-cell structure recorded at initial turn-ON time during resistive switching simulation. (b) Electron concentration contour plot of D-MOSFET complete-cell structure recorded at initial turn-ON time during resistive switching simulation (zoomed-in view).

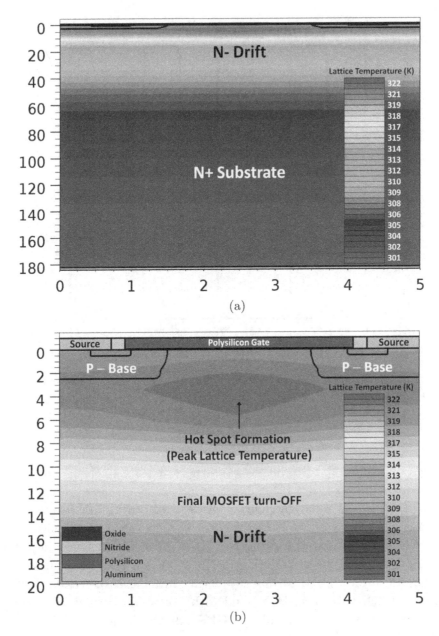

Fig. 43. (a) Lattice temperature contour plot of D-MOSFET complete-cell structure recorded at final turn-OFF time instant during resistive switching simulation. (b) Lattice temperature contour plot of D-MOSFET complete-cell structure recorded at final turn-OFF time instant during resistive switching simulation (zoomed-in view).

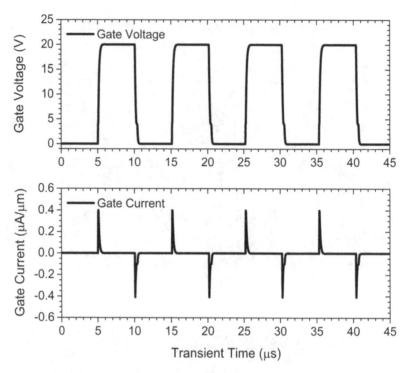

Fig. 44. Gate to source voltage (above) and gate current (below) waveforms during resistive switching simulation.

simulation which can result in the file being saved before or after maximum temperature point.

The gate voltage and gate current waveforms during resistive switching are shown in Fig. 44. The gate current is specified in $\mu A/\mu m$ since it was not feasible to calculate gate current density. Peak gate current magnitude of 0.4 $\mu A/\mu m$ was observed during the turn-ON and turn-OFF phase.

The gate voltage and current waveforms during turn-ON and turn-OFF instant are shown in Figs. 45(a) and 45(b), respectively. The gate current waveforms during turn-ON and turn-OFF indicate charging and discharging of the MOS capacitance. It has been observed during MOSFET transient simulation that the usage of high scaling factor (**width** parameter value) enables the viewing of detailed gate voltage waveform highlighting the gate plateau voltage and other turn-ON/turn-OFF phases. This is the reason why a low series resistance (**RSERIES**) was used during resistive switching which would cause the ON-state current to be unrealistically high, thereby making it mandatory to use a high value for the scaling factor/**width** parameter.

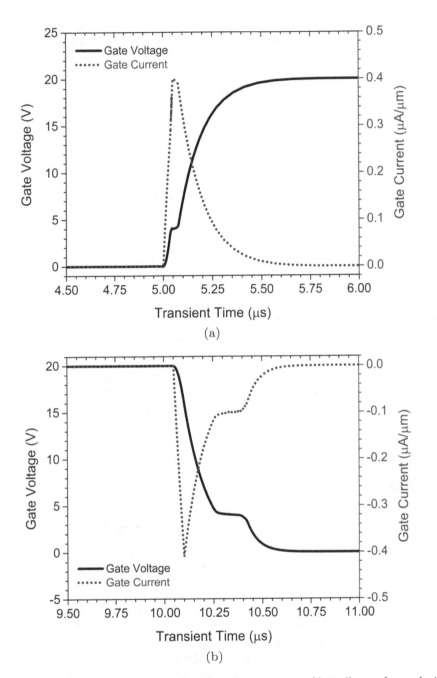

Fig. 45. (a) Gate to source voltage (solid) and gate current (dotted) waveforms during resistive switching MOSFET turn-ON. (b) Gate to source voltage (solid) and gate current (dotted) waveforms during resistive switching MOSFET turn-OFF.

There is a reversal of drain current at the end of **MOSFET** turn-OFF during resistive switching which responsible for negative power dissipation in the MOSFET. Due to the absence of any inductance in the circuit, the cause of current reversal is unknown and is currently under investigation.

9.5.3.2.5.   Clamped inductive switching simulation

The Clamped Inductive Switching (CIS) or double pulse circuit is a standard test circuit used to evaluate the turn-ON and turn-OFF switching energy loss in a MOSFET. CIS simulation was carried out in Silvaco© ATLAS using the circuit shown in Fig. 46. The circuit consists of DC voltage source (**VDC**) which sets the drain to source voltage to 2500 V (75% of rated blocking voltage 3300 V). The 10 mH inductor **L1** is in parallel with diode (**DDUM**) and the whole combination is in series with the MOSFET (**AMOSFET**). In order to reduce simulation time, built-in ideal diode model has been used in this simulation. A gate to ground resistor (**RGND**) of 10^{20} Ω was used to provide high impedance ground path and a series gate resistor (**RGATE**) of 10 Ω was used in series with the gate and gate voltage source (**VGATE**). A scaling factor of 1×10^6 was used in the **width** parameter to reduce the current density through the device. The value of scaling factor was obtained after multiple trial simulations since it is difficult to calculate the inductor current based on the ON-state resistance of a 2D MOSFET structure. Gate

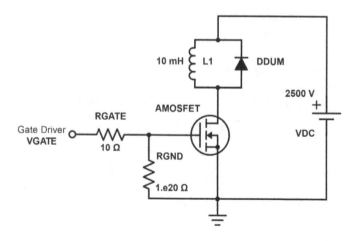

Fig. 46.   MOSFET CIS circuit.

to source voltage of 0/20 V was used to drive the MOSFET at 50 kHz switching frequency and 50% duty cycle.[11] To limit the simulation time, only four switching cycles were simulated.

The working of CIS circuit is based on the ability of a high value inductor to act as a constant current source. When the MOSFET transitions into ON-state, the series inductor stores energy as current through the MOSFET ramps up linearly to a magnitude determined by the duty cycle of the gate voltage and R_{DSON} of the MOSFET (assuming an ideal inductor). When the MOSFET turns OFF, inductor current re-routes through the forward-biased freewheeling diode due to inductive kickback. Due to the high inductance, inductor current almost remains constant during conduction through the diode. During subsequent turn-ON of the MOSFET, the drain current again starts ramping up, but this time, instead of starting from zero, current ramps up from the instantaneous inductor current value. The inductor current builds-up each time the MOSFET is in ON-state, which causes the MOSFET to turn ON and OFF at higher drain current magnitude as time progresses. Since the MOSFET turn-ON and turn-OFF event occur at same current magnitude, CIS circuit can be used to calculate turn-ON and turn-OFF switching energy loss for a range of drain current magnitudes. In order for the CIS circuit to work, inductor value must be large enough ($\approx$ mH) to act as a constant current source. Since the switching frequency is relatively high, the inductor will barely discharge during the MOSFET OFF-state. The following code was used to simulate the 3300 V SiC MOSFET complete-cell structure in a CIS circuit. The ON-state drain current density was controlled by the MOSFET ON-time, i.e. duty cycle. A brief explanation of the simulation program is provided in the code walkthrough (Table 10).

```
Sample code: Vertical D-MOSFET complete-cell structure clamped inductive switching simulation

1.   GO ATLAS SIMFLAGS ="-V 5.18.3.R -P 32 -160"
2.
3.   ##### 3300V D-MOSFET COMPLETE CIS CIRCUIT #####
4.
5.   MESH
6.
7.   ## X-MESH
8.
9.   X.MESH  loc=0.00    spac=0.08
10.  X.MESH  loc=1.00    spac=0.04
11.  X.MESH  loc=1.30    spac=0.025
12.  X.MESH  loc=1.50    spac=0.025
13.  X.MESH  loc=1.70    spac=0.15
14.  X.MESH  loc=3.20    spac=0.15
15.  X.MESH  loc=3.50    spac=0.025
16.  X.MESH  loc=3.70    spac=0.025
```

```
17. X.MESH   loc=4.00      spac=0.04
18. X.MESH   loc=5.00      spac=0.08
19.
20. ## Y-MESH
21.
22. Y.MESH   loc=-1.00     spac=0.94
23. Y.MESH   loc=-0.06     spac=0.94
24. Y.MESH   loc=-0.05     spac=0.025
25. Y.MESH   loc=0.00      spac=0.025
26. Y.MESH   loc=0.02      spac=0.098
27. Y.MESH   loc=1.00      spac=0.098
28. Y.MESH   loc=1.20      spac=0.1
29. Y.MESH   loc=1.80      spac=0.1
30. Y.MESH   loc=2.20      spac=0.1
31. Y.MESH   loc=3.50      spac=2.50
32. Y.MESH   loc=30.0      spac=5.0
33. Y.MESH   loc=31.5      spac=0.25
34. Y.MESH   loc=32.5      spac=0.25
35. Y.MESH   loc=33.0      spac=20
36. Y.MESH   loc=180.0     spac=20
37. Y.MESH   loc=182.0     spac=1.0
38. Y.MESH   loc=184.0     spac=1.0
39.
40. ##### DEFINING REGIONS
41.
42. REGION   num=1   y.max=0   material=Si3N4
43. REGION   num=2   x.min=0.91   x.max=4.09   y.min=-0.05   y.max=0 material=oxide
44. REGION   num=3   y.min=0   material=4H-SiC
45.
46. ##### DEFINING ELECTRODES
47.
48. ELECTRODE   name=source   x.min=0.0   x.max=0.75   y.max=0   material=aluminum
49. ELECTRODE   name=source   x.min=4.25   x.max=5.00   y.max=0   material=aluminum
50. ELECTRODE   name=gate   x.min=0.90   x.max=4.10   y.max=-0.05   material=polysilicon
51. ELECTRODE   name=drain   y.min=182   y.max=184   material=aluminum
52.
53. ##### DOPING DISTRIBUTION
54.
55. ## BULK DOPING
56. DOPING   uniform   n.type   conc=3.3e15   REGION=3
57.
58. ## N+ SOURCE DOPING
59. DOPING   uniform   n.type conc=1.e20   x.min=0.44   x.max=0.99   y.min=0 y.max=0.5
60. DOPING   uniform   n.type conc=1.e20   x.min=4.01   x.max=4.56   y.min=0 y.max=0.5
61.
62. ## P-BASE DOPING
63. DOPING   gauss   p.type conc=4.5e17   x.min=0.0   x.max=1.3 junc=2.0   rat=0.1
64. DOPING   gauss   p.type conc=4.5e17   x.min=3.7   x.max=5.0 junc=2.0   rat=0.1
65. DOPING   gauss   p.type conc=1.0e18   x.min=0.0   x.max=1.3 junc=2.5   rat=0.2
    start=2.0
66. DOPING   gauss   p.type conc=1.0e18   x.min=3.7   x.max=5.0 junc=2.5   rat=0.2
    start=2.0
67.
68. ## N+ SUBSTRATE DOPING
69. DOPING   uniform   n.type   conc=1.e20   y.min=32   y.max=182
70.
71. SAVE   outf=CIS_DMOS_Structure.str   master.out
72.
73. ##### STEADY STATE SIMULATION CIRCUIT #####
74.
```

```
75. GO ATLAS SIMFLAGS="-V 5.18.3.R -P 32 -160"
76.
77. .BEGIN
78.
79. VDC        1    0    0
80. L1         1    2    10m
81. DDUM       2    1    IDEAL
82. AMOSFET  2=drain  3=gate   0=source  infile=CIS_DMOS_Structure.str   width=1.e6
83. RGND       3    0    1e20
84. RGATE      3    4    10
85. VGATE      4    0    0
86.
87. .MODEL  IDEAL D()
88.
89. .NODESET  v(1)=0  v(2)=0  v(3)=0  v(4)=0
90. .NUMERIC  imaxdc=100
91. .LOG       outfile=CIS_DMOS_DC_log
92. .SAVE      outfile=CIS_DMOS_DC_Bias
93. .OPTIONS  m2ln  noshift  print  relpot
94.
95. .DC   VDC   0.      10.      0.5
96. .DC   VDC   10.     50.      5.
97. .DC   VDC   50.     100.     10.
98. .DC   VDC   100.    2500.    50.
99.
100. .END
101.
102. CONTACT  DEVICE=AMOSFET  NAME=GATE   n.polysilicon  EXT.ALPHA=10
103. CONTACT  DEVICE=AMOSFET  NAME=SOURCE             EXT.ALPHA=10
104. CONTACT  DEVICE=AMOSFET  NAME=DRAIN              EXT.ALPHA=10
105.
106. THERMCONTACT  DEVICE=AMOSFET  num=4  x.min=0  x.max=5  y.min=0.0  y.max=184
     alpha=10  ext.temp=300
107.
108. INTERFACE  DEVICE=AMOSFET REGION=2  charge=2.5e12  s.n=1.e4  s.p=1.e4  s.i
109.
110. MATERIAL  DEVICE=AMOSFET  material=4H-SiC REGION=3  permittivity=9.76
     eg300=3.26   affinity=3.7  egalpha=3.3e-2  egbeta=1.e+5  nc300=1.7e+19
     nv300=2.5e+19  arichn=146  arichp=30  augn=3.e-29  augp=3.e-29  taun0=3.33e-6
     taup0=6.7e-7  nsrhn=3.e+17  nsrhp=3.e+17  edb=0.050  eab=0.200  tcon.polyn
     tc.a=0.137534   tc.b=4.9662e-4   tc.c=0.000000354  hc.a=2.35  hc.b=1.75e-3
     hc.c=1.e-9  hc.d=-6.6e4
111.
112. MODELS DEVICE=AMOSFET  REGION=3 MATERIAL=4H-SiC FERMIDIRAC ANALYTIC CONWELL
     FLDMOB SRH BGN AUGER INCOMPLETE  LAT.TEMP  JOULE.HEAT  GR.HEAT  PRINT
113.
114. MOBILITY  DEVICE=AMOSFET material=4H-SiC REGION=3  vsatn=2.2e7  vsatp=2.2e7
     betan=1.2 betap=2  mu1n.caug=40  mu2n.caug=1136  ncritn.caug=2e17
     alphan.caug=-3  betan.caug=-3  gamman.caug=0.0  deltan.caug=0.76   mu1p.caug=20
     mu2p.caug=125  ncritp.caug=1.e19  alphap.caug=-3  betap.caug=-3
     gammap.caug=0.0  deltap.caug=0.5
115.
116. MOBILITY  DEVICE=AMOSFET  material=4H-SiC  REGION=3  n.angle=90  p.angle=90
     vsatn=2.2e7  vsatp=2.2e7  betan=1.2 betap=2  mu1n.caug=5  mu2n.caug=947
     ncritn.caug=2e17  alphan.caug=-3  betan.caug=-3  gamman.caug=0.0
     deltan.caug=0.76  mu1p.caug=2.5  mu2p.caug=20  ncritp.caug=1.e19
     alphap.caug=-3  betap.caug=-3  gammap.caug=0.0  deltap.caug=0.5
117.
```

```
118. IMPACT  DEVICE=AMOSFET  REGION=3  ANISO  E.SIDE  SELB  SIC4H0001  an1=3.44e6
     an2=3.44e6  bn1=2.58e7  bn2=2.58e7  ap1=3.5e6  ap2=3.5e6  bp1=1.7e7  bp2=1.7e7
     opphe=0.106
119.
120. METHOD  BLOCK climit=1.e-9  maxtraps=40  itlimit=50    max.temp=1000  dvmax=1.e8
     ix.tol=1.e-35  ir.tol=1.e-35  px.tol=1.e-35  pr.tol=1.e-30  cx.tol=1.e-45
     cr.tol=1.e-30
121.
122. GO ATLAS SIMFLAGS="-V 5.18.3.R -P 32 -160"
123.
124. ##### TRANSIENT SIMULATION CIRCUIT #####
125.
126. .BEGIN
127.
128. VDC      1     0     2500
129. L1       1     2     10m
130. DDUM     2     1     IDEAL
131. AMOSFET  2=drain  3=gate  0=source  infile=CIS_DMOS_Structure.str    width=1.e6
132. RGND     3     0     1e20
133. RGATE    3     4     10
134. VGATE    4     0     0        PULSE  0   20   5us   50ns   50ns   10us   20us
135.
136. .MODEL  IDEAL D()
137.
138. .NUMERIC  imaxtr=150  dtmax=1.e-7
139. .OPTIONS  m2ln.tr  noshift  print  relpot  write=50
140. .LOAD     infile=CIS_DMOS_DC_Bias
141. .SAVE     master=CIS_DMOS_Transient
142. .LOG      outfile=CIS_DMOS.log
143. .SAVE     outfile=CIS_DMOS.str
144.
145. .TRAN  10ns  105us
146.
147. .END
148.
149. CONTACT  DEVICE=AMOSFET  NAME=GATE    n.polysilicon  EXT.ALPHA=10
150. CONTACT  DEVICE=AMOSFET  NAME=SOURCE               EXT.ALPHA=10
151. CONTACT  DEVICE=AMOSFET  NAME=DRAIN                EXT.ALPHA=10
152.
153. THERMCONTACT  DEVICE=AMOSFET  num=4  x.min=0  x.max=5  y.min=0.0  y.max=184
     alpha=10  ext.temp=300
154.
155. INTERFACE  REGION=2 charge=2.5e12  s.n=1.e4  s.p=1.e4  s.i
156.
157. MATERIAL  material=4H-SiC REGION=3  permittivity=9.76    eg300=3.26
     affinity=3.7  egalpha=3.3e-2  egbeta=1.e+5  nc300=1.7e+19  nv300=2.5e+19
     arichn=146  arichp=30  augn=3.e-29  augp=3.e-29  taun0=3.33e-6  taup0=6.7e-7
     nsrhn=3.e+17  nsrhp=3.e+17  edb=0.050  eab=0.200  tcon.polyn  tc.a=0.137534
     tc.b=4.9662e-4   tc.c=0.000000354  hc.a=2.35  hc.b=1.75e-3  hc.c=1.e-9
     hc.d=-6.6e4
158.
159. MODELS  DEVICE=AMOSFET  REGION=3 MATERIAL=4H-SIC FERMIDIRAC ANALYTIC CONWELL
     FLDMOB SRH BGN AUGER INCOMPLETE LAT.TEMP JOULE.HEAT  GR.HEAT PRINT
160.
161. MOBILITY  material=4H-SIC  REGION=3  vsatn=2.2e7  vsatp=2.2e7  betan=1.2
     betap=2  mu1n.caug=40  mu2n.caug=1136  ncritn.caug=2e17  alphan.caug=-3
     betan.caug=-3  gamman.caug=0.0  deltan.caug=0.76  mu1p.caug=20  mu2p.caug=125
     ncritp.caug=1.e19  alphap.caug=-3  betap.caug=-3  gammap.caug=0.0
     deltap.caug=0.5
```

```
162.
163. MOBILITY  material=4H-SIC  REGION=3  n.angle=90 p.angle=90 vsatn=2.2e7
     vsatp=2.2e7  betan=1.2 betap=2  mu1n.caug=5  mu2n.caug=947  ncritn.caug=2e17
     alphan.caug=-3  betan.caug=-3  gamman.caug=0.0  deltan.caug=0.76
     mu1p.caug=2.5  mu2p.caug=20  ncritp.caug=1.e19  alphap.caug=-3  betap.caug=-3
     gammap.caug=0.0  deltap.caug=0.5
164.
165. IMPACT  DEVICE=AMOSFET  REGION=3  ANISO  E.SIDE  SELB  SIC4H0001  an1=3.44e6
     an2=3.44e6  bn1=2.58e7  bn2=2.58e7  ap1=3.5e6  ap2=3.5e6  bp1=1.7e7  bp2=1.7e7
     opphe=0.106
166.
167. METHOD  BLOCK.TRAN  climit=1.e-9  maxtraps=100  itlimit=150   dvmax=1.e8
     ix.tol=1.e-35  ir.tol=1.e-35  px.tol=1.e-35  pr.tol=1.e-30  cx.tol=1.e-45
     cr.tol=1.e-30
168.
169. OUTPUT  FLOWLINES
170.
171. GO ATLAS SIMFLAGS="-V 5.18.3.R -P 32 -160"
172.
173. QUIT
```

Table 10. Code walkthrough: Vertical D-MOSFET complete-cell structure CIS simulation.

Line No:	Functionality
1	Configure ATLAS simulator to use 160-bit extended precision and utilize 32 cores of the CPU if hardware resources are available. The version of ATLAS to be used by the simulator is set to 5.18.3.R using the $-V$ option in the simflags command.
5	Initialize device structure mesh information with width parameter.
7–38	X-axis and Y-axis mesh distribution.
42–44	Declare nitride, oxide, and 4H-SiC as the material for the areas specified by the x and y coordinates.
48–51	Electrode specifications for the MOSFET (Aluminum source and drain electrode and polysilicon gate electrode).
55–69	Specify doping profile, type, and concentration for different areas of the MOSFET complete-cell structure.
71	Save the device structure (**.str**) file on the local hard drive. The device structure can be viewed by opening the file via **TonyPlot** to troubleshoot/optimize the structure.
75	Initialize ATLAS simulator using GO ATLAS command (same as line 1).
77	Initialize the starting of SPICE-like code in Mixed-Mode steady-state simulation.
79–85	CIS circuit description in SPICE-like format. Width parameter with a value of 1×10^6 has been used for the MOSFET structure.
87	Invoke ideal diode model.
89	Declare the initial node voltage for the CIS circuit nodes

(*Continued*)

Table 10.   (*Continued*)

Line No:	Functionality
90	Set the maximum number of mixed circuit-device iterations to be performed during steady-state analysis (**imaxdc**) to 100.
91	Save log file after steady-state simulation completion.
92	Save file with bias information which will be used for transient simulation.
93	Specify Mixed-Mode steady-state simulation conditions. Modified two-level Newton solution method (**m2ln**), disable the shift of voltage for ATLAS devices (**noshift**), and enable the use of relative convergence criteria for potential especially when large voltage biases are involved (**relpot**).
95–98	Ramp up DC voltage to attain steady-state condition, i.e. VDC = 2500 V. This is split into multiple steps.
100	Initialize the ending of SPICE-like code in Mixed-Mode steady- state simulation.
102–104	Use contact statement to configure n-type polysilicon gate contact and specify heat transfer coefficient (**ext.alpha**) values.
106	Specify the thermal boundary for the MOSFET. Parameters includes boundary dimensions, heat transfer coefficient (**alpha**), and temperature of the thermal boundary (**ext.temp**) which is typically at 300 K.
108	Specify trapped charge density at the oxide–semiconductor interface.
110	Specify material parameters for 4H-SiC. Detailed description of these parameters is available in the Silvaco© ATLAS manual. The values for these parameters can either be obtained via material research or from literature.
112	Specify the various models to be included in the 4H-SiC MOSFET simulation.
114	Specify mobility parameters for 4H-SiC. Detailed description of these parameters is available in the Silvaco© ATLAS manual. The values for these parameters can either be obtained via material research or from literature.
116	Specify anisotropic mobility parameters for 4H-SiC. Detailed description of these parameters is available in the Silvaco© ATLAS manual. The values for these parameters can either be obtained via material research or from literature.
118	Specify Impact Ionization parameters for 4H-SiC. This statement is mandatory to obtain device breakdown characteristics.
120	Specify the BLOCK Newton solver type and the tolerance values to be used during the simulation. This is an extremely critical statement which can alter the simulation outcome.
122	Initialize ATLAS simulator using GO ATLAS command (same as line 1) for steady-state bias point simulation.

(*Continued*)

Table 10. (*Continued*)

Line No:	Functionality
126	Initialize the starting of SPICE-like code in Mixed-Mode transient simulation.
128–134	CIS circuit description in SPICE-like format. Width parameter with a value of 1×10^6 has been used for the MOSFET structure. The magnitude of DC voltage source is initialized at 2500 V, result obtained from the earlier steady-state simulation. Transient parameters have been added to the Gate voltage source to generate a square wave.
136	Invoke ideal diode model.
138	Set the maximum number of mixed circuit-device iterations to be performed during transient analysis (*imaxtr*) to 150 and maximum time-step to 100 ns.
139	Specify Mixed-Mode transient simulation conditions. Modified two-level Newton solution method for transient simulation (*m2ln.tr*), disable the shift of voltage for ATLAS devices (*noshift*), enable the use of relative convergence criteria for potential especially when large voltage biases are involved (*relpot*), and write structure file after every 50 time-step iterations.
140	Load the steady-state simulations results saved in line 92.
141	Save the structure file after every 50 time-step iterations specified in line 139.
142	Save log file after the completion of transient simulation.
143	Save the structure file after the completion of transient simulation.
145	Specify the initial time interval of 10 ns and total simulation time of 105 μs.
147	Initialize the ending of SPICE-like code in Mixed-Mode transient simulation.
149–165	Same as line 102 to line 118.
167	Specify the transient Block Newton solver type (*BLOCK.TRAN*) and the tolerance values to be used during the simulation.
169	Include current flowlines (*FLOWLINES*) in the output structure file.
171	Initialize ATLAS simulator using GO ATLAS command (same as line 1) for transient simulation.
173	Terminate the simulation.

9.5.3.2.6. Clamped inductive switching simulation results

The CIS circuit simulation was performed on a 3300 V SiC D-MOSFET complete-cell structure at a lattice temperature of 27°C. The simulation took approximately 5 days to complete on the computational platform discussed in Chapter 3. The drain to source voltage (V_{DS}) and drain current density

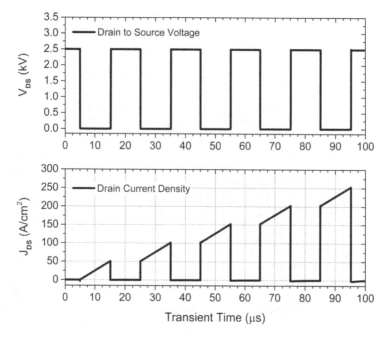

Fig. 47.   Drain to source voltage (above) and drain current density (below) waveforms during CIS simulation.

(J_{DS}) waveforms are shown in Fig. 47, and power dissipation density (P_{CIS}) and lattice temperature waveforms are shown in Fig. 48. The ramping up of drain current density waveform due to the inductor acting as a constant current source can be clearly seen in Fig. 47. The selection of ON-time of the gate voltage pulse is critical in determining the peak MOSFET ON-state current density. In this case, MOSFET turn-ON/OFF current densities of 50, 100, 150, and 200 A/cm^2 were obtained using a 10 mH inductor and gate voltage ON-time of 10 μs. Since the turn-ON/OFF current density is increasing with each pulse, there is a progressive increase in the switching power dissipation density (P_{CIS}) throughout the simulation.

At 100 A/cm^2 drain current density, peak power dissipation density of 252 kW/cm^2 was recorded at turn-ON and turn-OFF. As observed in the case of resistive switching, there is a build-up of lattice temperature over the course of the CIS simulation. Even though peak lattice temperature of 303.5 K was observed at the end of four switching cycles, a rapid rise in lattice temperature is expected due to the linear increase in current density with each switching cycle. The drain to source voltage (V_{DS}) and inductor current density (J_L) waveforms are shown in Fig. 49, and inductor current density and MOSFET drain current density (J_{DS}) waveforms are shown in Fig. 50.

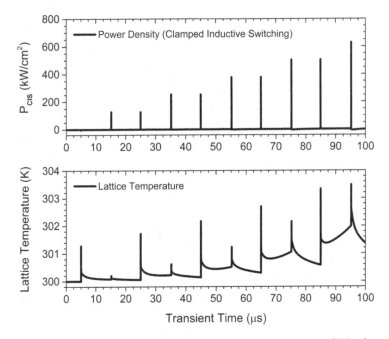

Fig. 48. Power dissipation density (above) and lattice temperature (below) waveforms during CIS simulation.

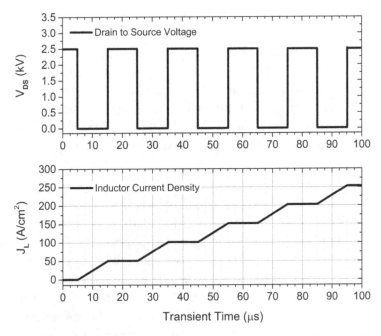

Fig. 49. Drain to source voltage (above) and inductor current density (below) waveforms during CIS simulation.

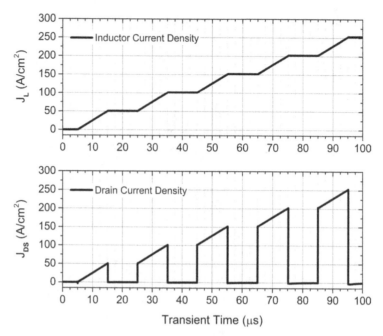

Fig. 50.   Inductor current density (above) and MOSFET drain current density (below) waveforms during CIS simulation.

Since the inductor and MOSFET are in series, the unit current density has been used for the inductor current even though it may not be technically applicable. The waveforms shown in Fig. 50 highlight the role of inductor in a CIS circuit. During MOSFET ON-state, drain to source current follows the inductor current to a peak value. The drain to source current becomes zero during OFF-state; however, inductor current stays constant as it conducts through the freewheeling diode. In the subsequent MOSFET ON-state, drain to source current increases linearly starting from the inductor's previous steady-state value.

 The use of built-in ideal diode model simplifies the simulation as there is no limit on the forward current and reverse-blocking voltage ratings. Moreover, it does not add mesh points to the existing device structure which could have severe implications on the simulation time. However, the built-in diode model does not account for reverse recovery and final log file generated does not include the electrical parameters associated with the diode.

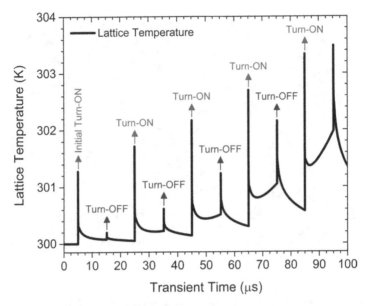

Fig. 51. Lattice temperature waveform during CIS simulation indicating the temperature change associated with relevant turn-ON/OFF events.

The lattice temperature waveform generated during CIS circuit simulation indicating MOSFET turn-ON/OFF events is shown in Fig. 51. Switching loss encountered during CIS circuit simulation is the dominant contributor to the overall lattice temperature rise in the device structure. However, the effect of conduction loss becomes significant especially once the current density exceeds 100 A/cm^2.

The lattice temperature contour plot of the MOSFET shown in Figs. 52(a) and 52(b) was extracted at the time instant corresponding to the initial turn-ON of the device. The initial turn-ON of the MOSFET is accompanied by the formation of thermal hot-spot in the JFET region which is due to current constriction by the depletion layers formed at the P-base/N− drift region interface.

The lattice temperature profile was also extracted at the time instant during final MOSFET turn-OFF when the temperature was at its maximum value. The contour plots shown in Figs. 53(a) and 53(b) highlight temperature distribution in the device structure. As compared to initial turn-ON in Fig. 52(b), ambient temperature is higher at the final turn-OFF instant along with thermal hot-spot in the JFET region as shown in Fig. 53(b).

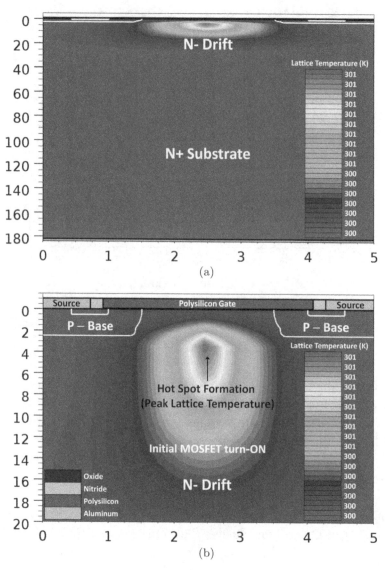

Fig. 52. (a) Lattice temperature contour plot of D-MOSFET complete-cell structure recorded at initial turn-ON time instant during CIS simulation. (b) Lattice temperature contour plot of D-MOSFET complete-cell structure recorded at initial turn-ON time instant during CIS simulation (zoomed-in view).

The power dissipation density waveform was integrated to obtain MOS-FET switching energy loss. The turn-ON, turn-OFF, and total switching energy loss (mJ/cm^2) as a function of drain current density is shown in Fig. 54. At lower current density, there was significant difference between

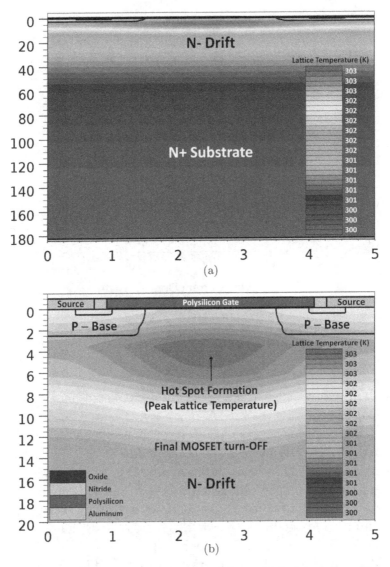

Fig. 53. (a) Lattice temperature contour plot of D-MOSFET complete-cell structure recorded at final turn-OFF time instant during CIS simulation. (b) Lattice temperature contour plot of D-MOSFET complete-cell structure recorded at final turn-OFF time instant during CIS simulation (zoomed-in view).

turn-ON and turn-OFF energy loss; however, as the drain current density became higher, the difference between turn-ON and turn-OFF energy loss became smaller. At 100 A/cm^2, total switching energy loss of 2.67 mJ/cm^2 was observed during simulation.

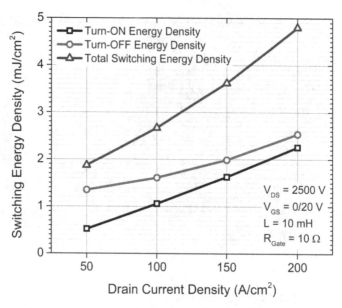

Fig. 54. Switching energy density as a function of drain current density for D-MOSFET complete-cell structure.

9.5.3.2.7. RLC ring-down circuit simulation

The D-MOSFET complete-cell structure was simulated under high current density pulsed condition using RLC ring-down circuit. The circuit parameters were designed to generate a 5 μs wide current pulse with a peak current value that would correspond to 1000 A/cm^2 in the MOSFET. RLC ring-down circuit simulation was carried out in Silvaco$^©$ ATLAS using the circuit shown in Fig. 55. The only difference between the RLC ring-down circuits used for MOSFET and diode simulation is that MOSFET simulation does not require resistors acting as a switch since the MOSFET is a controlled switching device as compared to a diode.[12] Before proceeding with Silvaco$^©$ Mixed-Mode simulation, the circuit was first simulated in *LTspice* to finalize the circuit components values and electrical parameters.

 It is highly recommended that the user first simulates the circuit using a SPICE-based program before proceeding with ATLAS Mixed-Mode simulation in scenarios where it is feasible.

The circuit consists of DC voltage source (**VDC**), which sets the drain to source voltage to the 650 V (DC voltage had to be increased to compensate

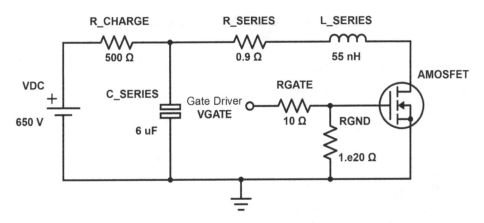

Fig. 55. MOSFET RLC ring-down circuit.

for the higher ON-state loss). The series RLC circuit is formed by the 6 μF capacitor bank (**C_SERIES**), 0.9 Ω resistor (**R_SERIES**), and 55 nH inductor (**L_SERIES**). A 500 Ω resistor (**R_CHARGE**) was used to charge the capacitor (**C_SERIES**) to the DC bus voltage (**VDC**). Since the MOSFET (**AMOSFET**) is in series with the RLC circuit, the same current will be experienced by all the circuit components. A gate to ground resistor (**RGND**) of 10^{20} Ω was used to provide high impedance ground path, and a series gate resistor (**RGATE**) of 10 Ω was used in series with the gate and gate voltage source (**VGATE**). The circuit components used in this simulation would result in a current pulse with peak value of 600 A. To set the peak current density through the MOSFET structure with an active area of 5 μm^2, a scaling factor of 1.2×10^7 was used in the **width** parameter to reduce the drain current to 50 μA which corresponds to 1000 A/cm^2 drain current density. Gate to source voltage of 0/20 V was used to drive the MOSFET. Since this is a high current density pulsed operation, the simulation was executed for a single pulse only.

The working of the RLC ring-down circuit is based on the ability of a series RLC circuit to generate a current pulse whose characteristics can be controlled by the circuit parameters. When the MOSFET is in OFF state, Capacitor **C_SERIES** is charged to the DC voltage (650 V) through the charging resistor **R_CHARGE**. When the MOSFET turns ON, Capacitor **C_SERIES** discharges through RLC network consisting of resistor **R_SERIES** and inductor **L_SERIES** to generate a current pulse. The following code was used to simulate the 3300 V SiC MOSFET complete-cell structure in an RLC ring-down circuit. A brief explanation of the simulation program is provided in the code walkthrough (Table 11).

```
Sample code: SiC D-MOSFET complete-cell structure RLC ringdown circuit simulation

1.  GO ATLAS SIMFLAGS ="-V 5.18.3.R -P 32 -128"
2.
3.  ##### 3300V D-MOSFET COMPLETE CELL RLC CIRCUIT @ 1000 A/CM2 #####
4.
5.  MESH
6.
7.  ## X-MESH
8.
9.  X.MESH  loc=0.00    spac=0.08
10. X.MESH  loc=1.00    spac=0.04
11. X.MESH  loc=1.30    spac=0.025
12. X.MESH  loc=1.50    spac=0.025
13. X.MESH  loc=1.70    spac=0.15
14. X.MESH  loc=3.20    spac=0.15
15. X.MESH  loc=3.50    spac=0.025
16. X.MESH  loc=3.70    spac=0.025
17. X.MESH  loc=4.00    spac=0.04
18. X.MESH  loc=5.00    spac=0.08
19.
20. ## Y-MESH
21.
22. Y.MESH  loc=-1.00   spac=0.94
23. Y.MESH  loc=-0.06   spac=0.94
24. Y.MESH  loc=-0.05   spac=0.025
25. Y.MESH  loc=0.00    spac=0.025
26. Y.MESH  loc=0.02    spac=0.098
27. Y.MESH  loc=1.00    spac=0.098
28. Y.MESH  loc=1.20    spac=0.1
29. Y.MESH  loc=1.80    spac=0.1
30. Y.MESH  loc=2.20    spac=0.1
31. Y.MESH  loc=3.50    spac=2.50
32. Y.MESH  loc=30.0    spac=5.0
33. Y.MESH  loc=31.5    spac=0.25
34. Y.MESH  loc=32.5    spac=0.25
35. Y.MESH  loc=33.0    spac=20
36. Y.MESH  loc=180.0   spac=20
37. Y.MESH  loc=182.0   spac=1.0
38. Y.MESH  loc=184.0   spac=1.0
39.
40. ##### DEFINING REGIONS
41.
42. REGION  num=1   y.max=0   material=Si3N4
43. REGION  num=2   x.min=0.91  x.max=4.09   y.min=-0.05  y.max=0  material=oxide
44. REGION  num=3   y.min=0   material=4H-SiC
45.
46. ##### DEFINING ELECTRODES
47.
48. ELECTRODE  name=source  x.min=0.0   x.max=0.75  y.max=0    material=aluminum
49. ELECTRODE  name=source  x.min=4.25  x.max=5.00  y.max=0    material=aluminum
50. ELECTRODE  name=gate    x.min=0.90  x.max=4.10  y.max=-0.05 material=polysilicon
51. ELECTRODE  name=drain   y.min=182  y.max=184    material=aluminum
52.
53. ##### DOPING DISTRIBUTION
54.
55. ## BULK DOPING
56. DOPING uniform  n.type conc=3.3e15  REGION=3
57.
```

```
58. ## N+ SOURCE DOPING
59. DOPING  uniform  n.type conc=1.e20  x.min=0.44 x.max=0.99  y.min=0  y.max=0.5
60. DOPING  uniform  n.type conc=1.e20  x.min=4.01 x.max=4.56  y.min=0  y.max=0.5
61.
62. ## P-BASE DOPING
63. DOPING  gauss  p.type conc=4.5e17  x.min=0.0  x.max=1.3  junc=2.0   rat=0.1
64. DOPING  gauss  p.type conc=4.5e17  x.min=3.7  x.max=5.0  junc=2.0   rat=0.1
65. DOPING  gauss  p.type conc=1.0e18  x.min=0.0  x.max=1.3  junc=2.5   rat=0.2
    start=2.0
66. DOPING  gauss  p.type conc=1.0e18  x.min=3.7  x.max=5.0  junc=2.5   rat=0.2
    start=2.0
67.
68. ## N+ SUBSTRATE DOPING
69. DOPING  uniform   n.type   conc=1.e20   y.min=32    y.max=182
70.
71. SAVE  outf=CIS_DMOS_Structure.str  master.out
72.
73. ##### STEADY STATE SIMULATION CIRCUIT #####
74.
75. GO ATLAS SIMFLAGS="-V 5.18.3.R -P 32 -160"
76.
77. .BEGIN
78.
79. VDC        1    0    0
80. R_CHARGE   1    2    500
81. C_SERIES   2    0    6u
82. R_SERIES   2    3    0.90
83. L_SERIES   3    4    55n
84. AMOSFET    4=drain 5=gate  0=source infile=MOSFET_Structure.str  width=1.2e7
85. RGND       5    0    1e20
86. RGATE      5    6    10
87. VGATE      6    0    0
88.
89. .NODESET   v(1)=0  v(2)=0  v(3)=0  v(4)=0  v(5)=0  v(6)=0
90. .NUMERIC   imaxdc=100
91. .LOG       outfile=MOSFET_DC_log
92. .SAVE      outfile=MOSFET_RLC_Bias
93. .OPTIONS   m2ln  noshift  print  relpot
94.
95. .DC   VDC   0.     10.     0.25
96. .DC   VDC   10.    100.    10.
97. .DC   VDC   100.   650.    25.
98.
99. .END
100.
101. CONTACT  DEVICE=AMOSFET  NAME=GATE   n.polysilicon EXT.ALPHA=10
102. CONTACT  DEVICE=AMOSFET  NAME=SOURCE              EXT.ALPHA=10
103. CONTACT  DEVICE=AMOSFET  NAME=DRAIN               EXT.ALPHA=10
104.
105. THERMCONTACT DEVICE=AMOSFET num=4  x.min=0  x.max=5  y.min=0.0  y.max=184
     alpha=10  ext.temp=300
106.
107. INTERFACE DEVICE=AMOSFET  REGION=2 charge=2.5e12  s.n=1.e4  s.p=1.e4  s.i
108.
109. MATERIAL DEVICE=AMOSFET material=4H-SiC REGION=3 permittivity=9.76
     eg300=3.26  affinity=3.7  egalpha=3.3e-2  egbeta=1.e+5  nc300=1.7e+19
     nv300=2.5e+19 arichn=146 arichp=30 augn=3.e-29 augp=3.e-29 taun0=3.33e-6
     taup0=6.7e-7 nsrhn=3.e+17 nsrhp=3.e+17 edb=0.050 eab=0.200 tcon.polyn
     tc.a=0.137534  tc.b=4.9662e-4  tc.c=0.000000354  hc.a=2.35  hc.b=1.75e-3
     hc.c=1.e-9  hc.d=-6.6e4
```

```
110.
111. MODELS  DEVICE=AMOSFET  REGION=3  MATERIAL=4H-SiC FERMIDIRAC ANALYTIC CONWELL
     FLDMOB SRH BGN AUGER INCOMPLETE  LAT.TEMP  JOULE.HEAT  GR.HEAT  PRINT
112.
113. MOBILITY  DEVICE=AMOSFET material=4H-SiC REGION=3  vsatn=2.2e7  vsatp=2.2e7
     betan=1.2 betap=2  mu1n.caug=40  mu2n.caug=1136  ncritn.caug=2e17
     alphan.caug=-3 betan.caug=-3  gamman.caug=0.0 deltan.caug=0.76  mu1p.caug=20
     mu2p.caug=125 ncritp.caug=1.e19 alphap.caug=-3  betap.caug=-3
     gammap.caug=0.0 deltap.caug=0.5
114.
115. MOBILITY  DEVICE=AMOSFET material=4H-SiC  REGION=3  n.angle=90 p.angle=90
     vsatn=2.2e7  vsatp=2.2e7  betan=1.2 betap=2  mu1n.caug=5  mu2n.caug=947
     ncritn.caug=2e17 alphan.caug=-3  betan.caug=-3  gamman.caug=0.0
     deltan.caug=0.76  mu1p.caug=2.5 mu2p.caug=20  ncritp.caug=1.e19
     alphap.caug=-3 betap.caug=-3  gammap.caug=0.0 deltap.caug=0.5
116.
117. IMPACT  DEVICE=AMOSFET  REGION=3  ANISO  E.SIDE  SELB  SIC4H0001  an1=3.44e6
     an2=3.44e6  bn1=2.58e7  bn2=2.58e7  ap1=3.5e6  ap2=3.5e6  bp1=1.7e7  bp2=1.7e7
     opphe=0.106
118.
119. METHOD  BLOCK climit=1.e-9  maxtraps=40  itlimit=50  max.temp=1000 dvmax=1.e8
     ix.tol=1.e-35  ir.tol=1.e-35  px.tol=1.e-35  pr.tol=1.e-30  cx.tol=1.e-45
     cr.tol=1.e-30
120.
121. GO ATLAS SIMFLAGS="-V 5.18.3.R -P 32 -128"
122.
123. ##### TRANSIENT SIMULATION CIRCUIT #####
124.
125. .BEGIN
126.
127. VDC        1    0    650
128. R_CHARGE   1    2    500
129. C_SERIES   2    0    6u
130. R_SERIES   2    3    0.90
131. L_SERIES   3    4    55n
132. AMOSFET    4=drain 5=gate  0=source infile=MOSFET_Structure.str  width=1.2e7
133. RGND       5    0    1e20
134. RGATE      5    6    10
135. VGATE      6    0    0    PULSE  0    20    10us    100ns    100ns    40us    80us
136.
137. .NUMERIC  imaxtr=150
138. .OPTIONS  m2ln.tr  noshift  print  relpot  write=20
139. .LOAD     infile=MOSFET_RLC_Bias
140. .SAVE     master=MOSFET_Transient
141. .LOG      outfile=MOSFET_RLC_Ringdown.log
142. .SAVE     outfile=MOSFET_RLC_Ringdown.str
143.
144. .TRAN  0.01us  10us  dtmax=1.e-7
145. .TRAN  0.01us  11us  dtmax=1.e-8
146. .TRAN  0.01us  45us  dtmax=1.e-7
147.
148. .END
149.
150. CONTACT  DEVICE=AMOSFET  NAME=GATE    n.polysilicon  EXT.ALPHA=10
151. CONTACT  DEVICE=AMOSFET  NAME=SOURCE                 EXT.ALPHA=10
152. CONTACT  DEVICE=AMOSFET  NAME=DRAIN                  EXT.ALPHA=10
153.
154. THERMCONTACT DEVICE=AMOSFET  num=4  x.min=0  x.max=5  y.min=0.0  y.max=184
     alpha=10  ext.temp=300
155.
```

```
156. INTERFACE REGION=2 charge=2.5e12 s.n=1.e4 s.p=1.e4 s.i
157.
158. MATERIAL MATERIAL=4H-SiC REGION=3 permittivity=9.76  eg300=3.26
     affinity=3.7 egalpha=3.3e-2  egbeta=1.e+5 nc300=1.7e+19 nv300=2.5e+19
     arichn=146 arichp=30 augn=3.e-29 augp=3.e-29 taun0=3.33e-6 taup0=6.7e-7
     nsrhn=3.e+17 nsrhp=3.e+17 edb=0.050 eab=0.200 tcon.polyn tc.a=0.137534
     tc.b=4.9662e-4  tc.c=0.000000354 hc.a=2.35 hc.b=1.75e-3 hc.c=1.e-9
     hc.d=-6.6e4
159.
160. MODELS DEVICE=AMOSFET REGION=3 MATERIAL=4H-SIC FERMIDIRAC ANALYTIC CONWELL
     FLDMOB SRH BGN AUGER INCOMPLETE LAT.TEMP JOULE.HEAT  GR.HEAT PRINT
161.
162. MOBILITY material=4H-SIC REGION=3 vsatn=2.2e7 vsatp=2.2e7 betan=1.2
     betap=2 mu1n.caug=40 mu2n.caug=1136 ncritn.caug=2e17 alphan.caug=-3
     betan.caug=-3 gamman.caug=0.0 deltan.caug=0.76  mu1p.caug=20 mu2p.caug=125
     ncritp.caug=1.e19 alphap.caug=-3 betap.caug=-3 gammap.caug=0.0
     deltap.caug=0.5
163.
164. MOBILITY material=4H-SIC REGION=3 n.angle=90 p.angle=90 vsatn=2.2e7
     vsatp=2.2e7 betan=1.2 betap=2 mu1n.caug=5 mu2n.caug=947 ncritn.caug=2e17
     alphan.caug=-3 betan.caug=-3 gamman.caug=0.0 deltan.caug=0.76 mu1p.caug=2.5
     mu2p.caug=20 ncritp.caug=1.e19 alphap.caug=-3 betap.caug=-3 gammap.caug=0.0
     deltap.caug=0.5
165.
166. IMPACT DEVICE=AMOSFET REGION=3 ANISO E.SIDE SELB SIC4H0001 an1=3.44e6
     an2=3.44e6 bn1=2.58e7 bn2=2.58e7 ap1=3.5e6 ap2=3.5e6 bp1=1.7e7 bp2=1.7e7
     opphe=0.106
167.
168. METHOD BLOCK.TRAN climit=1.e-9 maxtraps=100 itlimit=150  dvmax=1.e8
     ix.tol=1.e-35 ir.tol=1.e-35 px.tol=1.e-35 pr.tol=1.e-30 cx.tol=1.e-45
     cr.tol=1.e-30
169.
170. OUTPUT FLOWLINES
171.
172. GO ATLAS SIMFLAGS="-V 5.18.3.R -P 32 -160"
173.
174. QUIT
```

Table 11. Code walkthrough: Vertical D-MOSFET complete-cell structure RLC ring–down simulation.

Line No:	Functionality
1	Configure ATLAS simulator to use 128-bit extended precision and utilize 32 cores of the CPU if hardware resources are available. The version of ATLAS to be used by the simulator is set to 5.18.3.R using the −V option in the simflags command.
5	Initialize device structure mesh information with width parameter.
7–38	X-axis and Y-axis mesh distribution.
42–44	Declare nitride, oxide, and 4H-SiC as the material for the areas specified by the x and y coordinates.
48–51	Electrode specifications for the MOSFET (Aluminum source and drain electrode and polysilicon gate electrode).

(*Continued*)

Table 11. (*Continued*)

Line No:	Functionality
55–69	Specify doping profile, type, and concentration for different areas of the MOSFET complete-cell structure.
71	Save the device structure (**.str**) file on the local hard drive. The device structure can be viewed by opening the file via **TonyPlot** to troubleshoot/optimize the structure.
75	Initialize ATLAS simulator using GO ATLAS command (same as line 1).
77	Initialize the starting of SPICE-like code in Mixed-Mode steady-state simulation.
79–87	RLC ring-down circuit description in SPICE-like format. Width parameter with a value of 1.2×10^7 has been used for the MOSFET structure.
89	Declare the initial node voltage for the RLC ring-down circuit nodes.
90	Set the maximum number of mixed circuit-device iterations to be performed during steady-state analysis (**imaxdc**) to 100.
91	Save log file after steady-state simulation completion.
92	Save file with bias information which will be used for transient simulation.
93	Specify Mixed-Mode steady-state simulation conditions. Modified two-level Newton solution method (**m2ln**), disable the shift of voltage for ATLAS devices (**noshift**), and enable the use of relative convergence criteria for potential especially when large voltage biases are involved (**relpot**).
95–97	Ramp up DC voltage to attain steady-state condition, i.e. VDC = 650 V. This is split into multiple steps.
99	Initialize the ending of SPICE-like code in Mixed-Mode steady-state simulation.
101–103	Use contact statement to configure n-type polysilicon gate contact and specify heat transfer coefficient (**ext.alpha**) values.
105	Specify the thermal boundary for the MOSFET. Parameters includes boundary dimensions, heat transfer coefficient (**alpha**), and temperature of the thermal boundary (**ext.temp**) which is typically at 300 K.
107	Specify trapped charge density at the oxide–semiconductor interface.
109	Specify material parameters for 4H-SiC. Detailed description of these parameters is available in the Silvaco© ATLAS manual. The values for these parameters can either be obtained via material research or from literature.
111	Specify the various models to be included in the 4H-SiC MOSFET simulation.
113	Specify mobility parameters for 4H-SiC. Detailed description of these parameters is available in the Silvaco© ATLAS manual. The values for these parameters can either be obtained via material research or from literature.

(*Continued*)

Table 11. (*Continued*)

Line No:	Functionality
115	Specify anisotropic mobility parameters for 4H-SiC. Detailed description of these parameters is available in the Silvaco© ATLAS manual. The values for these parameters can either be obtained via material research or from literature.
117	Specify impact ionization parameters for 4H-SiC. This statement is mandatory to obtain device breakdown characteristics.
119	Specify the BLOCK Newton solver type and the tolerance values to be used during the simulation. This is an extremely critical statement which can alter the simulation outcome.
121	Initialize ATLAS simulator using GO ATLAS command (same as line 1) for steady-state bias point simulation.
125	Initialize the starting of SPICE-like code in Mixed-Mode transient simulation.
127–135	RLC ring-down circuit description in SPICE-like format. Width parameter with a value of 1.2×10^7 has been used for the MOSFET structure. The magnitude of DC voltage source is initialized at 650 V, result obtained from the earlier steady-state simulation. Transient parameters have been added to the gate voltage source to generate a square wave.
137	Set the maximum number of mixed circuit-device iterations to be performed during transient analysis (***imaxtr***) to 150.
138	Specify Mixed-Mode transient simulation conditions. Modified two-level Newton solution method for transient simulation (***m2ln.tr***), disable the shift of voltage for ATLAS devices (***noshift***), enable the use of relative convergence criteria for potential especially when large voltage biases are involved (***relpot***), and write structure file after every 20 time-step iterations.
139	Load the steady-state simulations results saved in line 92.
140	Save the structure file after every 20 time-step iterations specified in line 138.
141	Save log file after the completion of transient simulation.
142	Save the structure file after the completion of transient simulation.
144–146	Split the simulation time into three steps with maximum time step (***dtmax***) for each step.
148	Initialize the ending of SPICE-like code in Mixed-Mode transient simulation.
150–166	Same as line 101 to line 117.
168	Specify the transient Block Newton solver type (***BLOCK.TRAN***) and the tolerance values to be used during the simulation.
170	Include current flowlines (***FLOWLINES***) in the output structure file.
172	Initialize ATLAS simulator using GO ATLAS command (same as line 1) for transient simulation.
174	Terminate the simulation.

9.5.3.2.8.   RLC ring-down circuit simulation results

The RLC ring-down circuit simulation was performed on a 3300 V SiC D-MOSFET complete-cell structure at a lattice temperature of 27°C. The drain to source voltage (V_{DS}) and drain current density (J_{DS}) waveforms are shown in Fig. 56, and power dissipation density and energy density waveforms are shown in Fig. 57. Peak drain to source voltage drop of 85.7 V was observed across the MOSFET at a peak drain current density of 1000 A/cm^2 which corresponds to a peak power dissipation density of 86 kW/cm^2. Integration of the power density waveform yielded an energy density of 274 mJ/cm^2.

Power dissipation in the MOSFET is determined by the drain to source voltage–current density crossover shown in Fig. 58, which is a zoomed-in version of Fig. 56. This crossover is highly dependent on the device capacitance discussed earlier. Pulsed evaluation of power MOSFETs using RLC ring-down is typically performed on an actual device followed by the comparison of hardware test results to the simulation results to estimate lattice temperature rise. Since the capacitance of a 2D MOSFET model is much smaller than an actual device, the user may have to add external gate to source, gate to drain, or drain to source capacitance to match the voltage–current crossover to the hardware test result waveform.

The variation of lattice temperature with power dissipation density and energy density during simulation is shown in Figs. 59 and 60, respectively.

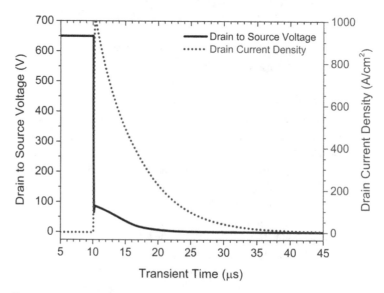

Fig. 56.   Drain to source voltage (solid) and current density (dotted) waveforms pertaining to 1000 A/cm^2 peak drain current density simulation.

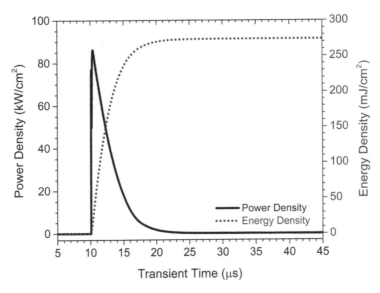

Fig. 57. Power density (solid) and energy density (dotted) waveforms pertaining to 1000 A/cm² peak drain current density simulation.

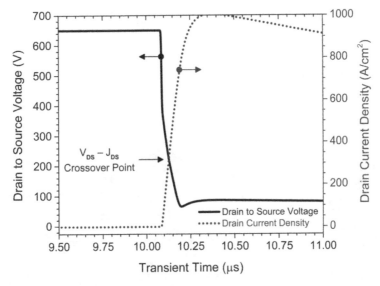

Fig. 58. Drain to source voltage (solid) and current density (dotted) waveforms pertaining to 1000 A/cm² peak drain current density simulation highlighting voltage–current density crossover.

Peak lattice temperature of 335 K was observed in the D-MOSFET structure during the pulsed operation. The lattice temperature profile of the D-MOSFET structure was extracted at peak current density and maximum temperature time instants.

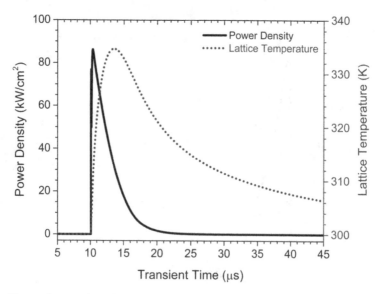

Fig. 59.   Power density (solid) and lattice temperature (dotted) waveforms pertaining to 1000 A/cm² peak drain current density simulation.

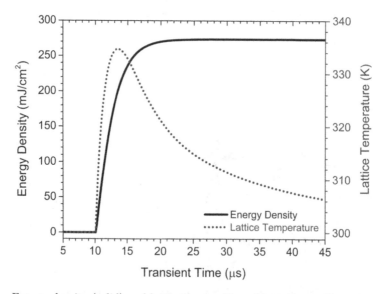

Fig. 60.   Energy density (solid) and lattice temperature (dotted) waveforms pertaining to 1000 A/cm² peak drain current density simulation.

The lattice temperature contour plots of the D-MOSFET structure recorded at the maximum current density time instant are shown in Figs. 61(a) and 61(b). The formation of thermal hot-spot in the JFET region can be seen in Fig. 61(b). Due to the dominant effect of ON-state resistance

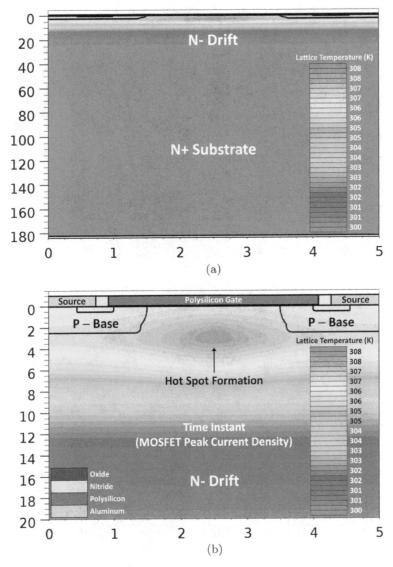

Fig. 61. (a) Lattice temperature contour plot of D-MOSFET complete-cell structure recorded at 1000 A/cm² current density time instant during RLC ring-down simulation. (b) Lattice temperature contour plot of D-MOSFET complete-cell structure recorded at 1000 A/cm² current density time instant during RLC ring-down simulation (zoomed-in view).

at 1000 A/cm², the drain to source voltage drop is significantly higher which reverse biases the P-base/N− drift region leading to the formation of much larger depletion region, thereby causing current constriction at elevated current density forward operation.

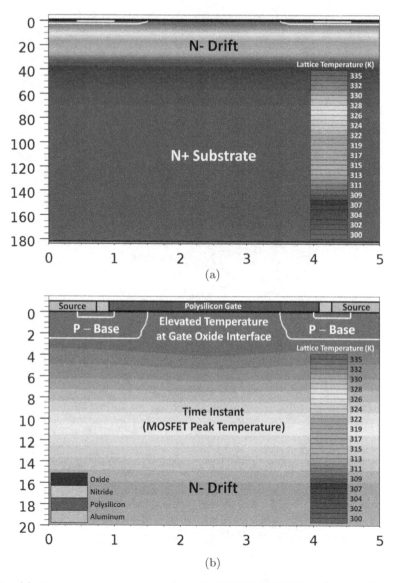

Fig. 62. (a) Lattice temperature contour plot of D-MOSFET complete-cell structure recorded at maximum temperature time instant during RLC ring-down simulation. (b) Lattice temperature contour plot of D-MOSFET complete-cell structure recorded at maximum temperature time instant during RLC ring-down simulation (zoomed-in view).

The lattice temperature contour plots of the D-MOSFET structure recorded at the maximum temperature time instant are shown in Fig. 62(a) and 62(b). Since the maximum lattice temperature is attained after peak current density time instant, spreading of heat from the JFET region to active area can be seen in Fig. 62(b). The lattice temperature profile also shows that the oxide–semiconductor interface is exposed to high temperature, which can cause gate oxide reliability issues.

References

1. IXYS Corp., High Voltage Power MOSFET, IXTU01N100 datasheet.
2. IXYS Corp., Polar^{TM} HiPerFET^{TM} Power MOSFET, IXFN32N120P datasheet.
3. Cree Inc., Silicon Carbide Power MOSFET C2M^{TM} MOSFET Technology, C2M0080120D datasheet, [Rev. C].
4. B. Baliga, *Fundamentals of Power Semiconductor Devices*, New York, NY: Springer Verlag, 2008.
5. J. Lutz, H. Schlangenotto, U. Scheuermann and R. D. Doncker, Semiconductor Power Device — Physics Characteristic Reliability, New York, NY: Springer-Verlag, 2011.
6. ATLAS User's Manual, September 11, 2014, [online] Available at: www.silvaco.com.
7. T. Kimoto, J. A. Cooper, *Fundamentals of Silicon Carbide Technology.*, Singapore: Wiley, 2014.
8. B. N. Pushpakaran, S. B. Bayne and A. A. Ogunniyi, Silvaco-based evaluation of 10 kV 4H-SiC MOSFET as a solid-state switch in narrow-pulse application, *2017 IEEE 21st International Conference on Pulsed Power (PPC)*, Brighton, 2017, pp. 1–5.
9. M. D. Kelley, B. N. Pushpakaran and S. B. Bayne, Single-Pulse Avalanche Mode Robustness of Commercial 1200 V/80 mΩ SiC MOSFETs, in *IEEE Transactions on Power Electronics*, vol. 32, no. 8, August 2017, pp. 6405–6415.
10. B. N. Pushpakaran, S. B. Bayne and A. A. Ogunniyi, Thermal analysis of 4H-SiC DMOSFET structure under resistive switching, in *Power Modulator and High Voltage Conference (IPMHVC), 2014 IEEE International*, vol., no., pp. 523–526, 1–5 June 2014.
11. B. N. Pushpakaran, S. B. Bayne and A. A. Ogunniyi, Physics-based simulation of 4H-SIC DMOSFET structure under inductive switching. *Journal of Computational Electronics*, 1–9 (2015).
12. B. N. Pushpakaran, S. B. Bayne, A. A. Ogunniyi, Electro-thermal transient simulation of silicon carbide power MOSFET, *Pulsed Power Conference (PPC), 2013 19th IEEE*, vol., no., pp. 1,6, 16–21 June 2013.

Index

Supplementary Materials

Thank you for purchasing this textbook.

To complement the contents of this book, we have prepared supplementary materials available for download from the World Scientific website (www.worldscientific.com).

The supplementary materials are high-resolution post-processed figures created using Silvaco© ATLAS Technology Computer-Aided Design (TCAD) software available in full color.

Downloading the supplementary materials

1. Enter the following URL into your browser (note: this access URL should be activated ONLY ONCE):

   https://www.worldscientific.com/r/10929-SUPP/

2. When you enter the site, you will be asked to login. If you have not previously registered on the World Scientific site, a simple (free) registration process will be required.

3. Once you have successfully logged in and reached the page for *Modeling and Electrothermal Simulation of SiC Power Devices*, select the "Supplementary" tab. This tab contains a direct link to the supplementary materials.

4. Clicking on the link will allow you to download the zipped file containing the figures.

5. If your computer automatically places downloaded files in a folder named "Downloads", you will want to relocate the zipped file to a convenient permanent directory before unzipping. The zipped file is named "Figures.zip" and after unzipping, it will produce an unzipped folder of the same name.

Please contact sales@wspc.com if you have any problems downloading the material.

CPSIA information can be obtained
at www.ICGtesting.com
Printed in the USA
BVHW051937210319
543278BV00002BA/3/P

9 789813 237827